A Catalogue of the Joanna Southcott Collection
at The University of Texas

A CATALOGUE

OF THE

Joanna Southcott

COLLECTION

AT THE

UNIVERSITY OF TEXAS

Compiled by
EUGENE PATRICK WRIGHT

THE UNIVERSITY OF TEXAS AT AUSTIN

To Wanda, Janet, Cindy and Patrick, with love and gratitude. E.P.W.

Published by
THE HUMANITIES RESEARCH CENTER
THE UNIVERSITY OF TEXAS AT AUSTIN
Distributed by
UNIVERSITY OF TEXAS PRESS
AUSTIN, TEXAS 78712
Printed in the United States of America

CONTENTS

Introduction : 1

I. PRINTED MATERIAL : 9
 A. JOANNA SOUTHCOTT : *Works Published During Her Lifetime* : 10
 B. JOANNA SOUTHCOTT : *Posthumous Publications* : 34
 C. JOANNA SOUTHCOTT : *Related Works* : 42
 D. JOANNA SOUTHCOTT : *Biographical Works* : 55
 E. JOANNA SOUTHCOTT : *Printed Broadsides, Leaflets, and Clippings* : 58
 F. RICHARD BROTHERS : 62
 G. MISCELLANEOUS PRINTED MATERIAL : 65

II. MANUSCRIPT MATERIAL : 67
 A. LETTERS : 68
 B. NOTES : 72
 C. SERMONS : 73
 D. DIVINE COMMUNICATIONS : 74
  1. *Given to Joanna* : 74
  2. *Given to Prophets other than Joanna* : 79
 E. NOTEBOOKS : 82
 F. PRAYERS : 94
 G. POEMS AND SONGS : 95
 H. SEALS : 97
 I. SCROLLS : 99
 J. MISCELLANEOUS MANUSCRIPT MATERIAL : 101

III. PAINTINGS : 103

IV. ENGRAVINGS : 107
 A. PORTRAITS OF JOANNA SOUTHCOTT : 107
 B. PORTRAITS OF RICHARD BROTHERS : 109
 C. PORTRAIT OF JOHN FINLAYSON : 109

V. PHOTOGRAPHS : 111

Index : 113

Illustrations follow page 66

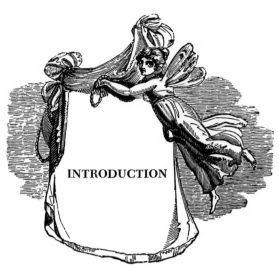

INTRODUCTION

The majority of the Joanna Southcott collection, consisting of manuscript material, paintings, portraits, pamphlets, books, miscellaneous scrolls and seals, and personal effects of Joanna Southcott, was acquired by the University of Texas Library in 1962 and housed in the Miriam Lutcher Stark Library. The collection was formed by George Bennett, late publisher of the London newspapers *The Standard* and *The Evening Standard*. Mr. Bennett was a descendant of George and Sarah Bennett, both followers of Joanna.

The importance of the collection is not easy to determine. First, it is difficult to discover just which manuscripts came from Joanna herself and which are later, perhaps inaccurate, copies, for Joanna dictated virtually all her works. Nor is it easy to determine how large a part of the total number of original manuscripts is now in this library, because there is no way to discover how much she wrote. It is probably safe to assume, however, that the manuscript part of the collection is as complete as it could have been, for it is obvious that at least part of the collection, and probably most of it, was part of the personal collection of Lavinia Elizabeth Chapman Jones, who began to collect unpublished Southcott manuscripts soon after Joanna's death. Had Mrs. Jones not begun her collection early, certainly the unpublished manuscripts would have been scattered among Joanna's followers and eventually lost. One lot of extant manuscript material is not in this collection; Joanna's "Box of Sealed Writings" is still held by her followers in England awaiting the Bishops' request to open it. It reportedly weighs one hundred and fifty-six pounds and must contain a large number of prophecies. Even this important omission in the present collection was almost filled at one time. G. R. Balleine (see item 208) reports that as the rather dynamic Mrs. Lavinia Jones searched England hunting manuscripts, she attempted to walk off with the box of prophecies. Had she been able to carry off this prize, Joanna's followers might be fewer today, but the collection at The University of Texas would possess an additional one hundred and fifty-six pounds of unpublished manuscript material.

The originality and completeness of the published works are easier to evaluate. There are first edition copies of every work Joanna published during her lifetime, as well as later editions of many. In addition, a number of her manuscripts were printed after her death by Lavinia Jones's printer husband, Daniel Jones, and the collection contains no less than fifty of these, nearly as many as the total number of books published by Joanna during her lifetime. There are books about Joanna written by polemicists on both sides of the question as well as by those who wrote of her more objectively.

The second difficulty in determining the importance of the collection is caused by Joanna herself. The question is, how can the incoherent writings of a religious fanatic of a century and a half ago be of any interest to scholars today? Admittedly Joanna Southcott's poetry is nothing more than doggerel, and Joseph Prescott's paintings are amateurish. Still the insight into the source of Joanna's poetry and Prescott's paintings cannot fail to attract one interested in the history and literature of the early nineteenth century, for many of the pressures which stirred the Southcottians were the same as those which affected important writers of the time. The political and social problems which caused Blake, Wordsworth, Coleridge, and others to lament or to be indignant are the same problems that caused Joanna and her followers to turn to a rather extreme, yet certainly traditional, form of religious activity.

Joanna was born on April 26, 1750, in East Devon, the fourth daughter of a family of four daughters and a son. Her father, William Southcott, was a poor farmer. Although she seldom writes of her mother, Hanna Southcott, her later experiences with her spirit show that Joanna depended on her mother for comfort. Joanna's early life seems to have been normal enough in the account she gives in her writings. For forty years she lived the simple life of a peasant-farmer's daughter. She frequently admits her youthful shortcomings and her early infatuations with young men. But the two childhood traits that most influenced her later life were her detailed knowledge of even the most obscure books of the Bible gained by her constant study and her fascination with the superstitious tales which were circulated in her village. Stories of direct or indirect supernatural occurrences, such as the appearances of angels and devils and the forewarnings of death by animals, were very real to Joanna. If Blake saw God and angels as a child, Joanna grew up with Satan and his angels to battle on every hand.

Still Joanna's early life was not extraordinary. She attended the Methodist church, and like any village woman she believed every word in the Bible to be the literal word of God. She earned her keep as a domestic servant and faced the problems of eluding the lustful intentions of her masters as did many a pretty peasant girl. But in 1792, when she was 42, Joanna had a strange experience. At this time all of Europe was disturbed by the chaos in France. The growth of both industry and population in England had caused social ills which often produced spirited controversy and riots; and Joanna, whose early training had been only in the Bible and in the mysterious stories of supernatural participation in human affairs, became convinced that the disturbances which were so great to her unsophisticated mind were nothing other than the "locusts of Abaddon" loosed upon a sinful world by an angry God. She insists that at this very time a "Voice" spoke to her explaining the source of the troubles and offering a solution.

When Joanna herself became convinced that her "Voice" was friendly and not evil, she felt the need to warn the world that "Christ's Second Coming is nigh." She sought to enlist the aid of the established church by sending her prophecies to ministers, but she was generally ignored. Not to be denied the opportunity of fulfilling her divine mission, she took her life savings of £100 to a printer in Exeter where, in February 1801, she published her first book, *The Strange Effects of Faith*. During the next thirteen years she published sixty-five books, and she circulated manuscripts and letters enough to have filled many more.

Her books were read and received with various results. Naturally she met with much ridicule, but before her death late in 1814 she was to attract over a hundred thousand followers, some from the highest places in society and some who should have been in Bedlam. She was never the dynamic evangelist in the movement that bore her name. So mild and polite was she that her closest followers called her "Mother." And even when she died without bringing to birth the promised Shiloh, most of her followers refused to stop believing. Such a blow should have killed the movement, but although Joanna was dead, her work continued. Three rival theories were evolved for Joanna's dying without giving birth to the child. One group thought that Joanna was taken away by God because of the unbelief of the Bishops, but would be brought back. Others said that the birth was never meant to be physical, but that the child had actually been born in spirit. Another group thought that the child had been born but was snatched up to heaven immediately to return later. The latter view was probably the most popular.

From this point on, the Southcottian movement has been led by various of her converts, some stronger leaders than others, some saner than others. An epidemic of "voices" and visions ran its course among Joanna's followers, and the order of worship began to vary from one group to another depending upon the communications received by the followers. Balleine reports that one group ended a prayer meeting by letting loose a small black pig, which they attacked with knives and sticks until they killed it. They then burned it and scattered the ashes on their heads. But the next real leader of the movement was George Turner, one of Joanna's disciples. Many of her followers looked to Turner for guidance after Joanna's death, probably because his message was more familiar than that of any of his rivals. He prophesied the end of the world on January 28, 1817. His followers threw their money away and many burned their possessions. Turner was much disturbed that his "Voice" had failed him, and he died in 1822 after having been completely mad for several years.

The leaders in succeeding years remembered Joanna, but each had his own peculiar approach to her ideas. William Shaw prophesied that if the world did not accept the meek Christ child, then Jesus would come as a warrior. John Wroe, who was the major leader from 1824 to 1863, was torn between his devotion to his prophetic duties and his desire for pretty, young girls. Wroe was followed by James White, called James Jezreel, who led the movement from 1875 until near the turn of the century when he was sentenced to four years in prison for bragging that he could seduce 72,000 women (half of the 144,000 of God's chosen would surely be women). He meant that as Eve had seduced Adam into evil, he, James Jezreel, would seduce women into good, but his ambiguity and his refusal to explain his prophecies to nonbelievers led him to jail. As leader he was followed by two women, Helen Exeter and Mabel Barltrop, called "Octavia" because she was the eighth modern prophet. Octavia, who died on October 16, 1934, began the current-day practice of sending patches of cloth soaked in "holy" water to the sick. Her "Voice" had given her the power to heal, and the Panacea Society, which she founded, began sending their healing water to every applicant without charge.

The Southcottian movement has thus been active since 1792 to the present day, and today her followers are active in several sects, the largest perhaps being the Panacea Society of Bedford, England (see especially item 275). This group of followers has in its possession the "Box of Sealed Writings" which Joanna sealed up before her death. Another and different Southcottian sect better known in America is the House of David.

What makes the Southcottian movement different from many other enthusiastic sects is that Joanna and some of her followers declared that they received communications by supernatural means. In short, Joanna and a few others claimed mystical powers. These communications were private, always directed to one person. It is true that several persons in different places would report similar messages, but even when several were present during a communication, only the prophet was affected. The communication could occur in any one of three different ways: as a "voice" which the prophet hears; as "visions" which appeared to the prophet at any time, asleep or awake; or as messages written by the prophet automatically and unconsciously. The messages received covered a range of subjects. The major theme of the prophecies is that man must turn to God because the end of the world is near. The myriad of additional themes, such as the defense of the Southcott position, explanations of scriptures, and comments on historical events, all are used to support the major theme.

Joanna's teachings made her one of the most widely known personages in England during the early nineteenth century. Not only did she attract thousands of followers from the ranks of the commonalty, but she was also often the subject of conversation in the higher ranks of English society. Most of the literary figures of the day knew of Joanna, and many of them mention her in their writings. It is ironic that such men as Blake, Southey, Byron and Keats knew of and talked about Joanna while Joanna herself seems never to have heard of any of them. There is even the suggestion by Henry Crabb Robinson in his diary that William Sharp, Blake's fellow engraver, "had endeavoured to make a convert of Blake to Joanna Southcott."

Blake was not, of course, a follower of Joanna, nor is it conceivable that he could be. His short poem on Joanna suggests that he neither knew nor could know the truth or falsity of her claims. Other poets of the period were not quite so objective as Blake, however. Keats, in a letter to George and Georgiana Keats in 1819, called Joanna and those of her ilk "nuisances" sired by the Devil. Byron, in canto 3 of *Don Juan* uses Joanna's failure to bring her divine child to birth as a means of satirizing Wordsworth's poem "The Excursion."

> But Wordsworth's poem, and his followers, like
> Joanna Southcote's Shiloh, and her sect
> Are things which in this century don't strike
> The public mind, —so few are the elect;
> And the new births of both their stale virginities
> Have proved but dropsies, taken for divinities.

But the most interested in hurling jibes at Joanna was Robert Southey. He looked upon Joanna and her followers as freaks and was constantly amazed that the public took her seriously. In a letter to J. Neville White Southey says, "Had she been sent to Bedlam ten years ago, how many hundred persons would have been preserved from this infectious and disgraceful insanity!"

It would be handy to dismiss Joanna's "Voice" as either the acting of a mountebank or the ravings of a frustrated spinster. But Joanna's constant questioning of her own powers and her lifelong poverty suggest that she was not consciously a fraud. Some of her last words were, "If I have been misled, it has been by some spirit good or evil." Neither is it easy to dismiss her visions simply as products of a confused mind, for to dismiss all visions as impossible is to dismiss not only such visionaries as Socrates, St. Joan, St. Theresa, Henry Vaughan, and William Blake, but also the recognition of a number of modern psychologists of a seeming clairvoyant or precognitive power in certain people. To lend support to Joanna's admittedly tenuous case, one must realize that many of her specific prophecies did come true. Even her last prophecy, that she was a virgin pregnant by the Holy Spirit with the Christ child, whom she called "Shiloh," even this highly unbelievable suggestion was documented by some of the most respected physicians in London. Finally more than thirty doctors declared her pregnant.

The characters who participate in this almost unbelievable story are ones that cannot be found even in Dickens. Mary Bateman, whose chickens laid eggs with misspelled inscriptions, is someone we would expect to find in a television comedy sketch. Jezreel, who set out to erect a Pantisocracy all in one gigantic tower, inspires more laughter than Coleridge's ode "To a Young Ass" because it is misguided idealism on a grander scale. But Joanna and her movement are valuable for more than entertainment. Theology students will find a case study of the treatment of a prophet among his contemporaries. Church officials can review here the lack of communication between what Balleine calls "University Religion" and the gropings of the lower middle-class. Psychologists will find here a detailed history of one who claims, with some justification, to possess clairvoyant and precognitive powers. Those interested in the study of mysticism have in Joanna's work a fresh history of the same unusual happenings explained in less detail by medieval saints. Students of literature can find a better understanding of the pressures and needs of the society of the period as well as occasional glimpses of an uneducated opinion of poetic diction or an analysis of a novel. All of these elements lie virtually undisturbed in the history of the Southcottian Movement, a record of which is very adequately represented in this collection.

The two books which are most valuable as appraisals of Joanna and her work are those by Balleine (item 208) and Matthews (item 210). While neither work is either complete or scholarly, both approach the subject objectively. Short references to and sketches of Joanna are plentiful. So well known was she in the early nineteenth century that newspapers and journals of the period abound with advertisements, letters, parodies and articles about her. In addition, her followers have taken care to insure against her being forgotten. Besides the pamphlets on her put out by the Panacea Society (see items 225-229), several of her followers have published biographies of her. Alice Seymour's two-volume work (see item 211) explains Joanna from the point of view of a twentieth-century follower. Joanna's critics were many, and several books treat her as anything from a deluded old woman to a clever entrepreneur. In this collection items 209 and 212-216 all treat Joanna unsympathetically.

The arrangement of this Catalogue is patterned after a work done some years ago on the Byron manuscripts in the University of Texas Library by Professor Willis W. Pratt, although it has been necessary to deviate from the pattern at times because of the nature of the material. All of the printed material, manuscripts, and paintings included in the "Southcott Collection" are described, although occasionally it was impossible to establish a relationship between a given work or manuscript and the Southcott Movement. Also included are those works in the main library stacks which seem by virtue of their subject matter to belong with the collection. Only stray scraps of paper and two items which, while interesting, are of little literary, historical, social, or religious importance have been omitted. There are a hair ring which belonged to Joanna and her satin slippers.

The description for published items in this Catalogue is given in a maximum of three parts:
I. (1) author. (2) title. (3) place of publication. (4) date. (5) printer. (6) sellers. (7) price.
II. (1) size. (2) number of pages. (3) binding. (4) cover title. (5) volume, location of work in the volume, and number of volumes in the set [a designation of "III (1/7) of VI" would be translated to mean that the work was bound first in a volume of seven separate works (1/7) and that it appears in volume three of a six-volume set (III of VI)].
III. additional description.

For manuscripts the description is given in a maximum of three parts:
I. For letters and notes: (1) writer. (2) type of manuscripts, signed

or unsigned. (3) place of origin. (4) date.
For poetry: (1) writer. (2) title or first line. (3) date.
II. (1) number of leaves. (2) size in centimeters.
III. additional description.
In case of both printed materials and manuscripts, the three parts are compressed into fewer when clarity will not suffer.

As a last word it must be said that this Catalogue makes no attempt to be a formal bibliography. It is at best a brief description of the materials in the collection, and it is designed to be used as a first source for anyone interested in particular works in the collection or in a general view of the material as a whole.

I must acknowledge the help of many in the preparation of this work. Special thanks are due to Professors Willis W. Pratt and William B. Todd for reading the manuscript several times and making valuable suggestions. I thank Professors Edwin T. Bowden and W. O. S. Sutherland also for their help. The librarians in the Miriam Lutcher Stark Library, especially Mrs. Sally Leach, were both helpful and patient. Finally, I acknowledge the immeasurable help of my wife, Wanda, who not only typed tirelessly, but who also endured.

Austin, Texas; August, 1966   EUGENE P. WRIGHT

**I. PRINTED
MATERIAL**

The printed material in the collection consists of items as small as newspaper clippings to multi-volume publications. By far the most numerous, however, are the short pamphlets which make up the "Books" of Joanna Southcott. A "Catalogue of Books Published by Joanna South-cott," printed sometime after 1852 by Daniel Jones, is a convenient reference to the sixty-five books published by Joanna during her lifetime. Jones lists time and place of publication and publisher for the various editions, although he often neglects to list part or all of this information for any given edition. Jones's list is indispensable, however, because members of the sect almost invariably refer to Joanna's works by number, the number corresponding to the number of the work as listed by Jones. In addition, the two indexes in the collection refer to the various works by their numbers rather than by title.

The annotations which appear in many of the publications in this collection are often interesting. Most were inscribed by followers who wanted to record their enthusiastic concurrence with the text. Often the annotations consist of nothing more than the marking of parts of the text considered important by some reader or of notations of scriptures which parallel a prophecy in the text.

The first sixty-five titles listed here correspond to the works of Joanna Southcott as listed by Daniel Jones. Additional works by Joanna are then listed according to date of publication, followed by the other printed material. It is interesting to note that four of the works listed by Jones as "Books Published by Joanna Southcott" are by someone other than Joanna. All four, however, contain extensive quotations from Joanna's manuscripts.

A : JOANNA SOUTHCOTT:

WORKS PUBLISHED DURING HER LIFETIME

1a(1): THE STRANGE EFFECTS OF FAITH; WITH REMARKABLE PROPHE-
CIES (MADE IN 1792, & C.) OF THINGS WHICH ARE TO COME: ALSO
SOME ACCOUNT OF MY LIFE [FIRST PART]. Exeter, n. d. [The text
is dated January, 1801, on p. i]. "Printed for the author by
T. Bride." Inscribed in ink on colophon page "and sold by E. J.
Field, 3 Broad Court, Longacre."

8°, pp. [i-iii]iv, [5]-48. Cover title: SOUTHCOTT'S PROPHECIES—1.
I(2/11) of VI.

The name "Perkins" inscribed on title page.

(2): Another copy. Disbound. Some underscoring.

1b: Second Edition. London, n. d. Printed by A. Seale. Sold by
E. J. Field, E. Carpenter, C. Abbott, W. Symonds, Miss Eveleighs,
and Mr. Child. Price 1 shilling.

Cover title: JOANNA SOUTHCOTT—1. I(1/10) of III.

Described as a "reprint" on the title page, but this is really a
second edition. A note on p. 48 explains, "The first edition was
printed with many errors, which remain in this, because the book
was not to be altered." A 12-line statement of purpose by Joanna,
dated Exeter, January, 1801, is found on the title page.

1c: Second Edition. N. d. Printed by Galabin & Marchant. Sold by
W. Tozer, W. Symonds, the Miss Eveleighs, S. Hirst, J. Middleton,
and James Light. Price 1 shilling ("and Three Pence" struck out
in ink).

Disbound.

Described as a "second edition" on the title page, probably printed
from and published after the Seale "second edition." The note on
p. 48 is repeated.

1d: [Third edition: *not seen*]

1e: Fourth Edition. London, June, 1816. Printed "from the Third
Edition, printed in May, 1810." Printed by W. Marchant. Sold
by the Miss Eveleighs, S. Hirst, James Light, Edmond Baker, and
C. Bradley. Price 1 shilling, 3 pence.

Disbound.

A preface calling for ministers to judge Joanna and a "Hierogliphic as appeared in Moores Almanack A. D. 1779" appear in this copy.

2a(1): THE STRANGE EFFECTS OF FAITH. SECOND PART. Exeter, n. d. [Jones: 1801]. Printed "for Joanna Southcott" by G. Floyde. Inscribed in ink on colophon page "And Sold by E. J. Field, 3 Broad Court, Longacre." Price to subscribers 6 d, non-subscribers 8 d.

8°, pp. [49]-96. Cover title: SOUTHCOTT's PROPHECIES—1. I(3/11) of VI.

The name "Perkins" inscribed on title page.

(2): Another copy. Disbound. Annotated and underscored.

2b: [Second edition, first printing: *not seen*]

2c: Second Edition, second printing. London, July 21, 1806, "from the First Edition, published 29 March, 1801." Printed by W. Marchant. Sold by E. J. Field, C. Abbott, W. Symonds, the Miss Eveleighs, S. Hirst, J. Middleton, and James Light. The price "Nine-Pence" is inked out and "0/1" is inserted.

Disbound.

2d: [Third edition: *not seen*]

2e: Fourth Edition. London, July, 1814. Printed by W. Marchant. Sold by T. Huntley, W. Tozer, the Miss Eveleighs, S. Hirst, W. Wadman, James Light, Edmund Baker, C. Bradley, John Nesbit, and T. Turpin.

Unbound.

3a(1): THE STRANGE EFFECTS OF FAITH. THIRD PART. Exeter, n. d. [Jones: 1801]. Printed by G. Floyde and J. Winter. Inscribed in ink on colophon page "And Sold by E. J. Field, 3 Broad Court, Longacre." Price 9 pence.

8°, pp. [97]-144. Cover title: SOUTHCOTT's PROPHECIES—1. I(4/11) of VI.

The name "Perkins" inscribed on title page. Joanna admits on the last page of this work that people cannot tell from her first two works whether she is inspired or deranged, but she warns that her next book "will puzzle them much more."

(2): Another copy. Disbound. Annotated and underscored.

3b: Second Edition. London, n. d. [Jones: 1804]. Printed by S. Rousseau. Sold by E. J. Field, C. Abbott, W. Tozer, W. Symonds, the Miss Eveleighs, Samuel Hirst, J. Middleton, and James Light.* The Price "Nine Pence" inked out and "0/1" written in.

Disbound. Annotated and underscored.

3c: [Third edition: *not seen*]

3d: Fourth Edition. London, August, 1814. Printed by W. Marchant. Sold by T. Huntley, W. Tozer, the Miss Eveleighs, S. Hirst, W.

Wadman, James Light, Edmund Baker, C. Bradley, John Nesbit, and T. Turpin. Price 1 shilling.

Unbound. Annotated and underscored.

4a(1): THE STRANGE EFFECTS OF FAITH; WITH REMARKABLE PROPHE-CIES, MADE IN 1792 & C. OF THINGS WHICH ARE TO COME. FOURTH PART. Exeter, n. d. [Jones: 1801]. Printed by G. Floyde. Sold at Mr. Symons's and, inked out in this copy, "Sold by George Riebau, No. 2, Blandford Street, Manchester-Square." Followed in ink by "And Sold by E. J. Field, 3 Broad Court, Longacre." Price 9 pence.

8°, pp. [145]-192. Cover title: SOUTHCOTT'S PROPHECIES—1. I(5/11) of VI.

There is included in this copy an engraving (20.5 x 30 cm.) of a vision in two "appearances" called "Open Vision," which Joanna was told of by an unnamed clergyman in London and concerning which she had a communication. In "Appearance I" there is a beast walking on a small island on its hind legs, being followed from the continent, across the water, by hundreds of people walking three abreast. In "Appearance II" the people are gone. On the island is another beast, a leopard, with an alligator and a bison on the water. A note on the back of the engraving reads "This to bound [sic] between Pages 168- & 169—4th Book." The name "Perkins" inscribed on title page.

(2): Another copy, but without the inked inscription on p. 192 and without the engraving called "Open Vision." Disbound. Marginal notes in pencil.

4b: [Second edition: *not seen*]

4c: Third Edition. London, January, 1812, "from the Second Edition, published in August, 1806." Printed by Galabin and Marchant. Sold by W. Tozer, W. Symonds, the Miss Eveleighs, S. Hirst, J. Middleton, and James Light. Price 1 shilling.

Disbound. Some annotation and underscoring.

4d: Fourth Edition. London, January, 1814, "from the Third Edition, printed in Jan. 1812." Printed by W. Marchant. Sold by W. Tozer, W. Symonds, the Miss Eveleighs, S. Hirst, W. Wadman, James Light, Edmund Baker, C. Bradley, R. Goldsmith, and T. Turpin. Price 1 shilling.

Sewn. Underscored.

4e: [A late printing.] Plymouth, 1912. Printed by J. H. Keys. Sold by Miss Seymour. Price 1 shilling.

Original printed wrappers.

5a(1): THE STRANGE EFFECTS OF FAITH; WITH REMARKABLE PROPHE-CIES, MADE IN 1792, & C. OF THINGS WHICH ARE TO COME. FIFTH PART. Exeter, n. d. [Jones: December, 1801]. "Printed for Joanna

Southcott by G. Floyde." Sold at Mr. Symons's and, inked out in this copy, "at Mr. G. Riebau's, No. 2. Blandford-Street, Manchester-Square, London." Followed in ink by "and Sold by E. J. Field, 3 Broad Court, Longacre." Price 9 pence.

8°, pp. [193]-240. Cover title: SOUTHCOTT'S PROPHECIES—1. I(6/11) of VI.

Brings to light much of the supernatural lore Joanna came into contact with during her childhood including visions and visitations. The name "Perkins" inscribed on title page.

(2): Another copy with Riebau's name and address not inked out.

Unbound. Annotated and underscored.

5b: [Second edition: *not seen*]

5c: Third Edition. London, October, 1808, "from the first Edition, printed Dec. 1, 1801." Printed by W. Marchant. Sold by E. J. Field, W. Tozer, W. Symonds, the Miss Eveleighs, S. Hirst, J. Middleton, and James Light.

Disbound. Annotated and underscored.

5d: Fourth Edition. London, October, 1813, "from the Third Edition, printed in Oct. 1808." Printed by W. Marchant. Sold by W. Tozer, W. Symonds, the Miss Eveleighs, S. Hirst, W. Wadman, James Light, Edmund Baker, C. Bradley, R. Goldsmith, and T. Turpin. Price 1 shilling.

Sewn. Some annotation and underscoring.

6a(1): THE STRANGE EFFECTS OF FAITH; WITH REMARKABLE PROPHECIES, MADE IN 1792, & C. OF THINGS WHICH ARE TO COME. SIXTH PART. Exeter, January 2, 1802. Printed by G. Floyde. Sold at Mr. Symons's, and, inked out in this copy, "and at Mr. G. Riebau's, No. 2 Blandford-Street, Manchester-Square, London." Followed in ink by "and Sold by E. J. Field, 3 Broad Court, Longacre." Price 9 pence.

8°, pp. [241]-288. Cover title: SOUTHCOTT'S PROPHECIES—1. I(7/11) of VI.

Comments on the Judgment Day. The name "Perkins" inscribed on title page.

(2): Another copy with Riebau's name and address not inked out.

Disbound. Annotated.

6b: [Second edition: *not seen*]

6c: Third Edition. London, October, 1808, "from the First Edition, printed by W. Marchant."

Pp. 287-288 missing from this copy. Disbound.

6d: Fourth Edition. London, October, 1813, "from the third Edition, printed Oct. 1808." Printed by W. Marchant. Sold by W. Tozer, W. Symonds, the Miss Eveleighs, S. Hirst, W. Wadman, James

Light, Edmund Baker, C. Bradley, R. Goldsmith, and T. Turpin. Price 1 shilling.

Disbound.

7a(1): A CONTINUATION OF PROPHECIES, BY JOANNA SOUTHCOTT, FROM THE YEAR 1792, TO THE PRESENT TIME. Exeter, n. d. [Jones: 1802]. Printed by G. Floyde. Sold by Mr. Symons's and by Mr. Elias Jameson Field. Price 9 pence.

8°, pp. [1]-56. Cover title: SOUTHCOTT's PROPHECIES—1. I(8/11) of VI.

The name "Perkins" inscribed on title page. Contains several letters from Basil Bruce, Esq. Also included is a list of prophecies already fulfilled and another of those "Hastening on."

(2): Another copy. Disbound. Annotated.

7b: Second Edition. London, 1807, "from the first Edition, printed in March, 1802." Printed by S. Rousseau. Sold by E. J. Field, W. Tozer, W. Symonds, the Miss Eveleighs, Samuel Hirst, J. Middleton, and James Light. Price 1 shilling.

Disbound.

A defective copy, but containing a key to the "Thoughts on the Sixth Book," inscribed in ink on pp. 38-42. Incongruously, there is folded inside the book loose a newspaper clipping of jokes, called "Far-fetched Fun," dated November 17, 1860.

8(1): THE STRANGE EFFECTS OF FAITH: BEING A CONTINUATION OF JOANNA SOUTHCOTT's PROPHECIES OF THINGS WHICH ARE TO COME. London, n. d. [Jones: 1802]. Printed by E. Spragg. Sold by E. J. Field and W. Simmonds. Price 9 pence.

8°, pp. [57]-108. Cover title: SOUTHCOTT's PROPHECIES—1. I(9/11) of VI.

Further defense of Joanna's powers against non-believers. The name "Perkins" inscribed on title page.

(2): Another copy. Cover title: None. I(1/5) of I.

(3): Another copy. Disbound.

9(1): LETTERS, & C. [DIVINE AND SPIRITUAL LETTERS OF PROPHECIES]. London, November 18, 1801. Printed by E. Spragg. Sold by George Riebau.

8°, pp. [1]-48. Cover title: SOUTHCOTT's PROPHECIES—1. I(10/11) of VI.

Letters by Joanna Southcott, Stanhope Bruce, William Sharp, and others. The title "Divine and Spiritual Letters of Prophecies, sent to Reverend Divines and other Spiritual good men; that are now ordered to be put in print, by Divine Command, for the good of the Public, and to try the Wisdom of Mankind, to what Spirit they will allude this Strange Revelation" appears on the last page because of a "divine command" that it "must be inserted here, instead of a title page at the beginning." There is much double-column printing in this work because "the book should contain neither more nor less than forty-eight pages." The name "Perkins" inscribed on title page.

(2): Another copy. Unbound.

10(1): DIVINE AND SPIRITUAL LETTERS OF PROPHECIES SENT TO REVEREND DIVINES, AND OTHER SPIRITUAL GOOD MEN AND WOMEN, THAT ARE NOW ORDERED TO BE PUT IN PRINT BY DIVINE COMMAND FOR THE GOOD OF THE PUBLIC, AND TO TRY THE WISDOM OF MANKIND TO WHAT SPIRIT THEY WILL ALLUDE THIS STRANGE REVELATION. London, n. d. Printed by E. Spragg. Sold by E. J. Field and Mr. W. Simmonds. Price 9 pence.

8°, pp. [49]-96. Cover title: SOUTHCOTT'S PROPHECIES—1. I(11/11) of VI.

Another collection of letters. The name "Perkins" inscribed on title page.

(2): Another copy. Disbound.

11(1): A DISPUTE BETWEEN THE WOMAN AND THE POWERS OF DARKNESS. London, n. d. [Jones: 1802]. Printed by E. Spragg. Sold by E. Field and W. Simmonds. Price 2 shillings, 6 pence.

8°, pp. [1]-128. Cover title: SOUTHCOTT'S PROPHECIES—2. II(1/6) of VI.

A seven-day dialogue between Joanna and Satan, or Satan's friends. Satan curses God and calls Joanna "Thou infamous bitch!" But Joanna talks everyone into submission. The final page is dated August 31, 1802.

Crosses inscribed in ink are on pp. 46 and 50. A circle containing a large cross and four small ones is on p. 51. These marks are explained by Joanna in *The Answer of the Lord to the Powers of Darkness* (see item 12), p. 56.

(2): Another copy. Disbound. Annotated.

12(1): THE ANSWER OF THE LORD TO THE POWERS OF DARKNESS. London, November 8, 1802. Printed "verbatim" by E. Spragg. Sold by E. J. Field and W. Simmonds. Price 2 shillings, 6 pence.

8°, pp. [1]-128. Cover title: SOUTHCOTT'S PROPHECIES—2. II(2/6) of VI.

A symbol used in her writings is explained on p. 56. On p. 92 appears a printed representation of the seal found by Joanna with two stars and the initials "I. C." [J. C.?] in it. Along side is an actual imprint in red sealing wax of the seal, but the imprint is in an inverted position.

A long letter "To the Public" by William Sharp appears at the end. Here he proclaims his support for Joanna.

(2): Another copy. Disbound. Annotated.

13a(1): A COMMUNICATION GIVEN TO JOANNA, IN ANSWER TO MR. BROTH-ERS' LAST BOOK, PUBLISHED THE END OF THIS YEAR, 1802. London, n. d. [Jones: December, 1802]. Printed "verbatim" by E. Spragg. Sold by E. J. Field and W. Simmonds. Price 4 pence—halfpenny.

8°, pp. [1]-22. Cover title: SOUTHCOTT'S PROPHECIES—2. II(3/6) of VI.

Printing errors on p. 11 are corrected in ink. These errors do not appear in the Second Edition. Joanna is told by God that Brothers' book "was written under the influence of the devil."

(2): Another copy. Disbound. Annotated.

13b(1): Second Edition. London, July, 1815. Printed by W. Marchant. Price 6 pence.

Cover title: Unreadable. III (2/12) of III. Seemingly sewn in the bound volume at a later date.

13b(2): Another copy. Cover title: None. I (3/5) of I.

14a(1): PROPHECIES. A WARNING TO THE WHOLE WORLD, FROM THE SEALED PROPHECIES OF JOANNA SOUTHCOTT, AND OTHER COMMUNI-CATIONS GIVEN SINCE THE WRITINGS WERE OPENED ON THE 12TH OF JANUARY, 1803. London, n. d. [Jones: March, 1803; watermarks read 1802]. Printed "verbatim" by E. Spragg. Sold by E. J. Field and W. Simmonds. Price 2 shillings, 6 pence.

8°, pp. [i]-ii, [1]-128. Cover title: Unreadable. III(3/12) of III.

Commonly referred to as "The First Book of Visions" and "The First Book of Sealed Prophecies." Various prophecies ranging from October 1794 to March 1803. Most interesting here is the reference on pp. 113-120 to the paintings or visions by "a youth" named Joseph Prescott. These are no doubt the paintings described later. Interesting also are the marginal notes reading "God be Praised" and "Happy Day."

Pp. [i]-ii were printed by W. Smith.

(2): Another copy. Cover title: SOUTHCOTT'S PROPHECIES—2. II(4/6) of VI.

(3): Another copy. Disbound.

14b: THE FIRST BOOK OF THE SEALED PROPHECIES. London, n. d. Printed by Marchant and Galabin. Sold by W. Tozer, W. Symonds, the Miss Eveleighs, S. Hirst, W. Wadman, James Light, Edmund Baker, C. Bradley, R. Goldsmith, and T. Turpin. Price 2 shillings, 6 pence.

8°, pp. [3]-128. Unbound.

A variant, probably the second edition. Missing are pp. i-ii which appear in the edition listed above. This copy is annotated and underscored.

15a(1): THE CONTINUATION OF THE PROPHECIES OF JOANNA SOUTHCOTT. A WORD IN SEASON TO A SINKING KINGDOM. London, n. d. [Jones: June, 1803]. Printed by E. Spragg. Sold by E. J. Field and W. Simmond's. Price 10 pence.

8°, pp. [1]-56. Cover title: Unreadable. III(4/12) of III.

Continuation of a description of Joseph Prescott's visions and divine communications given to Joanna about the visions.

(2): Another copy. Cover title: SOUTHCOTT'S PROPHECIES—2. II(5/6) of VI.

(3): Another copy. Disbound. Annotated and underscored.

15b: [Second edition: *not seen*]

15c: Third Edition. London, August, 1810. Printed by Galabin and Marchant. Sold by M. Jones, W. Tozer, W. Symonds, the Miss Eveleighs, Samuel Hirst, J. Middleton, and James Light. Price 1 shilling.

Unbound. Annotated.

16a(1): THE SECOND BOOK OF VISIONS. London, n. d. [Jones: August, 1803]. Printed "verbatim" by E. Spragg. Sold by E. J. Field and at W. Simmond's. Price 1 shilling, 3 pence.

8°, pp. [1]-72. Cover title: Unreadable. III(5/12) of III.

A continuation of Joseph Prescott's visions, most of which are represented in the paintings described later. Also here are some of Joanna's visions and her "Answer to the False Reports Concerning the Sealing of the People."

(2): Another copy. Cover title: SOUTHCOTT'S PROPHECIES—2. II(6/6) of VI.

(3): Another copy. Unbound. Annotated.

16b(1): Second Edition. London, November, 1813. Printed by W. Marchant, "from the First Edition, printed in August, 1803." Sold by W. Tozer, the Miss Eveleighs, S. Hirst, W. Wadman, James Light, Edmund Baker, C. Bradley, John Nesbit, and T. Turpin. The price "Eighteen-pence" struck out in ink and "1/3" inscribed on p. 71.

Unbound.

(2): Another copy. Cover title: None. I(2/5) of I.

17a: A WORD TO THE WISE; OR A CALL TO THE NATION, THAT THEY MAY KNOW THE DAYS OF THEIR VISITATION FROM THE PROPHECIES THAT ARE GIVEN TO JOANNA SOUTHCOTT, WITH THE REASONS ASSIGNED WHY THE SPIRIT OF PROPHECY IS GIVEN TO A WOMAN; AND WHICH

IS EXPLAINED FROM THE SCRIPTURES IN THE FOLLOWING PAGES. Stourbridge, August, 1803. Printed by J. Heming.

8°, pp. [1]-59. Cover title: Unreadable. III(8/12) of III.

A short explanation of the purpose and content of Joanna's prophecies. Note on the colophon page reads "This thousand to be given away." On p. 1: A. N. inviting letters of inquiry concerning Joanna. Part of the note cropped off in binding.

17b(1): First Edition, Second Printing. Printed by J. Heming. Sold by E. J. Field, Mr. Symonds, Miss Eveleighs, and Mr. Childs. Price 10 pence. Note on colophon page reads "This Thousand to be sold."

Cover title: SOUTHCOTT'S PROPHECIES—3. III(2/7) of VI.

(2): Another copy. Disbound.

17c: Second Edition. London, June, 1810. Printed by Galabin and Marchant, "from the 1st. Edition, printed at Stourbridge in August, 1803." Sold by W. Tozer, W. Symonds, the Miss Eveleighs, S. Hirst, J. Middleton, and James Light. Price 1 shilling.
Unbound.

17d: Third Edition. London, July, 1813, "from the 2nd. Edition, printed in June, 1810." Printed by Marchant and Galabin. Sold by W. Tozer, W. Symonds, the Miss Eveleighs, S. Hirst, James Light, Edmund Baker, C. Bradley, R. Goldsmith, and T. Turpin. Price 1 shilling.
Unbound.

18a(1): DIVINE AND SPIRITUAL COMMUNICATIONS, WRITTEN BY JOANNA SOUTHCOTT: ON THE PRAYERS OF THE CHURCH OF ENGLAND; THE CONDUCT OF THE CLERGY, AND CALVINISTIC METHODISTS, WITH OTHER PARTICULARS. London, 1803. Printed by S. Rousseau. Sold by E. J. Field. Price 8 pence.

8°, pp. [i-iii]-x, [11]-44. Cover title: Unreadable. III(9/12) of III.

An introduction by William Sharp in which Sharp aligns himself with Sir Isaac Newton and others who believed in the literal truth of the Bible.

(2): Another copy. Cover title: SOUTHCOTT'S PROPHECIES—3. III(1/7) of VI.

(3): Another copy. Disbound. Annotated.

18b: Second Edition. London, 1809. Printed by Galabin and Marchant. Price 10 pence.

18c: Third Edition. ("Second Edition" printed on title page, but this is actually a third edition.) London, 1823. Printed by W. Marchant. Price 1 shilling.

19a(1): SOUND AN ALARM IN MY HOLY MOUNTAIN. Leeds, n. d. [Jones: 1804]. Printed by Edward Baines. Sold by E. J. Field, Mr. Symonds, Miss Eveleigh, and Jonathan Priestly. Price 1 shilling.

8°, pp. [1]-76. Cover title: SOUTHCOTT'S PROPHECIES—3. III(3/7) of VI.

Discusses the meaning of Sealing and the end of Satan's kingdom. This copy annotated.

(2): Another copy. Cover title: Unreadable. III(10/12) of VI.

(3): Another copy. Unbound. Annotated.

19b: [Second edition: *not seen*]

19c: [Third edition: *not seen*]

19d: [Fourth edition: *not seen*]

19e: [Fifth edition: *not seen*]

19f: Sixth Edition. London, September, 1811, "from the Fifth Edition, published April, 1810." Printed by Marchant and Galabin. Sold by M. Jones, W. Tozer, W. Symonds, the Miss Eveleighs, S. Hirst, J. Middleton, and James Light. Price 1 shilling, 3 pence.

Disbound. Annotated.

19g: Seventh Edition. London, December, 1812, "from the Sixth Edition, published September, 1811." Printed by Marchant and Galabin. Sold by W. Tozer, W. Symonds, the Miss Eveleighs, S. Hirst, W. Wadman, James Light, Edmund Baker, C. Bradley, R. Goldsmith, and T. Turpin. Price 1 shilling, 3 pence.

Unbound.

19h: [Eighth edition: *not seen*]

19i: Ninth Edition. London, 1816, "from the Eighth Edition, published October, 1813." Published by Marchant and Galabin. Sold by the Miss Eveleighs, S. Hirst, James Light, Edmond Baker, and C. Bradley. Price 1 shilling, 3 pence.

Unbound.

20(1): A WARNING TO THE WORLD. JOANNA SOUTHCOTT'S PROPHECIES. London, April 25, 1804. Printed by S. Rousseau. Sold by E. J. Field. Price 18 pence.

8°, pp. [1]-100. Cover title: JOANNA SOUTHCOTT—2. II(7/8) of III.

A prophecy dated London, May 10th, 1804. Joanna here admits that she does not understand her prophecies; only her judges, picked and inspired by God, can understand.

(2): Another copy. Cover title: Unreadable. III(12/12) of III.

(3): Another copy. Cover title: SOUTHCOTT'S PROPHECIES—3. III(4/7) of VI.

(4): Another copy. Disbound. Title page signed "Mr. Lewick." Annotated.

(5): Another copy. Disbound. Annotated.

21a(1): ON THE PRAYERS FOR THE FAST DAY, MAY, 1804. London, June, 1804. Printed by S. Rousseau. Sold by E. J. Field, the Miss Eveleighs, and W. Simmons. Price 9 pence.

8°, pp. [1]-48. Cover title: SOUTHCOTT'S PROPHECIES—4. IV(1/10) of VI.

Pp. 1-8 (the first gathering) are sewn with pp. 9-48 (the last five gatherings) of LETTERS ON VARIOUS SUBJECTS, FROM MRS. JOANNA SOUTHCOTT TO MISS TOWNLEY. Page 9 of this copy begins "with blackness. . . ," the middle of a prose sentence which does not follow from the last line of poetry on p. 8. Another copy of the latter work (see item 21b) contains the first eight pages which this copy lacks. Jones lists both works under the same number.

(2): Another copy. Contains the same odd composition of gatherings as item 21a. Unbound. Annotated.

(3): Another copy. Printer's note on p. 1 reads "Printed by Marchant and Galabin," but the colophon on p. 48 reads "Printed by S. Rousseau." [Jones lists Rousseau as the printer of the first edition, but lists no other editions.] The first six pages of this copy vary in several respects from the copies listed above; however, pp. 8-48 appear identical to them.

Unbound.

21b: LETTERS ON VARIOUS SUBJECTS FROM MRS. JOANNA SOUTHCOTT TO MISS TOWNLEY. London, 1804. Printed by S. Rousseau. Sold by E. J. Field, the Miss Eveleighs, and W. Simmonds. Price 9 pence.

8°, pp. [1]-48. Sewn.

Listed by Jones along with ON THE PRAYERS FOR THE FAST DAY, although the works are different and separate. Some letters in this work concern the Fast Day.

22(1): COPIES AND PARTS OF COPIES OF LETTERS AND COMMUNICATIONS, WRITTEN FROM JOANNA SOUTHCOTT, AND TRANSMITTED BY MISS TOWNLEY TO MR. W. SHARP, IN LONDON. London, 1804. Printed by S. Rousseau. Sold by E. J. Field and the Miss Eveleighs. Price 18 pence.

8°, pp. [1]-92. Cover title: SOUTHCOTT'S PROPHECIES—3. III(5/7) of VI.

The title "Little Flock of Sheep," by which, according to Jones, the work was commonly known, appears at the tops of the pages inscribed in ink.

A short tale in prose and poetry and some dramatic dialogue called "The Parable of the Hermit" on pp. 26-29 is interesting.

Also here is "The History of Joanna's Life" on pp. 10-26, and several tales in verse.

(2): Another copy. Disbound.

23(1): MR. JOSEPH SOUTHCOTT, THE BROTHER OF JOANNA SOUTHCOTT, WILL NOW COME FORWARD AS DINAH'S BRETHREN DID; THAT THEY SHALL NOT DEAL WITH HIS SISTER, AS THEY WOULD WITH A HARLOT; FOR SO THEY ARE NOW DEALING WITH HER. AND HE WILL PROVE TO THE WORLD WHERE THE ADULTERY IS COMMITTED, BY MEN WHO ARE "UNCIRCUMCISED IN HEART AND LIFE"; AND NOW HE WILL EXPEND ALL THAT HE HAS IN THE WORLD, IF REQUIRED, IN THE HONEST DEFENCE OF HER CHARACTER—TILL HE HAS SLAIN THE UNCIRCUMCISED PHILISTINES, AND ENTIRELY FREED HIS SISTER FROM THE "REPROACHES OF THEIR ADULTERY." London, 1804. Printed by S. Rousseau. Sold by E. J. Field, and the Miss Eveleighs. Price 2 shillings.

8°, pp. [1]-112. Cover title: JOANNA SOUTHCOTT—1. I(4/10) of III.

Contains letters, divine communication, and diary entries from Joseph Southcott and others defending the character and abilities of Joanna.

(2): Another copy. Cover title: SOUTHCOTT'S PROPHECIES—3. III(6/7) of VI.

(3): Another copy. Disbound. Annotated and underscored.

24(1): LETTERS AND COMMUNICATIONS OF JOANNA SOUTHCOTT. THE PROPHETESS OF EXETER: LATELY WRITTEN TO JANE TOWNLEY. Stourbridge, June, 1804. Printed by J. Heming. Sold by E. J. Field, Miss Eveleighs, and Thomas Childs. Price 2 shillings, 3 pence.

8°, pp. [1-3]-128. Cover title: JOANNA SOUTHCOTT—1. I(8/10) of III.

Letters and copies of letters from Joanna to Jane Townley and Rev. T. P. Foley of Oldswinford, Worcestershire, and from Townley to Foley. Commonly called "What Manner of Communications Are These?" because those words appear on the title page. The title comes from Luke 24:17. Sections entitled "Continuation of Joanna's History" appear interspaced with the letters: pp. 26-28, 32-35, 63-75.

(2): Another copy. Cover title: SOUTHCOTT'S PROPHECIES—3. III(7/7) of VI. The name "Perkins" inscribed on title page.

(3): Another copy. Disbound. A seal of the London Chamber of Commerce on a separate sheet is folded loose in this copy.

(4): Another copy. Bound October 2, 1940, by U. T. Library.

25a(1): THE TRIAL OF JOANNA SOUTHCOTT, DURING SEVEN DAYS, WHICH COMMENCED ON THE FIFTH, AND ENDED ON THE ELEVENTH, OF DECEMBER, 1804. AT THE NECKINGER HOUSE, BERMONDSEY, NEAR LONDON. London, 1804. Printed by S. Rousseau. Sold by E. J. Field, W. Symonds, and the Miss Eveleighs. Price 3 shillings.

8°, pp. [i-iii]-xi, [41]-152. Cover title: SOUTHCOTT'S PROPHECIES—4. IV(2/10) of VI.

Contains dialogues between judges and witnesses during Joanna's trial. A long introduction explains the cause and purpose of the trial: to clear Joanna from the charge of "deluded imposter." Much information concerning Joanna's life and character is found here. On the last page Joanna refutes both those who would make her "more than human" and those who say that her writings "are from the devil."

(2): Another copy. Cover title: JOANNA SOUTHCOTT—1. I(3/10) of III.

(3): Another copy. Disbound. Some annotation and underscoring.

25b: Second Edition. Plymouth, 1916. Published by Jas. H. Keys. Printed by Butler and Tanner. Price 2 shillings.

Paper wrappers.

26(1): JOANNA SOUTHCOTT'S ANSWER TO GARRETT'S BOOK, ENTITLED "DEMOCRACY DETECTED—VISIONARY ENTHUSIASM CORRECTED; OR, SIXPENNYWORTH OF GOOD ADVICE SELECTED FROM THE SCRIPTURES OF TRUTH: BY THE REV. JEREMIAH LEARNOULT GARRETT, AUTHOR OF 'RAYS OF EVERLASTING LIGHT'." ALSO, REMARKS ON AN ENGRAVED PRINT, PUBLISHED BY THE SAID GARRETT OF HIS OWN HEAD: WITH MARVELOUS AND WONDERFUL ACCOMPANIMENTS, WHEREIN THE DEMON IS DETECTED, DISSECTED—WHO SOON WILL BE CORRECTED, AND ALL HIS ADHERENTS REJECTED. London, n. d. [Jones: 1805]. Printed by A. Seale. Sold by E. J. Field, E. Carpenter, C. Abbott, W. Symonds, Miss Eveleighs, and Mr. Child. Price 6 pence.

8°, pp. [i-ii], [1]-22. Cover title: JOANNA SOUTHCOTT—2. II(8/8) of III.

Joanna answers Garrett's attack on her by reporting that God had called him "a proud, vain, boasting Pharisee." Interesting here is the description of a print by Garrett which shows Satan with his arms around Joanna and Garrett as a protector of things holy.

(2): Another copy. Cover title: SOUTHCOTT'S PROPHECIES—4. IV(3/10) of VI.

(3): Another copy. Cover title: None. I(4/5) of I.

(4): Another copy. Unbound.

27(1): JOANNA SOUTHCOTT'S ANSWER TO FIVE CHARGES IN THE "LEEDS MERCURY," FOUR OF WHICH ARE ABSOLUTELY FALSE; BUT AS IN THE

FIRST CHARGE, HER ACCUSER MIGHT HAVE SOME ROOM FOR CAV-
ILLING, SHE WISHES TO MAKE EVERY ALLOWANCE; AND GIVE A CLEAR
ANSWER, HOW THAT WAS MISUNDERSTOOD: AND NOT ONLY TO ANSWER
THE FOUR FALSE CHARGES THAT ARE BROUGHT AGAINST HER; BUT
SHE HAS BROUGHT FOUR CHARGES AGAINST HER ADVERSARIES, WHICH
WILL BE SEEN IN THE FOLLOWING PAGES. London, n. d. [Jones:
1805]. Printed by A. Seale. Sold by E. J. Field, E. Carpenter,
C. Abbott, W. Symonds, Miss Eveleighs, and Mr. Child. Price 6
pence.

8°, pp. [1-3]-24. Cover title: JOANNA SOUTHCOTT—1. I(10/10) of
III.

Joanna answers charges that four of her major prophecies were
false by allowing the Spirit to defend her, generally by saying, "It
is not for man to know." The charges involve the prophecies concerning the end of sealing, a French invasion of England, a crop
failure, and Joanna's "awful trial."

(2): Another copy. Cover title: SOUTHCOTT'S PROPHECIES—4.
IV(4/10) of VI.

(3): Another copy. Unbound. Pp. 3-6, 7-10 uncut in this copy.

28(1): THE TRUE EXPLANATION OF THE BIBLE REVEALED BY DIVINE COM-
MUNICATIONS TO JOANNA SOUTHCOTT. PART THE FIRST. TO WHICH
ARE ADDED LETTERS TO AND FROM THE REV. MR. POMEROY. London,
1804. Printed by S. Rousseau. Sold by E. J. Field and the Miss
Eveleighs. Price 18 pence.

8°, pp. [1-3]-96. Cover title: JOANNA SOUTHCOTT—2. II(1/8) of
III.

Joanna's reflections and communications upon certain Biblical pas-
sages and characters. Largely the work consists of letters to the
Rev. Mr. Pomeroy condemning him for his calling Joanna a "de-
luded woman." One letter is signed by 24 believers: Rev. Stanhope
Bruce, Rev. T. P. Foley, Rev. Tho. Webster, George Turner, W.
Jowett, William Harwood, E[lias] Carpenter, John Wilson, Peter
Morison, William R. Wetherell, William Sharp, Charles Taylor,
William Belk, Charles Abbott, John Torin, Thomas Stephens, John
Young, John Morris, Richard Law, George Stocks, Elias Jameson
Field, William Layton Winter, William Owen, and John Hows.

(2): Another copy. Cover title: SOUTHCOTT'S PROPHECIES—4.
IV(5/10) of VI.

(3): Another copy. Disbound. "Mr. Lewick" inscribed in ink on
title page.

29(1): TRUE EXPLANATIONS OF THE BIBLE. PART THE SECOND. London,
n. d. [Jones: 1804]. Printed by S. Rousseau. Price 18 pence.

8°, pp. [97]-192. Cover title: JOANNA SOUTHCOTT—2. II(2/8) of
III.

Besides comments, generally in the voice of God, on several Biblical books, there is here a comment on her "awful trial."

(2): Another copy. Cover title: SOUTHCOTT'S PROPHECIES—4. IV(6/10) of VI.

(3): Another copy. Disbound.

30(1): TRUE EXPLANATIONS OF THE BIBLE. PART THE THIRD. London, n. d. [Jones: 1804]. Printed by S. Rousseau. Sold by E. J. Field, C. Abbott, W. Symonds, the Miss Eveleighs, and Mr. Child. Price 18 pence.

8°, pp. [193]-288. Cover title: JOANNA SOUTHCOTT—2. II(3/8) of III.

Further ponderings and divine communications on Biblical books. Further, there is a divine assurance to Joanna that her hatred of Pomeroy was like His [God's] hatred of Satan: "Thy heart is like my heart, and thy feeling is like my feeling. . . ."

(2): Another copy. Cover title: SOUTHCOTT'S PROPHECIES—4. IV(7/10) of VI.

(3): Another copy. Unbound.

31(1): TRUE EXPLANATIONS OF THE BIBLE. PART THE FOURTH. DISPUTES AND CONTROVERSIES WITH MANKIND. London, n. d. Printed by S. Rousseau. Sold by E. J. Field, E. Carpenter, C. Abbott, W. Symonds, the Miss Eveleighs, and Mr. Child. Price 18 pence.

8°, pp. [289]-384. Cover title: JOANNA SOUTHCOTT—2. II(4/8) of III.

Besides further comments on Biblical passages, Joanna answers two published criticisms against her, one by "B. H., a Mechanic," and by "the Rev. Mr. Garrett."

(2): Another copy. Cover title: SOUTHCOTT'S PROPHECIES—4. IV(8/10) of VI.

(3): Another copy. Disbound.

32(1): TRUE EXPLANATIONS OF THE BIBLE. PART THE FIFTH. London, n. d. Printed by S. Rousseau. Sold by E. J. Field, E. Carpenter, C. Abbott, W. Symonds, the Miss Eveleighs, and Mr. Child. Price 1 shilling, 6 pence.

8°, pp. [385]-480. Cover title: JOANNA SOUTHCOTT—2. II(5/8) of III.

Further comments on Biblical passages and remarks on the errors of the Arians and Calvinists.

(2): Another copy. Cover title: SOUTHCOTT'S PROPHECIES—4. IV(9/10) of VI.

(3): Another copy. Disbound.

33(1): TRUE EXPLANATIONS OF THE BIBLE. PART THE SIXTH. London, n. d. [Jones: 1805]. Printed by S. Rousseau. Sold by E. J. Field, E. Carpenter, C. Abbott, W. Symonds, the Miss Eveleighs, and Mr. Child. Price 1 shilling, 6 pence.

8°, pp. [481]-576. Cover title: JOANNA SOUTHCOTT—2. II(6/8) of III.

(2): Another copy. Cover title: SOUTHCOTT'S PROPHECIES—4. IV(10/10) of VI.

(3): Another copy. Disbound.

34a: AN EXPLANATION OF THE PARABLES PUBLISHED IN 1804. London, n. d. [Jones: 1806]. Printed by S. Rousseau. Sold by E. J. Field, C. Abbott, W. Tozer, W. Symonds, the Miss Eveleighs, Samuel Hirst, J. Middleton, and James Light. Price 1 shilling.

8°, pp. [1]-64. Cover title: SOUTHCOTT'S PROPHECIES—5. V(1/9) of VI.

Inscribed in ink on p. 1: "5 Volm. 34 Book. Pray read this Book with Serious Attention and you will see the Wisdom of God."

34b: Second Edition. London, April, 1811. Printed by Galabin and Marchant. Sold by M. Jones, W. Tozer, W. Symonds, the Miss Eveleighs, Samuel Hirst, J. Middleton, and James Light. Price 1 shilling, 3 pence.

Disbound. Annotated and underscored.

34c: Third Edition. London, August, 1823. Printed by W. Marchant. Price 18 pence.

Unbound. Annotated and underscored.

35(1): THE KINGDOM OF CHRIST IS AT HAND. BEING AN ANSWER TO A BOOK, DATED APRIL 8, 1805, PRINTED AT HALIFAX IN YORKSHIRE, AND SIGNED A LOVER OF THE TRUTH OF GOD; BY JOANNA SOUTHCOTT: WITH AN EXPLANATION HOW THE LORD PLEADED WITH MEN IN PAST AGES, AND HOW HE WILL PLEAD WITH ALL FLESH AT HIS SECOND COMING; ALSO AN EXAMINATION OF BAPTISM, AND THE USE AND MEANING OF CHURCH ORDINANCES, AND OF THE SEALING OF THE PEOPLE, IN THESE LATTER DAYS. London, n. d. Printed by A. Seale. Sold by E. J. Field, E. Carpenter, C. Abbott, W. Symonds, Miss Eveleighs, and Mr. Child. Price 1 shilling.

8°, pp. [i-iii]iv, [5]-62. Cover title: JOANNA SOUTHCOTT—1. I(7/10) of III.

After including a quotation from Ephesians 14:21 ("Let all Bitterness, and Wrath, and Anger, and Clamour, and Evil Speaking, be put away from you, with all Malice") on the title page, Joanna calls a critic ignorant and inconsistent and "void of reason." She defends her teachings by referring to the Bible and to her "Divine Communications."

(2): Another copy. Cover title: SOUTHCOTT'S PROPHECIES—5. V(2/9) of VI.

(3): Another copy. Disbound. The name "Waring" inscribed in upper margin of title page. Annotated and underscored.

36a(1): THE SECOND BOOK OF THE SEALED PROPHECIES. London, n. d. [Jones: 1805]. Printed by S. Rousseau. Sold by E. J. Field, E. Carpenter, C. Abbott, W. Symonds, Miss Eveleighs, and Mr. Child. Price 2 shillings, 6 pence.

8°, pp, [1]-136. Cover title: JOANNA SOUTHCOTT—1. I(2/10) of III.

Contains various letters, dreams, and poems. One poem, "Neglect of the Shepherds Proved," is reminiscent in theme of part of Milton's "Lycidas."

Leaves 3 and 4 of the Q gathering unopened at the top, although several other sections of the work are annotated.

(2): Another copy. Cover title: SOUTHCOTT'S PROPHECIES—5. V(3/9) of VI.

(3): Another copy. Disbound. Annotated and underscored.

36b: Second Edition. London, September, 1812, "from the First Edition printed in March, 1805." Printed by Marchant and Galabin. Sold by W. Tozer, W. Symonds, the Miss Eveleighs, S. Hirst, W. Wadman, James Light, Edmund Baker, C. Bradley, and R. Goldsmith. Price 2 shillings, 6 pence.

Unbound.

37a(1): THE ANSWER OF THE REV. THOMAS P. FOLEY, TO THE WORLD, WHO HATH BLAMED HIS FAITH IN BELIEVING IT WAS A COMMAND FROM THE LORD TO PUT IN PRINT SUCH PARABLES, AS HE PRINTED LAST YEAR AT STOURBRIDGE, UNDER THE TITLE "WHAT MANNER OF COMMUNICATIONS ARE THESE?" [By Thomas Foley]. Oldswinford, November, 1805. Printed by J. Heming. Sold by E. J. Field, C. Abbott, W. Tozer, W. Symonds, Miss Eveleighs, Samuel Hirst, and James Light.

8°, pp. [1-3]-96. Cover title: SOUTHCOTT'S PROPHECIES—5. V(4/9) of VI.

Generally included by the catalogers as Book 37 of Joanna Southcott's publications. The work referred to in the title is item 24.

(2): Another copy. Disbound. Annotated and underscored.

37b: Second Edition. London, 1824, "from the First Edition in 1805." Printed by W. Marchant. Price 18 pence.

Disbound. Some annotation and underscoring.

38(1): THE CONTROVERSY BETWEEN JOANNA SOUTHCOTT AND ELIAS CAR-
PENTER, ONE OF HER JUDGES, MADE PUBLIC. PART I. London, n. d.
[Jones: 1805]. Printed by S. Rousseau. Price 9 pence.

8°, pp. [1]-48. Cover title: SOUTHCOTT'S PROPHECIES—5. V(5/9)
of VI.

Carpenter is indicted for following "A different teaching from
Henry Prescott, whom they call Joseph." Prescott is the creator
of the paintings described later.

(2): Another copy. Disbound.

39(1): PART II [of the CONTROVERSY BETWEEN JOANNA SOUTHCOTT AND
ELIAS CARPENTER]. London, n. d. [Jones: 1805]. Printed by S.
Rousseau. Sold by E. J. Field, C. Abbott, W. Tozer, W. Symonds,
the Miss Eveleighs, Samuel Hirst, and James Light. Price 9 pence.

8°, pp. 49-96. Cover title: SOUTHCOTT'S PROPHECIES—5. V(6/9)
of VI.

(2): Another copy. Disbound.

40(1): PART III [of the CONTROVERSY BETWEEN JOANNA SOUTHCOTT AND
ELIAS CARPENTER]. London, n. d. [Jones: 1805]. Printed by S.
Rousseau. Sold by E. J. Field, C. Abbott, W. Tozer, W. Symonds,
the Miss Eveleighs, Samuel Hirst, and James Light. Price 9 pence.

8°, pp. 97-144. Cover title: SOUTHCOTT'S PROPHECIES—5. V(7/9)
of VI.

(2): Another copy. Disbound.

41(1): PART IV [of the CONTROVERSY BETWEEN JOANNA SOUTHCOTT AND
ELIAS CARPENTER]. London, n. d. [Jones: 1805]. Printed by S.
Rousseau. Sold by E. J. Field, C. Abbott, W. Tozer, W. Symonds,
the Miss Eveleighs, Samuel Hirst, and James Light. Price 9 pence.

8°, pp. 145-192. Cover title: SOUTHCOTT'S PROPHECIES—5. V(8/9)
of VI.

(2): Another copy. Disbound.

42(1): PART V [of the CONTROVERSY BETWEEN JOANNA SOUTHCOTT AND
ELIAS CARPENTER]. London, n. d. [Jones: 1805]. Printed by S.
Rousseau. Sold by E. J. Field, C. Abbott, W. Tozer, W. Symonds,
the Miss Eveleighs, Samuel Hirst, and James Light. Price 9 pence.

8°, pp. 193-240. Cover title: SOUTHCOTT'S PROPHECIES—5. V(9/9)
of VI.

(2): Another copy. Disbound.

43: AN ANSWER TO THE WORLD, FOR PUTTING IN PRINT A BOOK IN 1804,
CALLED "COPIES AND PARTS OF COPIES OF LETTERS AND COMMUNICA-
TIONS, WRITTEN FROM JOANNA SOUTHCOTT," AND TRANSMITTED BY
MISS TOWNLEY TO MR. W. SHARP IN LONDON. BEGINNING WITH THE

PARABLE OF THE LITTLE FLOCK OF SHEEP: IN WHICH REASONS ARE GIVEN, IN ANSWER TO THE MOCKERY AND RIDICULE OF MEN, FOR PRINTING THE PARABLES AND FABLES, WHICH WERE PUBLISHED FROM DIVINE COMMAND IN THAT BOOK. [By William Sharp.] London, 1806. Printed by S. Rousseau. Price 1 shilling, 6 pence.

8°, pp. [1-3]-96. Sewn.

Sharp defends Joanna's dreams, visitations of angels, and parables generally against "literary characters of the present age." He mentions the names of no specific attackers or non-believers.

44: THE FULL ASSURANCE THAT THE KINGDOM OF CHRIST IS AT HAND, FROM THE SIGNS OF THE TIMES. London, n. d. [Jones: 1806]. Printed by W. Marchant.

8°, pp. [1]-64. Disbound.

A catalogue of famines, storms, earthquakes, and other world-wide disasters with accompanying communications to prove that they were signs of the end to come.

This copy is perhaps a second edition, for Jones lists Rousseau as the original printer in 1806. However, the initial leaves in the A and B gatherings in this copy bear watermarks which appear to read 1806.

45: [REMARKS AND INQUIRIES ON THE REV. I. COCKIN'S SERMON]. Jones lists this title as Book 45. However, no book with such a title exists in the collection or, perhaps, anywhere. Present-day followers of Joanna Southcott refer to John Crossley's LETTERS, AND OBSERVATIONS, TO MINISTERS as Book 45 (see item 163). Since the first letter in this latter work is to "The Rev. Mr. Cockin" commenting on a sermon by him, almost certainly the two are the same.

46: THE LONG-WISHED-FOR REVOLUTION ANNOUNCED TO BE AT HAND IN A BOOK LATELY PUBLISHED, BY L. MAYER, WHEN, AS HE SAYS, "GOD WILL CLEANSE THE EARTH BY HIS JUDGMENTS, AND WHEN ALL DOMINIONS SHALL SERVE THE MOST HIGH." EXPLAINED BY JOANNA SOUTHCOTT; WITH LETTERS TO HER, FROM THE AUTHOR OF THAT BOOK, AND HER ANSWERS; TO WHICH ARE ADDED OBSERVATIONS UPON HIS WRONG APPLICATION OF THE SCRIPTURE PROPHECIES IN GENERAL, AND HIS IGNORANCE, PARTICULARLY IN WISHING FOR A PERIOD OF JUDGMENTS, WITHOUT EXPLAINING WHAT WILL BRING THIS HAPPY DELIVERANCE IN THE END, WHICH SHALL BE TO THE GLORY OF GOD, AND TO THE GOOD OF THE WHOLE HUMAN RACE, BY BEING UNITED TO HIS SPIRIT, AND BEARING HIS IMAGE, AND SATAN CAST OUT, SO THAT THE EARTH MAY BE AT REST FOR ONE THOUSAND YEARS. London, 1806. Printed by S. Rousseau. Sold by E. J. Field, C. Abbott, W. Tozer, W. Symonds, the Miss Eveleighs, Samuel Hirst, J. Middleton, and James Light.

8°, pp. [1-3]-96. Disbound. Annotated and underscored.

Lewis Mayer's answer to this book by Joanna is listed as item 186.

47: ANSWER TO MR. BROTHERS'S BOOK, PUBLISHED IN SEPTEMBER 1806, AND OBSERVATIONS ON HIS FORMER WRITINGS; ALSO, A LETTER SENT TO MR. HUNTINGTON WITH REMARKS ON THE CALVINIST AND ROMAN CATHOLIC DOCTRINES, & C. & C. AND THE UNBELIEF OF THE JEWS AT THE DESTRUCTION OF JERUSALEM. London, n. d. [Jones: December, 1806]. Printed by S. Rousseau. Sold by E. J. Field, C. Abbott, W. Tozer, W. Symonds, the Miss Eveleighs, Samuel Hirst, J. Middleton, and James Light. Price 1 shilling.

8°, pp. [1]-64. Disbound. Annotated and underscored.

48a: A CAUTION AND INSTRUCTION TO THE SEALED, THAT THEY MAY KNOW FOR WHAT THEY ARE SEALED. London, n. d. [Jones: 1807]. Printed by W. Marchant. Sold by E. J. Field, W. Tozer, W. Symonds, the Miss Eveleighs, S. Hirst, J. Middleton, and James Light.

8°, pp. [1]-24. Disbound. Annotated and underscored.

48b: [Second edition: *not seen*]

48c: [Third edition: *not seen*]

48d: Fourth Edition. London, March, 1814. Printed by Marchant and Galabin. Sold by W. Tozer, the Miss Eveleighs, S. Hirst, W. Wadman, James Light, Edmund Baker, C. Bradley, John Nesbit, and T. Turpin. Price 6 pence.

Unbound.

49: AN ACCOUNT OF THE TRIALS ON BILLS OF EXCHANGE, WHEREIN THE DECEIT OF MR. JOHN KING AND HIS CONFEDERATES, UNDER THE PRETENCE OF LENDING MONEY IS EXPOSED, AND THEIR ARTS BROUGHT TO LIGHT. London, n. d. [Jones: July, 1807]. Printed by S. Rousseau. Sold by E. J. Field, W. Tozer, W. Symonds, the Miss Eveleighs, Samuel Hirst, J. Middleton, and James Light.

8°, pp. [1]-72. Disbound.

Some annotation. Numbers of pages in the volume from which this copy was taken are inscribed in the upper margin (from 1959-2030).

50: AN ANSWER TO A SERMON PUBLISHED AND PREACHED BY MR. SMITH, ON TUESDAY EVENING, MARCH 15, 1808, AT BEERSHEBA-CHAPEL, PROSPECT-PLACE, ST. GEORGE'S FIELD. London, n. d. [Jones: June, 1808]. Printed by W. Marchant. Sold by E. J. Field, W. Tozer, W. Symonds, the Miss Eveleighs, S. Hirst, J. Middleton, and James Light. Price 2 shillings.

8°, pp. [1]-83. Disbound.

The title of Smith's book was THE LYING PROPHETESS DETECTED. This copy annotated and underscored. Errata on p. 83 notes that the page numbers in the E gathering were the numbers for the F gathering: instead of E being pp. 33-40, the numbers should be 25-32.

51: No Title [Jones: ANSWER TO FALSE DOCTRINES, AND THE CRYING SINS OF THE NATION]. London, 1808. Printed by W. Marchant. Sold by E. J. Field, W. Tozer, W. Symonds, the Miss Eveleighs, S. Hirst, J. Middleton, and James Light.

8°, pp. [1]-48. Disbound.

A note to readers on p. 1 proclaims "From this Publication the Readers may discern what is hastening upon the Land, as they are daily provoking the Lord to Anger, by false Doctrine, as well as the crying Sins of the Nation." Annotated.

52: A TRUE PICTURE OF THE WORLD AND A LOOKING-GLASS FOR ALL MEN. London, n. d. [Jones: 1809]. Printed by Galabin and Marchant. Sold by E. J. Field, W. Tozer, W. Symonds, the Miss Eveleighs, S. Hirst, J. Middleton, and James Light. Price 1 shilling.

8°, pp. [1]-48. Disbound. Annotated.

53(1): TRUE EXPLANATIONS OF THE BIBLE. PART THE SEVENTH. London, March, 1810. Printed by Galabin and Marchant. Sold by E. J. Field, W. Tozer, W. Symonds, the Miss Eveleighs, S. Hirst, J. Middleton, and James Light. Price 1 shilling.

8°, pp. [577]-624. Cover title: SOUTHCOTT'S PROPHECIES [−6]. VI(2/14) of VI.

There is included here also "An Answer to Hann's False Assertions in his Handbills & Advertisements: Together with an Account of Ann Moore Living Without Food, & c."

(2): Another copy. Sewn.

54(1): THE CONTROVERSY OF THE SPIRIT WITH THE WORLDLY WISE, AS GIVEN THROUGH JOANNA SOUTHCOTT. London, 1811. Printed by Galabin and Marchant. Sold by M. Jones, W. Tozer, W. Symonds, the Miss Eveleighs, Samuel Hirst, and James Light. Price 1 shilling.

8°, pp. [1-2]-52. Cover title: SOUTHCOTT'S PROPHECIES [−6]. VI(4/14) of VI.

(2): Another copy. Disbound. Annotated.

55(1): A CONTINUATION OF THE CONTROVERSY WITH THE WORLDLY WISE. London, April 30, 1811. Printed by Galabin and Marchant. Sold by M. Jones, W. Tozer, W. Symonds, the Miss Eveleighs, Samuel Hirst, J. Middleton, and James Light.

8°, pp. [1]-52. Cover title: SOUTHCOTT'S PROPHECIES [—6]. VI(4/14) of VI.

(2): Another copy. Sewn. Annotated.

(3): Another copy. Unbound. The following inscribed on p. 1: "Elias Galpin—The Gift of his Brother Robt. Hoadby-ashe, D. D."

56(1): AN ANSWER TO THOMAS PAINE'S THIRD PART OF THE AGE OF REASON, PUBLISHED BY D. I. EATON; LIKEWISE TO S. LANE, A CAL-VINISTIC PREACHER, AT YEOVIL, IN SOMERSETSHIRE; AND TO HEWSON CLARKE, EDITOR OF "THE SCOURGE," AND LATE OF EMANUEL COL-LEGE, CAMBRIDGE. London, n. d. [Jones: 1812]. Printed by Marchant and Galabin. Sold by W. Tozer, W. Symonds, the Miss Eveleighs, S. Hirst, J. Middleton, James Light, Edmund Baker, and C. Bradley. Price 1 shilling, 3 pence.

8°, pp. [1-2]-66. Cover title: SOUTHCOTT'S PROPHECIES [—6]. VI(5/14) of VI.

(2): Another copy. Unbound.

57(1): THE BOOK OF WONDERS, MARVELLOUS AND TRUE. London, 1813. Printed by Marchant and Galabin. Sold by W. Tozer, W. Symonds, the Miss Eveleighs, S. Hirst, W. Wadman, James Light, Edmund Baker, C. Bradley, R. Goldsmith, and T. Turpin. Price 2 shillings.

8°, pp. [1-3]-88. Cover title: SOUTHCOTT'S PROPHECIES [—6]. VI(6/14) of VI.

By "Wonders" Joanna means "miraculous happenings," such as her receiving divine communications.

(2): Another copy. Sewn and uncut.

58(1): THE SECOND BOOK OF WONDERS, MORE MARVELLOUS THAN THE FIRST. London, 1813. Printed by Marchant and Galabin. Sold by W. Tozer, W. Symonds, the Miss Eveleighs, S. Hirst, W. Wadman, James Light, Edmund Baker, R. Goldsmith, and T. Turpin. Price 2 shillings, 6 pence.

8°, pp. [1-3]-116. Cover title: SOUTHCOTT'S PROPHECIES [—6]. VI(7/14) of VI.

(2): Another copy. Unbound.

59(1): COPIES OF LETTERS SENT TO THE CLERGY OF EXETER, FROM 1796 TO 1800, WITH COMMUNICATIONS AND PROPHECIES PUT IN THE NEWSPAPERS IN 1813. London, 1813. Printed by Marchant and Galabin. Sold by W. Tozer, the Miss Eveleighs, W. Wad-man, James Light, Edmund Baker, C. Bradley, John Nesbit, and T. Turpin. Price 1 shilling, 3 pence.

8°, pp. [1-3]-64. Cover title: SOUTHCOTT'S PROPHECIES [—6].
VI(8/14) of VI.

(2): Another copy. Disbound.

(3): Another copy. Unbound. Annotated.

60(1): WISDOM EXCELLETH THE WEAPONS OF WAR, AND HEREIN IS
SHEWN THAT JUDGMENTS ARE THE STRANGE WORKS OF THE LORD,
BUT MERCY HIS DARLING ATTRIBUTE. London, 1814. Printed by
W. Marchant. Sold by W. Tozer, W. Symonds, the Miss Eveleighs,
S. Hirst, W. Wadman, James Light, Edmund Baker, C. Bradley,
R. Goldsmith, and T. Turpin. Price 1 shilling.

8°, pp. [1]-48. Cover title: SOUTHCOTT'S PROPHECIES [—6].

(2): Another copy. Unbound.

(3): Another copy. Unbound.

61(1): THE THIRD BOOK OF WONDERS, ANNOUNCING THE COMING OF
SHILOH; WITH A CALL TO THE HEBREWS. London, 1814. Printed by
W. Marchant. Sold by W. Tozer, the Miss Eveleighs, S. Hirst,
W. Wadman, James Light, Edmund Baker, C. Bradley, John Nesbit,
and T. Turpin. Price 1 shilling, 3 pence.

8°, pp. [1-3]-64. Cover title: SOUTHCOTT'S PROPHECIES [—6].
VI(10/14) of VI.

(2): Another copy. Disbound.

62(1): THE FOURTH BOOK OF WONDERS, BEING THE ANSWER OF THE
LORD TO THE HEBREWS. London, 1814. Printed by W. Marchant.
Sold by M. Jones, J. Hunt, W. Tozer, the Miss Eveleighs,
S. Hirst, W. Wadman, James Light, Edmund Baker, C. Bradley,
John Nesbit, and T. Turpin. Price 1 shilling, 6 pence.

8°, pp. [1-3]-80. Cover title: SOUTHCOTT'S PROPHECIES [—6].
VI(11/14) of VI.

(2): Another copy. Disbound.

63(1): THE FIFTH BOOK OF WONDERS, ANNOUNCING THE EVENT HAVING
TAKEN PLACE, WHICH WAS PROMISED IN THE FOURTH BOOK SHOULD
BE IN MAY. WITH A FURTHER EXPLANATION OF THE FOUR FORMER
BOOKS; ALSO AN ANSWER TO THE ADDRESS OF THE REV. JAMES HEARN,
CURATE OF BRIXHAM, DEVON; AND TO THE MOCKERY OF OTHERS.
London, 1814. Printed by W. Marchant. Sold by T. Huntley, W.
Tozer, the Miss Eveleighs, S. Hirst, W. Wadman, James Light,
Edmund Baker, C. Bradley, John Nesbit, and T. Turpin. Price 16
pence.

8°, pp. [1-3]-72. Cover title: SOUTHCOTT'S PROPHECIES [—6].
VI(12/14) of VI.

(2): Another copy. Disbound.

64(1): A COMMUNICATION SENT IN A LETTER TO THE REVEREND MR. P. IN 1797, WITH AN EXPLANATION THEREON NOW. London, 1814. Printed by W. Marchant. Sold by T. Huntley, W. Tozer, the Miss Eveleighs, S. Hirst, W. Wadman, James Light, Edmund Baker, C. Bradley, John Nesbit, and T. Turpin. Price 6 pence.

8°, pp. [1]-24. Cover title: SOUTHCOTT'S PROPHECIES [−6]. VI(13/14) of VI.

(2): Another copy. Unbound.

65(1): PROPHECIES ANNOUNCING THE BIRTH OF THE PRINCE OF PEACE, EXTRACTED FROM THE WORKS OF JOANNA SOUTHCOTT; TO WHICH ARE ADDED A FEW REMARKS THEREON, MADE BY HERSELF. London, n. d. [Jones: September, 1814]. Printed by W. Marchant. Sold by W. Tozer, the Miss Eveleighs, S. Hirst, W. Wadman, James Light, Edmund Baker, C. Bradley, John Nesbit, and T. Turpin. Price 10 pence.

8°, pp. [1]-40. Cover title: SOUTHCOTT'S PROPHECIES [−6]. VI(14/14) of VI.

Interesting here are Joanna's answers to those critics who accuse her of dishonesty.

(2): Another copy.

(3): Another copy. Disbound.

B : JOANNA SOUTHCOTT:

POSTHUMOUS PUBLICATIONS

66: THE SIXTH BOOK OF WONDERS! BEING A VERBATIM COPY OF THE SIX SEALED LETTERS DATED SEPTEMBER 1813, ANNOUNCING "THIS DAY THE REV. JOSEPH POMEROY MARRIED TO JOANNA SOUTHCOTT, THE GREAT PROPHETESS AND THE WONDER OF THE WORLD." Edited by Daniel Jones. Bath, 1852. Printed and published by Daniel Jones.

8°, pp. [1-4]-92. Paper wrappers.

67: ON THE FAST DAY, 1797, THE FOLLOWING WAS GIVEN TO JOANNA SOUTHCOTT, IN ANSWER TO THE REV. J. POMEROY, SAYING, "THAT THERE WERE MORE THAN FIFTY RIGHTEOUS TO SAVE THE NATION FROM GOD'S JUDGMENTS." Warrington, n. d. Printed by Hatton.

8°, pp. [1]-4. Unbound.

Not listed by Jones and therefore probably not printed prior to December, 1814.

68: THE SCRIPTURES OF THE HOLY TRINITY. THE NEW TESTAMENT EXPLAINED IN ENGLAND BY THE VOICE OF THE SPIRIT OF CHRIST. PART IV. HEBREWS TO TIMOTHY. Unknown editor. London, n. d. Published by Job Caudwell. Price 3 shillings.

8°, pp. [97]-200. Paper wrappers.

A collection of Joanna's comments on the scripture. A copy of Jones's "Catalogue of Books Published by Joanna Southcott" is printed on the verso of the front wrapper and both sides back wrapper.

69: PROVERB. N. p., n. d. Newspaper clipping.

1.5 x 6.8 cm.

Reads "To acknowledge our faults when we are blamed is modesty; to discover them to one's friends in ingenuousness is confidence; but to preach them to the world if one does not take care, is pride." Joanna's name is printed beneath the proverb, but Joanna rarely wrote so succinctly.

(70-153) A collection of pamphlets printed mostly from previously unpublished Southcott manuscripts by Daniel Jones and/or Lavinia Elizabeth Chapman Jones. The dates on the manuscripts range from 1792 to 1814 and the publications were issued in Bradford at various times between 1846 and 1860. Priced variously at 1d., 3d., and 6d. each, the pamphlets are all 8°. Occasionally two or three or more manuscripts will be published together, but generally each communication or letter is issued separately, the pagination starting over with each new pamphlet. All the pamphlets are unbound, seemingly removed from a volume. Titles, dates of the manuscripts, and dates of publication arranged according to date of publication are as follows:

70: COMMUNICATION BY THE SMALL STILL VOICE, ON MONARCHY IN FRANCE. MS dated London, December 21, 1804. Published in 1846. 13 pp. Printed with item 71.

71: COMMUNICATION FROM THE SPIRIT OF CHRIST. SMALL STILL VOICE,— JOANNA SOUTHCOTT, ON THE JUBILEE. MS dated October 28, 1809. Published in 1846. 3 pp. Printed with item 70.

72: COMMUNICATION GIVEN GOOD-FRIDAY, 1799. MS dated 1799. Published April, 1853. 5 pp.

73: COMMUNICATION ON THE LIKENESS OF MEN TO THE FALLEN ANGELS WHEN THEY WERE CAST OUT OF HEAVEN. MS dated May 1, 1801. Published April, 1853. 11 pp.

74: COMMUNICATION ON THE TEMPORAL AND SPIRITUAL SWORD. MS dated July 27, 1803. Published April, 1853. 9 pp.

75: COMMUNICATION UPON BAPTISM. N. d. Published April, 1853. 8 pp.

76: COMMUNICATION WHEREIN IT IS ASCERTAINED THAT IT IS THE SPIRIT, AND NOT THE BODY OF THE WICKED WHICH GOETH TO HELL. MS dated August 22, 1804. Published May, 1853. 2 pp. Printed with items 77 and 78.

77: COMMUNICATION IN ANSWER TO AN ENQUIRY CONCERNING MATTHEW XXV.—41 to 46. ON THE WORD "EVERLASTING." MS dated February 26, 1811. Published May, 1853. 3 pp. Printed with items 76 and 78.

78: COMMUNICATION CONCERNING ORDINATION. MS dated June 9, 1811. Published May, 1853. 3 pp. Printed with items 76 and 77.

79: COMMUNICATION UPON THE TWO WITNESSES. MS dated December 11, 1811. Published May, 1853. 10 pp. Printed with item 80.

80: A CONTINUATION AND FURTHER OPENING OF THE SUBJECT OF THE TWO WITNESSES. MS dated December 17, 1811. Published May, 1853. 8 pp. Printed with item 79.

81: COMMUNICATION UPON THE LAW AGAINST SATAN. MS dated July 18, 1813. Published May, 1853. 9 pp.

82: COMMUNICATION OF THE OATH OF SWEARING ALLEGIANCE. MS dated Old Swinford, August 7, 1803. Published June, 1853. 5 pp. Printed with item 83.

83: COMMUNICATION ON THE OATH OF ALLEGIANCE. MS dated Old Swinford, August 11, 1803. Published June, 1853. 3 pp. Printed with item 82.

84: COMMUNICATION ON PRAYER; IN WHICH IS INTRODUCED A REFERENCE TO THE CONDUCT OF DANIEL TOWARDS THE PRIESTS, IN THE HISTORY OF "BEL AND THE DRAGON." MS dated March 27, 1804. Published June, 1853. 7 pp.

85: COMMUNICATION: AN EXTRACT UPON THUNDER AND LIGHTNING. MS dated September 2, 1807. Published June, 1853. 3 pp.

86: ASTROLOGY AND WITCHCRAFT. MS dated July 11, 1808. Published June, 1853. 5 pp.

87: COMMUNICATION ON THE OATH. N. d. Published June, 1853. 7 pp.

88: COMMUNICATION [On Joanna's being misled]. MS dated January 9, 1800. Published July, 1853. 2 pp.

89: COMMUNICATION. PROPHECY UPON THE FRENCH NATION. MS dated August 31, 1803. Published July, 1853. 3 pp. Printed with item 93.

90: COMMUNICATION [On Joanna's persecution]. MS dated Wednesday, October 31, 1804. Published July, 1853. 4 pp.

91: COMMUNICATION ON THE PARABLE OF "THE HIGHWAYMAN." MS dated November 6-7, 1804. Published July, 1853. 9 pp. Printed with item 95.

92: COMMUNICATION OF COMING IN A CLOUD, CONTINUED. MS dated November 7, 1804. Published July, 1853. 6 pp.

93: EXTRACT FROM A LETTER TO MR. PRIESTLY. MS dated June 21, 1805. Published July, 1853. 3 pp. Printed with item 89.

94: COMMUNICATION ON ESDRAS, V. 5 AND VI. MS dated December 18, 1805. Published July, 1853. 4 pp.

95: EXTRACT FROM A LETTER ON NOT WEARING ANY MARK. MS dated December 13, 1814. Published July, 1853. 1 p. Printed with item 91.

96: COMMUNICATION OF SPIRITUAL AND TEMPORAL BUILDERS. MS dated May 26, 1806. Published September, 1853. 7 pp. Printed with item 98.

97: COMMUNICATION ON THE CHILDREN OF THIS WORLD ARE WISER IN THEIR GENERATION THAN THE CHILDREN OF LIGHT. MS dated November 26, 1806. Published September, 1853. 8 pp.

98: THE MEANING OF THE WORD "RULERS." N. d. Published September, 1853. 1 p. Printed with item 96.

99: COMMUNICATION IN ANSWER TO THE JUDGMENT OF FRIENDS AT BIRMINGHAM. N. d. Published October, 1853. 4 pp. Printed with items 100, 102, 103, and 104.

100: COMMUNICATION UPON CAIN'S MADNESS POSSESSING THREE-FOURTHS OF THE HABITABLE GLOBE. N. d. Published October, 1853. 1½ pp. Printed with items 99, 102, 103, and 104.

101: COMMUNICATION UPON THE PROPHECIES OF JOHN THE BAPTIST. N. d. Published October, 1853. 8 pp.

102: EXTRACT FROM A COMMUNICATION ON CHARGES. N. d. Published October, 1853. ½ p. Printed with items 99, 100, 103, and 104.

103: FRAGMENT FROM A COMMUNICATION: A WARNING TO ENGLAND. N. d. Published October, 1853. 1 p. Printed with items 99, 100, 102, and 104.

104: ON TEMPTATIONS. N. d. Published October, 1853. 1 p. Printed with items 99, 100, 102, and 103.

105: COMMUNICATION UPON THE DUTY OF THE JEWS. MS dated 1794. Published December, 1853. 1 p. Printed with items 107 and 109.

106: COMMUNICATION SENT TO MR. POMEROY. MS dated Christmas, 1800. Published December, 1853. 4 pp. Printed with items 108, 110, 111, and 112.

107: COMMUNICATION ON "JESUS CHRIST TO BE SEEN THREE DAYS AND THREE NIGHTS IN THE CENTRE OF THE EARTH." FOR EVERY EYE TO SEE. MS dated August 4, 1806. Published December, 1853. 8 pp. Printed with items 105 and 109.

108: COMMUNICATION IN EXPLANATION OF THE CONCEPTION. MS dated February 28, 1813. Published December, 1853. 9 pp. Printed with items 106, 110, 111, and 112.

109: COMMUNICATION ON SPIRITS IN PRISON. MS dated May 28, 1813. Published December, 1853. 1 p. Printed with items 105 and 107.

110: COMMUNICATION TAKEN OUT OF THE SEALED WRITINGS. MS dated Saturday, October 30, 1813. Published December, 1853. 2 pp. Printed with items 106, 108, 111, and 112.

111: AN EXPLANATION OF THE VISITATION OF THE SPIRIT TO JOANNA SOUTHCOTT. MS dated February 28, 1814. Published December, 1853. 10 pp. Printed with items 106, 108, 110, and 112.

112: COMMUNICATION ON QUEEN ESTHER. N. d. Pubished December, 1853. 2 pp. Printed with items 106, 108, 110, and 111.

113: EXTRACT FROM A LETTER ADDRESSED TO MR. G. WOOLCOTT, OF EXETER. MS dated December 6, 1806. Published February, 1854. 2 pp. Printed with items 114, 115, and 116.

114: EXTRACT FROM A LETTER RESPECTING THE SEALS BEING PUT INTO THE COFFIN WITH THE INDIVIDUAL WHO LEAVES THE EARTH. MS dated July 14, 1808. Published February, 1854. 2 pp. Printed with items 113, 115, and 116.

115: ORDERS ABOUT BELIEVERS GOING TO CHURCH. MS dated May 24, 1809. Published February, 1854. 13 pp. Printed with items 113, 114, and 116.

116: COMMUNICATION ON THE SACRAMENT TO BE RECEIVED AT THE CHURCH. MS dated November 7, 1809. Published February, 1854. 4 pp. Printed with items 113, 114, and 115.

117: COMMUNICATION BY THE SMALL STILL VOICE ON THE HISTORY OF JOSEPHUS. MS dated July 23, 1806. Published in 1856. 12 pp.

118: EXTRACT FROM A COMMUNICATION BY THE "SMALL STILL VOICE" ON MALICE IN MEN. MS dated 1797. Published in 1797. 1 p. Printed with item 128.

119: COMMUNICATION GIVEN BY THE "SMALL STILL VOICE" UPON "TO-
MORROW IS A DAY UNKNOWN." MS dated July 21, 1799. Published
in 1859. 1 p. Printed with items 121 and 122.

120: COMMUNICATION ON THE OLD AND YOUNG PROPHET. MS dated
May 24, 1802. Published in 1859. 5 pp. Printed with item 132.

121: COMMUNICATION IN ANSWER TO BARON SWEDENBORG'S DESCRIPTION
OF HEAVEN. MS dated July 10, 1802. Published in 1859. 2 pp.
Printed with items 119 and 122.

122: COMMUNICATION UPON THE TEACHINGS OF BARON SWEDENBORG.
MS dated July 10, 1802. Published in 1859. 5 pp. Printed with
items 119 and 121.

123: COMMUNICATION ON CHARITY. MS dated July 25, 1802. Published in 1859. 2 pp. Printed with item 126.

124: ANSWER TO MR. CARPENTER'S LETTERS, AND THE CHAPTERS IN THE
BIBLE, WHICH HE SENT TO JOANNA. MS dated August 11, 1803.
Published in 1859. 11 pp. Printed with items 127 and 140.

125: EXTRACT FROM A LETTER IN ANSWER TO MR. W. INGALL. MS dated
Old Swinford, August 29, 1803. Published in 1859. 6 pp. Printed
with item 134.

126: COMMUNICATION ON THE FOLLY OF DECEPTION. MS dated September 4, 1803. Published in 1859. 6 pp. Printed with item 123.

127: COMMUNICATION FROM THE SPIRIT OF THE SMALL STILL VOICE ON
PROTECTION FROM EVERY DANGER. MS dated December 6, 1803.
Published in 1859. 4 pp. Printed with items 124 and 140.

128: COMMUNICATION BY THE "SMALL STILL VOICE" IN EXPLANATION
OF MANY SCRIPTURES, ESPECIALLY ON THE SUBJECT OF THE MIGHTY
COUNSELLOR, & C. MS dated August 26-31, 1804. Published in
1859. 31 pp. Printed with item 118.

129: COMMUNICATION ON THE SUN DIAL AND GRAND DIAL. MS dated
July 12, 1805. Published in 1859. 10 pp.

130: COMMUNICATION UPON PARABLES. MS dated January 1, 1806.
Published in 1859. 4 pp.

131: COPY OF A LETTER: ENGLAND MAY BE A HAPPY LAND; ALSO THE
WARNING GIVEN BY MR. BROTHERS. MS dated April 2, 1806. Published in 1859. 10 pp.

132: COMMUNICATION IN ANSWER TO MR. BROTHER'S BOOK AND A VISION HE HAD OF TWO SUNS. MS dated May 3, 1806. Published in 1859. 11 pp. Printed with item 120.

133: COMMUNICATION, ON THE PERSECUTION CAUSED BY THE DEVIL AND THE POSSIBILITY OF HIS VISIBLE APPEARANCE. MS dated January 14, 1807. Published in 1859. 9 pp.

134: COMMUNICATION, HOW TO CONTEND WITH EVIL SPIRITS, AN EXTRACT. MS dated October 1, 1807. Published in 1859. 2 pp. Printed with item 125.

135: COMMUNICATION. LOVE AND ANGER. MS dated Sunday, September 9, 1810. Published in 1859. 10 pp.

136: COMMUNICATION UPON THE PROPRIETY OF THE FRIENDS MEETING TOGETHER. MS dated October 8, 1810. Published in 1859. 1 p. Printed with items 139 and 141.

137: COMMUNICATION ON THE COMET. MS dated 1811. Published in 1859. 5 pp. Printed with item 138.

138: COMMUNICATION GIVEN IN ANSWER TO A BELIEVER BEING BOUND FOR A FRIEND, AND WHO WAS CALLED UPON TO PAY THE BOND. N. d. Published in 1859. 3 pp. Printed with item 137.

139: COMMUNICATION ON THE SECOND SEALING. N. d. Published in 1859. ½ p. Printed with items 136 and 141.

140: FRAGMENT SHEWING THE PRAYER FOR THIS PRESENT TIME. N. d. Published in 1859. 1 p. Printed with items 124 and 127.

141: THE SMALL STILL VOICE. N. d. Published in 1859. ½ p. Printed with items 136 and 138.

142: COMMUNICATION BY THE "SMALL STILL VOICE" ON PSALM XCII. MS dated July 25, 1803. Published in 1860. 3 pp. Printed with items 144 and 148.

143: COMMUNICATION IN ANSWER TO A CIRCUMSTANCE WHICH CAUSED SOME DISPUTE. MS dated February 8, 1806. Published in 1860. 8 pp.

144: LETTER TO MR. WADMAN, RESPECTING THE DUTY OF WARNING THE PEOPLE. MS dated August 8, 1806. Published in 1860. 3 pp. Printed with items 142 and 148.

145: COMMUNICATION BY THE "SMALL STILL VOICE" ON THE MEANING OF THE STONE CUT OUT WITHOUT HANDS. MS dated September 2, 1806. Published in 1860. 8 pp.

146: COMMUNICATION GIVEN BY THE "SMALL STILL VOICE" ON THE SEVENTH ANGEL SOUNDED. MS dated February 28, 1810. Published in 1860. 4 pp. Printed with item 147.

147: COMMUNICATION IN ANSWER TO THE PEOPLE AT BIRMINGHAM, WHO MADE GREAT DISTURBANCE BY THROWING BLOOD AND GRAINS INTO THE MEETINGS, AND OTHER ANNOYANCES. MS dated February 4, 1814. Published in 1860. 4 pp. Printed with item 146.

148: COMMUNICATION GIVEN BY THE "SMALL STILL VOICE" ON THE COT. MS dated May 10, 1814. Published in 1860. 2 pp. Printed with items 142 and 144.

149: COMMUNICATION GIVEN BY THE SPIRIT ON THE VISION OF THE CANDLE, ALSO AN EXPLANATION OF JOANNA'S ILLNESS. MS dated August 26, 1814. Published in 1860. 10 pp.

150: COMMUNICATION ON TROUBLES IN ENGLAND. MS dated Sunday morning, August 10, 1800. N. d. 9 pp.

151: COMMUNICATION ON JOANNA'S DEATH: SHE BEING THE RISING AND SETTING SUN. MS dated October 2, 1803. N. d. 10 pp.

152: COMMUNICATION FROM THE "SMALL STILL VOICE IN EXPLANATION OF A DREAM UPON WAX WORK." MS dated January 5, 1806. N. d. 6 pp.

153: COMMUNICATION UPON THE BIBLE SOCIETY AND UPON "THE INFANT OF DAYS." N. d. 4 pp.

C : JOANNA SOUTHCOTT:

RELATED WORKS

154: "AMRAPHEL." TRUTH'S HUMBLE APPEAL UNTO ALL MEN. London, n. d. [Watermark reads 1804]. Printed by J. Barnes and W. Rutter. 8°, pp. [1-3]-15. Unbound.

An answer to "Boanerges, —J. T. —and Unbeliever," who were currently criticizing Joanna Southcott and Joseph Prescott.

155: BEAUMONT, REV. G[EORGE]. FIXED STARS; OR, AN ANALYZATION AND REFUTATION OF ASTROLOGY: THE PRINCIPLES OF THIS SCIENCE BEING PLAINLY LAID OPEN, AND THEIR ABSURDITY AND WICKEDNESS DEMONSTRATED. TO WHICH IS ADDED, THE TESTIMONIES OF MANY LEARNED MEN AGAINST THE SCIENCE OF ASTROLOGY. Leeds, 1803. Printed by Edward Baines. Sold by G. Beaumont, Binns, Bothamley, and Holmes; Brooke and Garnet; Edwards; Farrer; Todd; Canne; Smith; Thompson; Clark; and Pratt. Price 1 shilling.

8°, pp. [i-iii]-iv, [1-3]-40. Cover title: JOANNA SOUTHCOTT—1. I(9/10) of III.

Beaumont answers the arguments of certain astrologers, especially one who wrote in a letter to the *Leeds Mercury* that the stars were composed of water. Included also are other folk interpretations of the composition, structure, and origin of heavenly bodies.

156: BENNETT, G[EORGE]. A WARNING TO THE NATION, FROM THE PROPHECIES OF JOANNA SOUTHCOTT. London, n. d. Published by John Spencer. Printed by Hancock. Sold by "all Booksellers." Price 2 pence.

8°, pp. [1-3]-15. Unbound.

A review of Joanna's mission presented through extracts from her printed works. A note on p. 2 stating the purpose of the tract is signed by G[eorge] Bennett, Thomas Malby, John Hagger, John Pye, James Sinnock, John Spencer, and John Bennett.

157: ———. Another copy. Unbound.

158: CARPENTER, ELIAS. MODERN REALITIES; OR, THE SUBSTANCE FOL-
LOWING THE SHADOW: BEING A REPLY TO "MODERN VISIONARIES,"
BY J. T. WHEREIN ARE DISPLAYED THE FALLACY OF JUDGING WITHOUT
INQUIRY, AND THE INJUSTICE OF CONDEMNING CHARACTERS ON MERE
REPORT; SHEWING THAT THE SYSTEM IN WHICH WE ARE ENGAGED,
HAS NO OTHER OBJECT THAN THE PREPARING MEN'S MINDS FOR
THE GLORIOUS PERIOD THE POET HAD IN VIEW. London, 1805.
Printed by W. Marchant. Sold by E. J. Field.

8°, pp. [1-3]-16. Unbound.

159: ————. NOCTURNAL ALARM; BEING AN ESSAY ON PROPHECY &
VISION: OR A BRIEF EXAMINATION OF SOME REMARKABLE THINGS
UNDER THOSE HEADS WHICH HAVE RECENTLY APPEARED IN THE
WORLD: AND WHICH, FROM THEIR EXTRAORDINARY IMPORT, SEEM
WORTHY OF THE ENQUIRY AND CONSIDERATION OF ALL SERIOUS AND
WELL-DISPOSED CHRISTIANS. London, 1803. Printed by W. Smith.
Sold by E. J. Field. Price 18 pence.

8°, pp. [1-3]-114. Unbound.

The introduction argues for the necessity of the ignorant leading
the learned at times.

160: ————. WHO ARE THE DELUDED? OR MYSTERY UNMASKED: BEING
A FEW EXTRACTS FROM A FAITHFUL RECORD OF SPIRITUAL TEACH-
INGS: VIZ. REVELATIONS AND VISIONS, COMMUNICATED TO A DECEASED
CHARACTER: SUBMITTED, WITH HUMILITY, TO THOSE WHO WISH
TO EXPLORE THE TRUTH AND DETECT ERROR. London, 1805. Printed
by W. Marchant. Sold by E. J. Field.

8°, pp. [1-3]-100. Disbound.

Tells of an anonymous visionary (called "Jerusha" by Carpenter)
who had a series of strange visions of a religious nature. This
visionary is perhaps Joseph Prescott, whom Carpenter later followed.

161: CARPENTER, S. CATHERINE. ARE THESE THINGS SO? BEING REMARKS
ON "DEMOCRACY DETECTED": SHEWING THE ERRONEOUS STATEMENTS
OF THAT AUTHOR, AND PROVING THE SCRIPTURAL OPINIONS OF
JOANNA SOUTHCOTT, AND THOSE IN FAITH UNITED WITH HER. Lon-
don, 1805. Printed by W. Marchant. Sold by E. J. Field.

8°, pp. [1-2]-16. Blue paper wrappers.

Another answer to Garrett's book (see also item 26).

162: COPAS, THOMAS. AN APPEAL TO THE BELIEVERS IN THE DIVINE
MISSION OF JOANNA SOUTHCOTT. N. p., n. d.

8°, pp. [1-2]-24. Unbound.

A refutation of Samuel Jowett's concept that Joanna was not yet
a "free" woman, but must suffer further earthly pains. A note at
the end is signed by Thomas Malby, John Hagger, and John Pye.

163a: CROSSLEY, JOHN. LETTERS, AND OBSERVATIONS, TO MINISTERS. Bradford, March 26, 1814. Printed by T. Inkersley. Sold by J. Crowther and S. Hirst. Price 1 shilling.

8°, pp. [i-iii]-iv, [1]-48. Cover title: SOUTHCOTT'S PROPHECIES—[6]. VI (1/14) of VI.

Contains several letters, one from Joanna. Crossley's letters chastise several ministers for not believing in Joanna's prophecies.

163b: [Second edition: *not seen*]

163c(1): Third Edition. Bradford, n. d. Printed by T. Inkersley. Sold by J. Crowther and S. Hirst. Price 1 shilling.

Cover title: None. I (5/5) of I.

(2): Another copy. Disbound.

(3): Another copy. Sewn.

164: CROSSLEY, JOHN AND WILLIAM JOWETT. A VINDICATION OF JOANNA SOUTHCOTT'S WRITINGS; BEING A REPLY TO AN ANONYMOUS PAMPHLET PUBLISHED AGAINST HER AT HALIFAX. Leeds, 1805. Printed by Edward Baines. Sold by E. J. Field, J. Crowther, and W. Jowett.

8°, pp. [1-3]-28. Cover title: JOANNA SOUTHCOTT—1. I(6/10) of III.

A letter from Joanna and two articles by her followers defending her against an attack that she is an imposter.

165: FOLEY, REV. THOMAS P. COPY OF AN EPISTLE, WITH A FEW ALTERATIONS, ADDRESSED TO THE REV. THE VICE-CHANCELLORS OF CAMBRIDGE & OXFORD, BEING A PLAIN AND HONEST STATEMENT OF THE CHIEF AND LEADING EVENTS WHICH TOOK PLACE DURING THE YEARS 1801, 1802, & 1803, RESPECTING JOANNA SOUTHCOTT AND THE BELIEVERS IN HER DIVINE MISSION. Warrington, 1847. Printed "for the Southcottian Friends" by Richard Hatton.

8°, pp. [1-3]-11, [12]. Unbound.

Contains the "Examination of Prophecies."

166: HAGGER, JOHN, ET AL. A CALL TO THE BELIEVERS IN THE DIVINE MISSION OF THE LORD TO JOANNA SOUTHCOTT, STIMULATING THEM TO DO THEIR DUTY TO THEIR GOD, THEIR KING, THEIR COUNTRY, THEIR FAMILIES, AND THEMSELVES. London, 1843. Printed "for the Southcottian Friends, by A. Hancock."

8°, pp. [1-2]-20. Uncut, unbound.

Signed "In behalf of the London Church" by Hagger, Thomas Malby, John Spencer, James Sinnock, John Pye, William Parker, and G. Bennett.

167(1): ———. AN ADDRESS TO THE PROTESTANTS OF ENGLAND, ESPE-
CIALLY THE QUEEN, THE ARCHBISHOPS, BISHOPS, AND CLERGY, TO
EVERY SECT OF PROFESSING CHRISTIANS, AND EVERY ONE WHO
BELIEVES THE BIBLE TO BE THE TRUE WORD OF GOD. London, April
5, 1844. Second Edition. Printed "for the Southcottian Friends"
by Hancock. "To be Had Gratis" on the title page.

8°, pp. [1-2]-12. Unbound.

Members of the London church argue that the Protestants are
consistent with tradition: Eve protested against the serpent, and
God himself protested against "those who rebelled there." Signed
"by the Committee in behalf of the London Southcottian Church"
by Hagger, John Ley, John Pye, Jun., William Parker, John Bennett, George Hinds, Thomas Malby, John Pye, Sen., John Spencer,
George Bennett, James Sinnock, and George Davis.

(2): Another copy. Unbound.

168: ———. COPY OF AN ADDRESS TO THE CHAIRMAN OF THE ANTI-
CORN LAW CONFERENCE IN LONDON, GIVING THE CAUSE, AND SHEW-
ING THE REMEDY FOR THE PRESENT EVILS AND DISTRESSES, AS PROVED
FROM THE PROPHETIC WRITINGS OF THE LATE JOANNA SOUTHCOTT.
N. p., July 22, 1842.

8°, pp. [1]-4. Unbound.

Addressed to P. A. Taylor, the letter is signed by John Hagger,
Jas. Sinnock, Benjn. Howe, John Bennett, John Pye, jun., Thos.
Malby, Sen., John Bradbury, Wm. Parker, George Hinds, Edwin
Slater, John Pye, John Spencer, George Bennett, and John Ley.
The bottoms of the pages, including some of the text, are cropped
off for binding.

169: HAGGER, JOHN, editor. LETTERS TO THE BELIEVERS IN THE DIVINE
MISSION TO JOANNA SOUTHCOTT, IN REPLY TO THE VARIOUS LETTERS
RECEIVED IN CONNECTION WITH THEIR SECOND CIRCULAR. Holborn,
January 1, 1842. Printed by Hancock.

8°, pp. [1]-20. Unbound.

Includes three letters signed respectively by Thomas Copas, John
Pye, and Thomas Malby. Hagger signed the "Introduction."
Except for the first two leaves (and the quarter-sheet added to
form pp. 2-12) the gathering is uncut.

170: H[ARRISON], W. B. A LETTER ADDRESSED TO A FRIEND, PROVING
FROM REASON AND SCRIPTURE, THAT A FURTHER DIVINE REVELATION
WILL BE GIVEN FOR THE INSTRUCTION AND DIRECTION OF MANKIND,
PREVIOUS TO THE ESTABLISHMENT OF CHRIST'S KINGDOM ON EARTH.
Manchester, 1832. Printed and sold by T. Sowler.

8°, pp. [1-3]-75. Sewn.

171: HARRISON, W. B. A LETTER ADDRESSED TO AN EMINENT CLERGYMAN OF THE ESTABLISHED CHURCH OF ENGLAND, EXPLAINING THE NATURE AND OBJECT OF THE DIVINE MISSION OF THE LATE JOANNA SOUTHCOTT. Leeds, 1842. Printed by Samuel Jowett.

8°, pp. [i-iii]-iv, [5]-96. Sewn.

Dated from 86, Grosvenor Street, Manchester, on December 27, 1841.

172: HUDSON, T[HOMAS] P. COPIES OF DEEP AND IMPORTANT LETTERS, ADDRESSED TO THE QUEEN, PRINCE ALBERT, THE QUEEN DOWAGER, THE ARCHBISHOP OF CANTERBURY, AND OTHERS, ON THE CAUSE OF ENGLAND'S DISTRESS, AND THE REMEDY. London, June 15, 1843. Printed by Hancock.

8°, pp. [1-3]-23. Unbound.

173: [————]. THE ROYAL PROCLAMATION FOR THE CROWNING OF THE LORD JESUS CHRIST, KING OF KINGS AND LORD OF LORDS, IN THE NAME OF THE FATHER, SON, AND HOLY GHOST, ON SUNDAY, DECEMBER 26, 1847; IN ALL THE CHURCHES OF THE TRUE ISRAEL, IN ENGLAND. WITH THE FORM OF SERVICE FOR SUCH IMPORTANT PROCLAMATION, AS DECIDED ON BY THE CABINET COUNCIL, IN LONDON, DEC. 7, 1847. Birmingham, n. d. Printed by John Tonks, "by order of T. P. Hudson." Price 3 pence.

8°, pp. [1-3]-12. Disbound.

174: [INGALL, JOHN]. BEHOLD THE TENT! THE SWORD IS DRAWN!! ENGLAND AWAKE!!! THE ENEMY IS AMONG YOU!!!! London, 1804. Printed by E. Spragg. Sold by I. E. Field. Price 1 shilling.

8°, pp. [i-iii]-iv, [1]-56. Unbound.

A note on p. 56 identifies the author as Ingall. The tent referred to in the title is the one in Joseph Prescott's vision (see items 389 and 390). Interesting here is the fact that, with rare exceptions, when Joanna's name appears in print, it has been inked out.

175: JONES, DANIEL, printer and publisher. CATALOGUE OF BOOKS PUBLISHED BY JOANNA SOUTHCOTT. Bradford-on-Avon, n. d.

8°, 2 pp. Bound with THE SCRIPTURES OF THE HOLY TRINITY (see item 178).

A valuable list of Joanna's books giving titles, dates, and printers. The list is indispensable because her followers often refer to her works not by title, but by the corresponding number on this list.

176: ————. THE EVERLASTING GOSPEL, SATAN'S TEN PLAGUES. Bradford, July, 1864. Price 2 pence "by post."

8°, pp. [1]-4. Unbound.

Asserts that Richard Brothers and Joanna Southcott came as prophets from God but were ignored, therefore bringing plagues upon England and the world.

177: JONES, LAVINIA E[LIZABETH] C[HAPMAN], editor. COMMENTARY UPON THE PRAYERS AND ORDINANCES OF THE ENGLISH PROTESTANT CHURCH, EXTRACTED FROM REVELATIONS GIVEN BY THE SMALL STILL VOICE IN LONDON, DURING THE YEARS 1801 to 1814. Bradford, n. d. [1863?]. Printed and published by Daniel Jones.

8°, pp. [i-iii], 4, [5-6]-84, [85-88]. Paper wrappers.

A collection of Joanna's comments upon various things drawn from her published works and from unpublished manuscripts.

178: ————, editor. THE SCRIPTURES OF THE HOLY TRINITY. N. p., n. d.

8°, pp. [i-ii, 1]-288. Boards. Cover title: L. E. C. Jones.

On p. 1 appears the title "Revelation of Jesus Christ to John at Patmos, explained in England by the Spirit of Christ, During the Years 1792, to December 27, 1814." The work contains excerpts from Joanna's books which explain the book of Revelation verse by verse. Bound with this is a "Catalogue of Books Published by Joanna Southcott" (see item 175).

179: ————, editor. THE TIME FOR WORSHIPPING IN THE SPIRIT ILLUCIDATED FROM THE VISITATION OF PROPHECY TO JOANNA SOUTHCOTT DURING THE YEARS 1792-1814. PART I. Bath, 1853, "Printed for the Authoress, By D. Jones."

8°, pp. [i]-v, [6]-58. Brown paper wrappers.

Short excerpts from Joanna's works, a catalogue of which appears on pp. 15-16 of this copy.

180: JOWETT, SAMUEL. TO THE BELIEVERS OF JOANNA SOUTHCOTT'S VISITATION. Leeds, September, 1844. Printed by Samuel Jowett.

8°, pp. [1]-18. Sewn.

A statement of the belief of the later Southcottians in Leeds.

181: ————. TO MESSRS. HAGGER, COPAS, PYE AND MALBY, WITH OTHER LONDON BELIEVERS IN JOANNA SOUTHCOTT'S VISITATION. Leeds, n. d. Printed by Samuel Jowett.

8°, pp. [1]-6. Brown paper wrappers.

Involves a doctrinal dispute between the Leeds and London Southcottian churches.

182(1): LAW, RICHARD. COPY OF AN EPISTLE OF THE MOST EXTRA-
ORDINARY NATURE; SENT TO THE RIGHT HONOURABLE HENRY ADDING-
TON, PRIME MINISTER OF THE UNITED KINGDOM, ON AFFAIRS OF
THE UTMOST IMPORTANCE. JULY 19th, 1803. London, n. d. "Print-
ed for the Author, no. 3, Clipstone-Street, Mary-Le-Bone. By
Barnard & Sultzer." Price 4 pence.

8°, pp. [1-3]-19. Cover title: Unreadable. III (6/12) of III.
Law requests that the government obey the commands of God
(i.e. of Joanna Southcott). A special demand is that Richard
Brothers be released from prison.

(2): Another copy. Unbound.

(3): Another copy. Unbound.

183(1): LEWIS, F. AN ADDRESS TO THE CLERGY, PARTICULARLY THE
BENCH OF BISHOPS; CONTAINING SOME IMPORTANT FACTS WORTHY
THE CONSIDERATION OF ALL RANKS AND DENOMINATIONS AT THIS
DANGEROUS CRISIS. London, 1803. Printed by E. Spragg. Sold by
E. J. Field. Price 6 pence.

8°, pp. [1-3]-22. Cover title: Unreadable. III (7/12) of III.

An essay announcing that the end is near and begging the clergy
to wake up in time. On the title page is this:

> England is threatened!!!
> Our Sovereign in danger!!!
> The Enemy at the Door!!!
> What shall we do to be saved?

Napoleon is identified as the "beast" mentioned in the book of
Revelation in the Bible.

(2): Another copy. Disbound.

184: MALBY, THOMAS, ET AL. THE TESTIMONY OF THE SOUTHCOTTIAN
CHURCH IN LONDON, ON THE LATE VISITATION OF JOANNA SOUTHCOTT,
THAT THE CHILD WAS BORN ON THE 16TH OF DECEMBER, 1814,
PROVING IT TO BE THE MAN-CHILD MENTIONED IN HER WRITINGS;
ALSO TESTIFIED BY SCRIPTURAL AUTHORITY; AND TO BE NO OTHER
THAN CHRIST RE-BORN THE SECOND TIME, AND NO SECOND SAVIOR,
AS THE WORLD HAS REPORTED. Holborn, n. d. [January 1, 1843
inscribed in ink on title page]. Printed "for the Southcottian
Friends, by A. Hancock."

8°, pp. [1-3]-16. Unbound and uncut.

A policy statement of the later Southcottians signed by Malby,
John Hagger, John Pye, John Spencer, and William Parker as a
committee "in behalf of the London Church."

185: MASKELL, REV. WILLIAM, M.A. QUERIES AND REMARKS UPON A LATE
PAMPHLET ENTITLED, "THE QUESTION ANSWERED," BY MR. ALFRED
BISHOP. London, 1839. "Printed for J. G. F. & J. Rivington" by
Gilbert and Rivington.

8°, pp. [1-5]-34. Sewn.

The subject of discussion between Maskell and Bishop is the superiority of the Church of England over all other sects.

186: MAYER, L[EWIS]. THE WOMAN IN THE WILDERNESS, OR, THE WON-
DERFUL WOMAN, WITH HER WONDERFUL SEAL, WONDERFUL SPIRIT,
AND WONDERFUL CHILD, WHO "IS TO RULE THE NATIONS WITH A
ROD OF IRON." London, 1806. Printed by W. Nicholson. Sold by
Williams and Smith, J. Pearmain, and Sumner. Price 6 pence.

8°, pp. [1-3]-32. Paper wrappers.

An answer to Joanna's accusations and her ideas in her Book 46.

187: PULLEN, PHILIP. HYMNS, OR SPIRITUAL SONGS, COMPOSED FROM
THE PROPHETIC WRITINGS OF JOANNA SOUTHCOTT. London, 1814.
Fourth Edition. Printed by Marchant and Galabin. Sold by
W. Tozer, the Miss Eveleighs, S. Hirst, W. Wadman, James Light,
Edmund Baker, C. Bradley, J. Nesbit, and T. Turpin.

12°, pp. [i-iii]-x, [1]-4 (index), [1]-223 (songs), 1-4 (addenda).
Unbound.

The songs are numbered as well as the pages. There are 172 songs in this collection, two of which (66 and 143) are reprinted on separate leaves. One of these (66) varies slightly from the other printing in this edition.

188: ————. INDEX TO THE DIVINE AND SPIRITUAL WRITINGS OF JOANNA
SOUTHCOTT. London, 1815. Printed by T. Wood. Sold by W.
Tozer, the Miss Eveleighs, S. Hirst, W. Wadman, James Light,
Edm. Baker, C. Bradley, J. Nesbit, and T. Turpin.

8°, pp. [i-iii]-viii, [9]-240, [241-243]. Boards. Cover title: None.

Contains two pages of errata bound at the end. Pp. v-vi contain a "Catalogue of Books, Published by and for Joanna Southcott, and referred to in the following Index," and pp. vii-viii "The Catalogue attempted in Verse," a series of 24 amazingly bad quatrains. This catalogue is less complete than that published by Jones (see item 175), since printers and dates of editions are omitted. Both list the same 65 works.

189: SEYMOUR, A[LICE]. THE TWO WITNESSES, NO. 27. Ashford, n. d.
Printed and published by Alice Seymour. Price 3 pence.

8°, pp. [1-2]-11, [12]. Unbound.

This "monthly" succeeds the "Express Leaflets" (see item 190).
Subscription rate is 3 shillings, 6 pence or 85 cents per annum.
An advertisement on p. 12 lists a book store in San Diego, California, Carpenter's Book Store, as a place selling Southcott publications.

190: [————]. THE "EXPRESS" LEAFLETS, NO. 22. Plymouth, England, 1912. Printed by J. H. Keys. Price 3 pence.

8°, pp. [1-3]-12. Unbound.

Issued monthly, this publication reprinted selected of Joanna's prophecies. On p. 12 a note announces "The Subscription for 'The Express Leaflets' is 3 s. 6 d., or 85 cents, per annum, paid in advance, including postage." Miss Alice Seymour's name appears on p. 12 as the one who receives orders for the publication.

191: SPENCER, JOHN. A CIRCULAR ADDRESSED TO ALL THE BELIEVERS IN THE DIVINE MISSION OF THE LORD TO JOANNA SOUTHCOTT. London, 1841.

8°, pp. [1]-2, [3]-4. Unbound.

Printed with "A Prayer for the occasion To Almighty God, Founded on His Own Words" (pp. 3-4), signed by John Hagger, William Parker, John Pye, Thomas Malby, and John Spencer.

192: ————, ET AL. SECOND CIRCULAR. TO THE BELIEVERS IN THE DIVINE MISSION TO JOANNA SOUTHCOTT. London, 1841.

8°, pp. [1]-4. Unbound.

"Signed on the part of the London Believers," by John Spencer, John Pye, John Hagger, William Parker, and Thomas Malby. Corrections in ink of misprints on pp. 3 and 4.

193: TOWNLEY, JANE. LETTERS ON THE SIGNS OF THE TIMES. London, n. d. Printed by S. Rousseau. Sold by E. J. Field.

4° folded and bound in an 8° volume. Pp. [1]-3. Cover title: Unreadable. III(11/12) of III.

Inscribed on the verso of leaf 2: "Mr. C. Bowman." Contains ·a printed letter to "The Right Reverend The Lord Bishop of London" by Jane Townley, dated May 22, 1804, No. 9, Trinity Street, Bristol. Miss Townley explains a letter from Joanna concerning a warning. The letter from Joanna is included.

194: TURNER, GEORGE. A VINDICATION FOR THE HONOUR OF GOD, IN ANSWER TO J. AKED, HALIFAX. Leeds, 1807. Printed by Edward Baines. Sold by E. J. Field, Samuel Hirst, and Joseph Crowther. Price 10 pence.

8°, pp. [1-3]-55. Unbound.

An answer to a book, supposedly published by Aked, in which "the God of Richard Brothers, Joanna Southcott and George Turner" was called a "mushroom God, the God of apes, and an hobgobling God." Turner here says that God is not really any of these things.

195: WEBSTER, THOMAS. REASONS FOR THE FALL OF MAN. London, 1804. Printed by J. Greenham. Sold by E. J. Field and Thomas Webster. Price 6 pence.

8°, pp. [1-3]-24. Disbound.

One of Joanna's disciples warns England to "Prepare to meet your God."

196: WETHERELL, WILLIAM ROUNDELL. A TESTIMONY OF JOANNA SOUTH-COTT, THE PROPHETESS; SENT BY THE LORD, TO WARN THE PEOPLE OF HIS COMING. London, n. d. Printed by S. Rousseau. Sold by E. J. Field. Price 4 pence.

8°, pp. [1-3]-18. Disbound.

197: [?]. A CALL FROM THE MOST HIGH GOD, THE GOD OF ABRAHAM, THE GOD OF ISAAC, THE GOD OF JACOB, TO HIS ANCIENT PEOPLE THE JEWS, SCATTERED THROUGHOUT THE EARTH, BY HIS HOLY SPIRIT TO THE BRIDE, AS PROMISED THROUGH THE PROPHETS, THE GOSPEL AND THE APOSTLES, TO THE GENTILE CHURCH. London, November 19, 1845. Printed by A. Hancock.

8°, pp. [1-3]-11. Unbound.

An invitation to the Jews to learn of Joanna's prophecies.

198: [?]. CORRESPONDENCE OF THE SOUTHCOTTIAN CHURCH. N. p., n. d. Printed by Hancock.

8°, pp. [1]-8. Unbound.

Correspondence between several members of the Southcottian church and a Mr. W. B. Harrison on the teachings of Joanna.

199: [?]. THE FIRST AND SECOND COMING OF CHRIST. N. p., n. d.

8°, pp. [1-3]-8. Stapled.

A short treatise explaining people's reception of Christ at his first coming and what might be expected on his return.

200(1): [?]. A GENERAL INDEX TO THE WRITINGS OF JOANNA SOUTHCOTT, THE PROPHETESS. London, n. d. [1805?]. Printed by W. Marchant. Sold by E. J. Field, E. Carpenter, C. Abbott, W. Symonds, Miss Eveleighs, and Sam. Hirst. Price 1 shilling.

8°, pp. [i-ii], [1]-33. Unbound.

A note on the title page announces that the index begins "with her First Book, Published in 1801, and ending with the 'Answer to the Leeds Charges,' Printed March, 1805," thus indexing her first 25 books. For a more complete index see Pullen's work, item 188.

(2): Another copy. Title page missing. Cover title: JOANNA SOUTH-COTT—1. I(5/10) of III.

201: [?]. THE INDICTMENT AGAINST THAT TYRANNICAL, CRUEL, AND
BLOODY MONARCH, SATAN, THE GOD OF THIS WORLD; WHOM THE
CREATED CREATURES OF GOD INTEND, BY GOD'S DIRECTIONS, TO BRING
TO CONDIGN PUNISHMENT. ALSO, THE MINUTES OF THE MEMBERS
OF THE SOUTHCOTTIAN CHURCHES IN LONDON, FOR SEVEN DAYS,
FROM THE 19TH TO THE 25TH OF NOVEMBER, 1844. London, January 20, 1845. Printed "for the Southcottian Friends" by A. Hancock. Price 8 pence.

8°, pp. [1-2]-91. Sewn in blue paper wrappers.

The "Indictment Against Satan" condemns the devil for persecuting the "Sealed People" and for murdering Joanna Southcott. P. 91 includes a list of people, including their occupations and addresses, who "objected to the conference taking place, though professed Believers in the Divine Mission of Joanna Southcott."

202: [?]. THE PERIOD OF THE REDEMPTION OF MAN ILLUSTRATED; FROM
THE TASK, A POEM, BY WILLIAM COWPER. London, 1804. Printed
by S. Rousseau. Sold by E. J. Field.

12°, pp. [1-3]-8. Unbound.

Not listed in the *Dictionary of Anonymous and Pseudononymous Literature.* The work is printed as a long poem, but although there is some structural inversion (such as "Foretold by prophets, and by Poets sung. . . ."), there is neither rime nor rhythm. A printed note on p. 8 says that one who has "a heart to understand" must "finally acknowledge that the soul-animating, heart-churning doctrines contained in these lines, are clearly to be found in the writings of Joanna Southcott."

203: [?]. RETREAT OF THE FRENCH ARMY FROM RUSSIA; BEING A MOST
INTERESTING DETAIL OF THE IMPORTANT EVENTS AND DREADFUL
SUFFERINGS OF THE ALLIED FORCES, COMMANDED BY BONAPARTE,
DURING THEIR RETREAT FROM MOSCOW. London, 1813. Printed
by Gedge and Barker "for J. Deck, Bookseller." Price 1 shilling.

8°, pp. [1-3]-27. Unbound.

This pamphlet was written by "a German officer in the Russian service." A note on the title page explains that the work was "Translated from the German into French, and Printed at Berlin by J. Decker, from which this Translation is made." Annotations inscribed in ink show the events described in the work to be the fulfillment of a prophecy.

204: [?]. SCRIPTURES WHICH SHEW FOR WHAT CHRIST DIED; ALSO WHICH
SHEW HIS SECOND COMING, TO BRUISE SATAN'S HEAD, AND TO ESTAB-
LISH HIS PEACEABLE KINGDOM ON EARTH. THE DIFFERENCE SHEWN
OF CHRIST'S SECOND COMING AND LAST COMING; AND THE DIFFER-
ENCE OF THE FIRST RESURRECTION AND THE GENERAL RESURRECTION.
LIKEWISE THE REMARKABLE EVENTS OF 1811, SELECTED FROM THE

NEWSPAPERS. London, June 21, 1812. Printed by Marchant and Galabin. Sold by Mr. Darton, Mrs. Doebins, Mrs. Cole, Mrs. Powell, Mr. Wright, Mr. Porter, Mr. Layton, W. Symonds, the Miss Eveleighs, S. Hirst, J. Middleton, James Light, and Mr. Tozer. Price 1 shilling, 3 pence.

8°, pp. [1-2]-64. Unbound.

This copy signed by George Bennett. The author is identified only as "A Lover of Truth." The work attempts to show that contemporary international events as reported in newspapers match the events described in the Bible which were to precede the second coming of Christ.

205: [?]. THE TRIAL, CASTING, AND CONDEMNATION OF THE PRINCE OF THIS WORLD, THE OLD SERPANT, DEVIL, AND SATAN; AT THE COURT OF EQUITY, LITTLE JAMES STREET, GRAY'S INN LANE, LONDON, FROM THE 25TH TO THE 31ST OF DECEMBER, 1846. TO WHICH IS ADDED A LETTER TO THE ARCHBISHOP OF CANTERBURY, SOLICITING HIM TO PRESENT TO THE HOUSE OF LORDS A PETITION ON THE REAL CAUSE AND ONLY REMEDY FOR THE DISTRESS AND PERPLEXITIES IN ENGLAND AND ALL NATIONS. London, April 2, 1847. Printed by A. Hancock. Price 6 pence.

8°, pp. [1-3]-63. Blue paper wrappers with the title page reprinted on the cover.

A trial of Satan "By order of the Southcottian Church, in council assembled." Contains the transcript of the trial, perhaps a result of the indictment issued in item 201. Satan is found guilty of murdering Christ and Joanna.

206(1): [?]. TRUTH DEFENDED: OR, CHRIST'S GLORIOUS AND PEACEABLE REIGN IS AT HAND. JOANNA SOUTHCOTT VINDICATED IN HER CLAIM FOR THE DESTRUCTION OF SATAN'S POWER. London, 1840. Printed by A. Hancock. Sold by Mr. Spencer, Mr. Page, Mrs. Hawkins, Mr. Benn, W. Cripps, Mrs. Essam, and Mr. J. Lowe.

8°, pp. [1-3]-16. Unbound.

A long poem in rimed couplets "written in the year 1807, to a friend of the Author, an Unbeliever, but a professor of Religion, to whom he was desirous of imparting a knowledge of the fundamental principles contained in the Writings of Joanna Southcott, by the Spirit, and their agreement with the Word of God" (p. 2).

(2): Another copy. Sewn in blue paper wrappers.

207: [?]. THE UPLIFTING OF HANDS. Plymouth, 1913. Printed by J. H. Keys.

8°, pp. [1-3]-20. Sewn in purple paper wrappers.

On the title page is a note: "Order of Service for January 12th." The specific times of the various ceremonies are given, the "Uplifting of Hands" occurring "as near as possible to 7-30 p.m." This part of the service is very ritualistic, the believers chanting together the following:

The-will-of-the-Lord-be-done.
Come-Lord-Jesus-O-come-quickly.

Believers are instructed to "Repeat slowly each word together with uplifted hands; all lower them, then together raise again, repeating the above: do this three times" (p. 16).

D: JOANNA SOUTHCOTT:

BIOGRAPHICAL WORKS

208: BALLEINE, G[EORGE] R. PAST FINDING OUT. THE TRAGIC STORY OF JOANNA SOUTHCOTT AND HER SUCCESSORS. London, 1956. Published by S. P. C. K. Price 15 shillings, 6 pence.

8°, pp. [i-iv]-xi, 1-151. Boards.

Illustrated and indexed. A well-written and unbiased history of the Southcottian movement by an Anglican clergyman. Three appendixes on "The Shiloh Myth," "The Millennium," and "Southcottians and the Church" are helpful, as is the "Table of Southcottian Sects."

209: KIRBY, R. S. KIRBY'S WONDERFUL AND ECCENTRIC MUSEUM; OR MAGAZINE OF REMARKABLE CHARACTERS. INCLUDING ALL THE CURIOSITIES OF NATURE AND ART, FROM THE REMOTEST PERIOD TO THE PRESENT TIME, DRAWN FROM EVERY AUTHENTIC SOURCE. London, 1820. Printed by R. S. Kirby.

3 volumes. 8°, I. 428 pp.; II. 492 pp.; III. 430 pp. Half morocco binding. Cover titles: KIRBY'S WONDERFUL MUSEUM, I, II, III.

Volumes I and II contain sketches on Joanna. Volume I (pp. 336-363) presents a description of Joanna as a "deluded woman" and an "antiquated virgin" who wrote books containing "Vulgar language and indecent allusions" and who sold seals. The charges against Joanna here are numerous and harsh, but the proofs are thin. Volume II (pp. 344-349) relates actions by some of Joanna's followers several years after her death. They are treated as the other "curiosities of nature" discussed in these volumes, as freaks.

210: MATTHEWS, RONALD. ENGLISH MESSIAHS: STUDIES OF SIX ENGLISH RELIGIOUS PRETENDERS, 1656-1927. London, 1936. Published by Methuen and Company, Ltd.

8°, 230 pp. Boards.

An objective historical treatment of several enthusiasts. There are chapters on James Nayler, Joanna Southcott, Richard Brothers, John Nichols Toms, Henry James Prince, and John Hugh Smyth-Pigott.

211: SEYMOUR, ALICE. THE EXPRESS. London, 1909. Published by Simpkin, Marshall, Hamilton, Kent and Company, Ltd.

2 volumes. 8°, I. 366 pp.; II. 413 pp. Boards. Cover titles: THE EXPRESS, CONTAINING THE LIFE AND DIVINE WRITINGS OF JOANNA SOUTHCOTT—I, II.

Miss Seymour was a twentieth century follower of Joanna who felt called to give "to the World that which it so badly needs, though at present it is in ignorance of its pressing necessities." She includes interesting chapters on Joanna's poetry and prose. Her polemical biography of Joanna is drawn mainly from Joanna's works. Included also are illustrations of Joanna, the Box of Sealed Writings, the Communion Cup, Joanna's handwriting, a seal, and "The Patchwork Quilt." Balleine [see item 208] quotes from Seymour.

212: TIMBS, JOHN. ENGLISH ECCENTRICS AND ECCENTRICITIES. London, 1875. Published by Chatto and Windus.

8°, 578 pp. Bound in cloth, pictorially blocked.

Contains a section on "Joanna Southcote [sic], and the coming of Shiloh," which treats Joanna as a deluded old woman who unintentionally perpetrated a farce. Valuable for its references to important names and events connected with Joanna. Also listed are collections of Joanna's works.

213: WALFORD, EDWARD. OLD AND NEW LONDON: A NARRATIVE OF ITS HISTORY, ITS PEOPLE, AND ITS PLACES. VOLUME V. "The Western and Northern Suburbs." London, n. d. Published by Cassell Petter & Galpin.

4°, 576 pp. Bound in cloth, pictorially blocked, gilt extra.

Contains a brief sketch of Joanna's life, and locates the burial place of "the impostors, Richard Brothers and Joanna Southcott," pp. 251-253.

214: WILSON, HENRY AND JAMES CAULFIELD. THE BOOK OF WONDERFUL CHARACTERS: MEMOIRS AND ANECDOTES OF REMARKABLE AND ECCENTRIC PERSONS IN ALL AGES AND COUNTRIES. London, n. d. [1870?]. Published by John Camden. Price 7 shillings, 6 pence.

8°, 416 pp. Bound in cloth, pictorially blocked, gilt extra.

Contains inter alia "Joanna Southcott, An Extraordinary Fanatic." Joanna is sketched alongside such characters as pig-faced ladies and other freaks of nature. She is treated as a fool and an heretic.

215: [?]. RELIGIOUS IMPOSTERS. N. p., n. d.

8°, pp. 1-32. Unbound.

A portrait of Joanna appears on p. 1. Discussed besides Joanna are Munzer and Bockholt, Richard Brothers, Ann Lee, Jemima Wilkinson, Mrs. Buchan, Robert Matthews, John Nicholls Thoms [sic], and Sabbathais Zwi. The writer's attitude toward his subject is suggested in his first sentence: "All excesses are dangerous, and none perhaps more so than an excess in devotional feeling."

216: "The Folly of the Times Exemplified in the Attentions Obtained by Joanna Southcott," *Bell's Weekly Messenger*, September 4, 1814, p. 286.

The article accuses Joanna of selling her seals for "from ten shillings to one guinea each." Also here is a "Summary Account of the Prophetic Origin and History of Joanna Southcott."

217: "A Tragic Prophetess," *T. P.'s Weekly*, XXIV, no. 613, August 8, 1914, p. 188.

Contains a short sketch of Joanna's life.

E: JOANNA SOUTHCOTT:

PRINTED BROADSIDES,

LEAFLETS, AND CLIPPINGS

218: BRUCE, REV. STANHOPE, ET AL. "Examination of Prophecies." Paddington, January 22, 1803. Printed by J. Greenham. Sold by E. J. Field and Symons. Broadside.

1 leaf, one side. 28 x 20.5 cm. Cover title: SOUTHCOTT'S PROPHECIES—1. I(1/11) of VI.

A statement of faith in Joanna's divine inspiration signed by Rev. Stanhope Bruce, Peter Morison, William Jowett, William Sharp, Elias Carpenter, W. Roundell Wetherell, George Turner, Charles Taylor, John Wilson, Rev. Thomas Webster, Rev. Thos. P. Foley, Charles Abbott, Richard Law, Elias Jameson Field, George Stocks, John Morris, William Coy, William Belk, William Taylor, John Young, Wm. Layton Winter, John Torin, and Thomas Stephens.

219: FOX, MRS. [RACHEL]. "The Key to Happiness," *The Daily News*, n. d. [because W. W. I. is mentioned as "the last war," the article must be dated 1919 or later]. Newspaper article.

1 leaf, one side. 18.4 x 5.7 cm.

Mrs. Fox, the new leader of the Southcottian movement, explains the importance of Joanna's writings and announces the plans of the movement to grow.

220: JONES, DANIEL. "Table of the Kingdoms of Men and the Kingdom of God." 1839. Printed poster.

One side. 48.5 x 38.5 cm. Heavy paper laid on gauze.

A table showing the dates of the creation and final judgment (which will occur in 7000) and the kingdoms of men through the years.

221: JONES, LAVINIA E. C. "The Bible—The Dial." Bradford, n. d. Broadside.

1 leaf, one side. 22.5 x 14 cm.

222: ———. "Christ's Spirit, The Heir of the Promised Land." Bradford, n. d. Leaflet.

1 leaf, one side, double column. 22.5 x 14 cm.

A poem in couplets.

223: ———. "Let these words go forth to the ends of the earth." July, 1862. Preface.

8°, 1 p.

Obviously a preface to a book Mrs. Jones had compiled translating a prayer "into. . . a variety of languages." Included in the preface is Pope's Eclogue "Wrapt into future times."

224: LEES, G. FREDERIC. "Another Southcott Box." Hotel du Lac, Lugano [Switzerland], July 14, no year ["/27" inscribed in pencil]. Letter to the Editor of the [London?] *Times*.

10 x 7 cm.

Lees announces his finding a "large trunk" filled with baby clothes made for "Shiloh, Prince of Peace," some pictorial documents, and some "seals" made out with names of Cabinet Ministers. Lees claims to have retained photographs of the objects.

225: THE PANACEA SOCIETY. "England's Troubles, Difficulties, & Perplexities will continue to increase. . . . " *The Evening Standard*, [?] October, 1956. Newspaper article.

9.6 x 9.3 cm.

The people of England are warned that problems will increase until Joanna's box of sealed prophecies is opened. The same advertisement has been noted 9 June 1962 in the *Daily Mail*, 5 February 1966 in the *Evening News and Star*, and 9 April 1966 in the *Evening Standard*.

226: ———. "No Deliverance from Present World Conditions Until the Bishops Act. Bedford, n. d. [but after 11 July 1927]. Leaflet.

1 leaf, both sides. 22.5 x 14.4 cm.

Presents a picture of Joanna's box (which matches the picture in THE EXPRESS, I, p. 26. See item 211) as "The Real Box," and calls for the Bishops to open it. There is also the promise to "deliver" the believer "from Nerves, Consumption, Epilepsy, Paralysis, Rheumatism, Eye, Ear and Throat Troubles, Mental Anxiety, Business Worries, and Faults of Disposition."

227: ———. "What Fellowship with the Panacea Society Entails." Bedford, n. d. [but after 1923]. Leaflet.

1 leaf, both sides. 17.5 x 13.1 cm.

Addressed to those who are troubled or in poor health, offering "The Healing Water" which, if taken, will cure the ills.

228(1): ———. "Who is Joanna Southcott? What is her Ark or Box?" Bedford, n. d. [but after 1923]. Leaflet.

1 leaf, both sides. 21.9 x 13.9 cm.

Gives a general history of Joanna and the movement.

(2): Another copy.

229: ———. "The 'Whosoever' Religion." Bedford, n. d. [but after 1923]. Leaflet.

2 leaves, both sides. 21.9 x 14.1 cm.

The Society warns that although the last day will be no later than A. D. 2000, yet earthly conditions are so bad that God might "shorten" the time. The leaflet is a solicitation for membership in the Society.

230: "Prophecies of Joanna Southcott, Sold by Charles Abbott." London, n. d. Broadside.

1 leaf, one side. 24.5 x 20 cm.

An advertisement for THE TRIAL OF JOANNA SOUTHCOTT (see item 25). Inscribed in ink is "and [sold by] E. J. Field No. 189 High Holborn London."

231: SEYMOUR, ALICE. "The Prophecies of Joanna Southcott are Proved Undeniably True by Their Fulfilment." Blockley, Worcestershire, England, n. d. [but after February, 1917]. Leaflet.

1 leaf, both sides. 22.4 x 14.3 cm.

Miss Seymour takes issue with "so-called followers of Joanna Southcott" (obviously the Panacea Society) for unnecessary petitioning and false warnings. She accuses them of straying from the true Southcott line.

232(1): [ZEBULUN, JOSEPH]. "The Seal of the Kingdom of Christ on Earth." N. p., n. d. Broadside.

1 leaf, one side. 26.7 x 21 cm.

"N 1031—Ann Reuben. Aprl. 21—1842—" inscribed in bottom margin in Zebulun's hand.

(2): Another copy. Attached with wax to a MS: "This seed, is of me, saith the Lord. . . " (see item 311).

"N 1355—Elizabeth Reuben—June 11, 1844" inscribed in bottom margin in Zebulun's hand.

(3): Another copy. Attached with wax to a MS: "Come saith, Jah. Jehovah. . . " (see item 312).

"N 1366 William Reuben, July 22, 1844" inscribed in bottom margin in Zebulun's hand.

(4): Another copy.

"No. 1367—Mary Reuben, July—28—1844" inscribed in bottom margin in Zebulun's hand.

(5): Another copy. Attached with wax to a MS: "Thus saith the Lord, Creations, God. . . " (see item 314).

"N. 1368—Joseph Reuben—August 29, 1844" inscribed in bottom margin in Zebulun's hand.

233: [?]. "Bishops on the Box," *The Daily News*. July 28, no year. Newspaper article.

37.8 x 5.7 cm.

Reveals various answers to a *Daily News* letter to forty-nine Bishops of the Church of England asking their opinions about opening the box. Most were unwilling to meet Joanna's written requirements.

234: [?]. "Close the Box!" *Dallas Morning News*, 12 January 1964. Editorial.

17 x 13 cm.

An editorial comparing the "foolishness" of the United States Federal Government for trying to achieve a panacea by grants, financial programs, and aid to the "foolishness" of the Panacea Society for declaring that the box of sealed prophecies will solve all problems. Joanna's name is not mentioned, but her works are implicitly referred to.

235: [?]. "Go on Your Way Rejoicing." Signed "C. M. K." N. p., n. d. Clipping.

15.5 x 9.5 cm.

Seven quatrains riming abcb, defe, etc. Theme of anticipation of heavenly reward for "Ye toilers in a world of sin and sorrow." Clipped from a magazine or newspaper.

236: [?]. "The Lord's Prayer." Published by The Missions to Seamen, 4 Buckingham Palace Gardens, Victoria, London. N. d. Leaflet.

1 leaf, both sides. 10.1 x 1.6 cm. Folded in thirds.

Contains the Lord's Prayer and directions for its use ("Adopted from the Dictionary of Christ and the Gospels"); also here is "A Prayer for Absent Friends."

237: [?]. "On the Millennium." Printed by Clouter, Bristol. N. d. Broadside.

19.8 x 11.2 cm. Cover title: Unreadable. III (glued to front fly-leaf) of III.

Two poems on the subject of paradise lost and paradise regained, generally riming abab, cdcd, etc.

F: RICHARD BROTHERS

Brothers was a self-proclaimed prophet who was active before and during the time of Joanna Southcott. Although he and Joanna had no personal contact, surely he helped pave the way for her. When Brothers' prophecies did not materialize, his followers began to leave the fold, and it was to Joanna that they turned for succor.

Brothers, a young, retired naval officer, was influenced by occultism which he had encountered during a brief association with a Polish count, Tadeus Grabianka. Brothers himself began to see visions, and he became convinced that the day of judgment was at hand and that he was to be the world ruler. England was very important to Brothers because he believed that ten of the Biblical twelve tribes were merged into the the population of Great Britain (see item 244). In his second book (item 240) Brothers relieved King George III of his authority and demanded that the crown be turned over to him as the new ruler. Soon after this Brothers was confined in an asylum.

Brothers did not want for followers. William Sharp, the engraver; Mr. Halhed, M. P.; Thomas Webster, Lecturer in two London churches; Thomas P. Foley, Fellow of Jesus College, Cambridge; Stanhope Bruce, Vicar of Inglesham; his son Colonel Basil Bruce; and hundreds of others followed Brothers faithfully. Balleine describes him as "the most discussed writer in the Kingdom" in 1795 (see item 208, p. 34).

238: A REVEALED KNOWLEDGE OF THE PROPHECIES & TIMES, BOOK THE FIRST. WROTE UNDER THE DIRECTION OF THE LORD GOD, AND PUBLISHED BY HIS SACRED COMMAND; IT BEING THE FIRST SIGN OF WARNING FOR THE BENEFIT OF ALL NATIONS. CONTAINING, WITH OTHER GREAT AND REMARKABLE THINGS, NOT REVEALED TO ANY OTHER PERSON ON EARTH, THE RESTORATION OF THE HEBREWS TO JERUSALEM, BY THE YEAR OF 1798: UNDER THEIR REVEALED PRINCE AND PROPHET. London, 1794. (Name of printer inked out in this copy.) Sold by G. Riebau.

8°, pp. [1-3]-68. Cover title: A REVEALED KNOWLEDGE, 1794. I (1/2) of I.

Brothers' first publication.

239: A REVEALED KNOWLEDGE, OF THE PROPHECIES & TIMES. PARTIC-
ULARLY OF THE PRESENT TIME, THE PRESENT WAR AND THE PROPH-
ECY NOW FULFILLING. THE YEAR OF THE WORLD 1513. BOOK THE
SECOND. CONTAINING WITH OTHER GREAT AND REMARKABLE THINGS,
NOT REVEALED TO ANY OTHER PERSON ON EARTH, THE SUDDEN AND
PERPETUAL FALL OF THE TURKISH, GERMAN, AND RUSSIAN EMPIRES,
WROTE UNDER THE DIRECTION OF THE LORD GOD, AND PUBLISHED
BY HIS SACRED COMMAND; IT BEING A SECOND SIGN OF WARNING
FOR THE BENEFIT OF ALL NATIONS. BY THE MAN THAT WILL BE
REVEALED TO THE HEBREWS AS THEIR PRINCE AND PROPHET. Lon-
don, 1794. (Name of printer inked out in this copy.) Sold by
G. Riebau.

8°, pp. [i-iii]-vi, [7]-108. Cover title: A REVEALED KNOWLEDGE,
1794. I (2/2) of I.

240: A DESCRIPTION OF JERUSALEM: ITS HOUSES AND STREETS, SQUARES,
COLLEGES, MARKETS, AND CATHEDRALS, THE ROYAL AND PRIVATE
PALACES, WITH THE GARDEN OF EDEN IN THE CENTRE, AS LAID DOWN
IN THE LAST CHAPTERS OF EZEKIEL. ALSO THE FIRST CHAPTER OF
GENESIS VERIFIED, AS STRICTLY DIVINE AND TRUE. AND THE SOLAR
SYSTEM, WITH ALL ITS PLURALITY OF INHABITED WORLDS, AND
MILLIONS OF SUNS, AS POSITIVELY PROVED TO BE DELUSIVE AND
FALSE. London, 1801. Printed "for George Riebau, Bookseller to
the King of the Hebrews," by S. Rousseau.

8°, pp. [i-iv, 1]-145 (plus three 8° illustrations and three large
fold outs). Bound in full navy-blue calf, gilt. Cover title: DESCRIP-
TION OF JERUSALEM.

Brothers advertises himself as the one "who will be Revealed to
the Hebrews as their King and Restorer." This copy contains three
foldouts: 1. A drawing of the "New Jerusalem" (40.5 x 38 cm.)
bound before the title page; 2. The plan for the "Garden of
Eden" (38.5 x 32 cm.) bound between pp. 12-13; and 3. "The
Royal Banner or Ensign of the Hebrews" (19 x 21 cm.) adorned
with watercolors, bound between pp. 40-41. Several other 8° size
illustrations are bound in. This volume has some textual corrections
inscribed in ink.

241: A LETTER TO THE SUBSCRIBERS FOR ENGRAVING THE PLANS OF
JERUSALEM, THE KING'S PALACE, THE PRIVATE PALACES, COLLEGE-
HALLS, CATHEDRALS, AND PARLIAMENT-HOUSES. London, 1805.
Printed by E. Spragg. Sold by George Riebau. Price 1 shilling,
6 pence.

8°, pp. [1-3]-46. Cover title: BROTHERS TRACTS. I(2/4) of I.
Green polished calf binding, gilt extra.

Signature of Bar Prescot in top margin of title page, and beneath
the name of the author he has inscribed "In the 11th year of his
captivity under Mr. Pitt's government." Some annotation by
Prescot.

242: THE RUINS OF BALBEC AND PALMYRA, IN THEIR PRESENT STATE, DESCRIBED AND EXPLAINED FROM THE PLATES OF ROBERT WOOD, ESQ. UNDER SECRETARY OF STATE TO HIS BRITANIC MAJESTY, PROVED TO BE LEBANON HOUSE AND TADMOR IN THE DESERT, THE PALACES OF SOLOMON, KING OF ISRAEL. London, 1821. Printed by R. George. Sold by G. Riebau.

8°, pp. [i]-ii, [1]-31. Cover title: BROTHERS TRACTS. I(2/4) of I.

A prefatory letter to the Prince Regent asks that certain plates of classical Greek buildings be distributed by the government, that a new Royal Palace be built in imitation of Greek structures, and that bridges over the Thames be newly constructed according to certain requirements laid down by Brothers.

243: A DESCRIPTION OF JERUSALEM, ACCORDING TO THE SCRIPTURE; PUBLISHED IN SUPPORT OF THE BIBLE, AND THE DIVINE REVELATION IT CONTAINS, FOR THE BENEFIT OF ALL DENOMINATIONS AND DISTINCTIONS OF PEOPLE ON EARTH. London, July, 1821. Printed by R. George. Sold by G. Riebau.

8°, pp. [1]-88. Cover title: BROTHERS TRACTS. I(3/4) of I.

Contains lists of architectural measurements of streets, gardens, buildings, etc.

244: A CORRECT ACCOUNT OF THE INVASION AND CONQUEST OF THE ROMAN COLONY OF AILBANE, OR BRITAIN, BY THE SAXONS, NEVER PUBLISHED BEFORE: AND WHICH IS VERY INTERESTING TO THE PRESENT ENGLISH, WHO ARE DESCENDED FROM THOSE GREAT AND BRAVE MEN. London, 1822. Printed by R. George. Sold by G. Riebau.

8°, pp. [i]-viii, [1]-142. Cover title: BROTHERS TRACTS. I(4/4) of I.

Brothers here links Britains with their forgotten Israelite ancestors. Bede and other ancient historians are refuted as Brothers offers an interesting narrative account of the Saxon invasion of Britain with exact names, dates, and exact quotations from participants. In his A REVEALED KNOWLEDGE, BOOK THE FIRST (item 238) Brothers explains his source of such knowledge: "I was . . . instructed by Revelation. . . . " A. N. S. on the title page by Bar Prescot and annotations throughout.

G: MISCELLANEOUS PRINTED MATERIAL

245: H[UTCHINSON], W. H. POEMS. London, 1818. Printed by I. Cunningham. Sold by Sherwood, Neely, and Jones; Knight and Son; and Cole.

8°, 81 pp. Bound in original boards, rebacked.

Miscellaneous poems by "W. H. H., a Gentleman of Greenwich." Although a few of the poems are of a religious nature, they seem to have nothing to do with the Southcottian movement.

246: MOLYNEUX, REV. CAPEL, B. A. ABOUNDING IN HOPE. London, n. d. Published by Mrs. J. B. Sumner.

8°, pp. 1-6. Unbound.

A sermon "Preached in St. Paul's Church, Onslow Square, South Kensington, On Sunday Morning, December 5, 1869."

(247-254): SPURGEON, C. H. Sermons. Reprints of eight Spurgeon sermons by the "Metropolitan Tabernacle Pulpit." Published "every Thursday" and printed by Passmore and Alabaster. The works are all 8° and numbered variously as parts of volumes. Each sermon contains 12 pp. All are unbound. The title, dates delivered, and publication dates are as follows:

247: GLORIOUS PREDESTINATION. Delivered "Lord's Day Morning, March 24, 1872." N. d.

248: A CALL FOR REVIVAL. Delivered on "Lord's Day Morning, August 18, 1872." N. d.

249: OUR LORD'S QUESTION TO THE BLIND MEN. Delivered on "Lord's-Day Evening, May 13, 1877." Published May 31, 1877.

250: SHEEP AMONG WOLVES. Delivered on "Lord's-Day Morning, August 19, 1877." Published August 30, 1877.

251: EVERYDAY RELIGION. Delivered on "Lord's-Day Morning, May 22, 1881." Published May 26, 1881.

252: A GREATER SOLOMON. Delivered on "Lord's-Day Evening, February 6, 1881." Published May 26, 1881.

253: WHAT THE FARM LABOURERS CAN DO AND WHAT THEY CANNOT DO. Delivered on "Lord's-Day Morning, June 12, 1881." Published June 16, 1881.

254: SITTING BY. "Intended for Reading on Lord's-Day, November 13, 1887." Published November 10, 1886 [?].

Engraving of Joanna Southcott by an unknown artist (399)

Joanna Southcott.

Painting: *Under his Wings shalt thou Trust* (392)

Painting: of an angel leading a two-horse chariot toward heaven (388)

Painting of the Last Day (393)

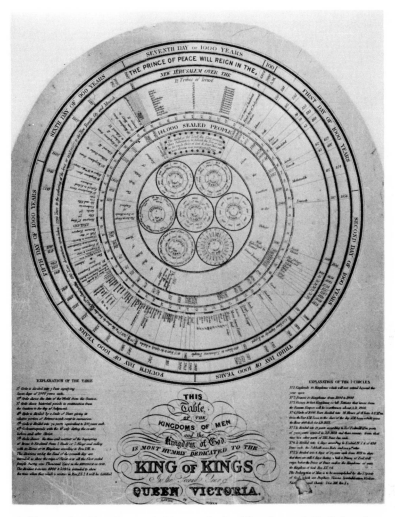

Table of the Kingdoms of Men and the Kingdom of God (220)

Painting: *Rock of Ages* (391)

The Rock of Ages.

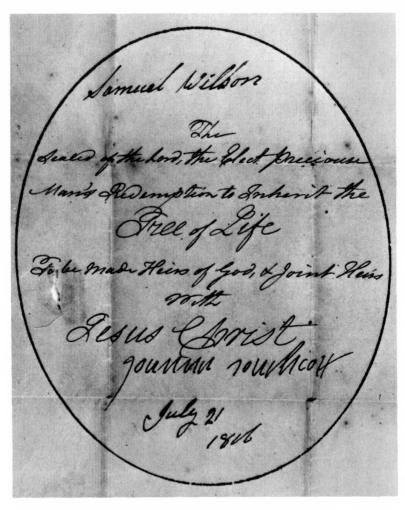

A typical seal (367)

Painting of a celestial figure ("Our Lord") on horseback (382)

Painting of Celestial Tent (389)

A Representation of the Knowledge of The Lord in Every Heart (384)

ABOVE: Richard Brothers, engraved by "Monk" (407)
BELOW: John Finlayson, engraved by I. Kay (409)

II. MANUSCRIPT MATERIAL

With rare exceptions, which are noted, the manuscripts in this collection are autograph manuscripts. Often they are signed, but since many of the manuscripts are copies, the signatures are copies also. Items 279 through 366 are all autograph manuscripts, and therefore individual identifying symbols are not included.

A: LETTERS

255: ALLEN, W. W. A. L. S., Spring Field, July 6, 1841. To Daniel Bird, Rhy Markett, Stone Bridge.

2 leaves, both sides of leaf 1, address and post mark on verso of leaf 2. Recto of leaf 2 blank. 23.2 x 18.3 cm.

Allen inquires about the well-being of his sick brother and requests a letter from Bird. A curious note added to the first page of the letter asks that the return letter be dictated.

256: MOLINEAUX, T. & S. A. L. S., Woodlund Bunk, Timperley, January 13, 1891. To Mr. George Bennett, n. p.

2 leaves, both sides of one and one side of leaf 2. 17.6 x 11.4 cm. Wishes recipient well and asks about the health of Mrs. Bennett. Announces faith in the promises made to Joanna.

257: MOLINEAUX, T. A. L. S., Woodlund Bunk, Timperley, July 11, 1898. To [George] Bennett, n. p.

2 leaves, both sides. 18.1 x 11.3 cm.

The letter, which describes a recently held meeting of Southcottian faithfuls, is only one page long. The balance of the pages is taken up by the copying of part of one of Joanna's communications received in 1796.

258: ———. A. L. S., Woodlund Bunk, Timperley, Cheshire, August 24, 1900. To "Dear Friend," n. p.

1 leaf, one side. 17.7 x 11.2 cm.

A short letter announcing the enclosure of a communication to Joanna "In answer to a man who said the Bible would be no more Revealed than it was," received July 7, 1802 (see item 286).

259: ———. A. L. S., n. p., n. d. To "Dear Friend," n. p.

1 leaf, one side. 17.5 x 11.4 cm.

A letter sent with a copy of the divine communication "Given to Joanna Southcott Nov. 9th, 1804" expressing the hope that the communication might be given to some "thirsty Believer."

260: NYLAND, JOHANNA. A. L. S., Rotterdam, August 4, [18]27. To Mr. and Mrs. Neilson, n. p.

2 leaves, both sides. 17.9 x 13.9 cm.

Discusses the health of Johanna Nyland and her family, the time of the Jewish Sabbath, and the happenings in the Church community in Rotterdam.

261: PUGHE, WILLIAM OWEN. A. L. S., London, March 26, 1825. To the Rev. T. P. Foley, n. p.

2 leaves, both sides leaf 1, leaf 2 blank except for address. 22.9 x 18.6 cm.

Reports the death of [Jane] Townley. There are appended two diary-like entries concerning communications seemingly given to the writer, both in the same hand and dated earlier than the letter.

262: ————. A. L. S., "For the True Believers in Joanna Southcott's Divine Mission and Inspired Writings," December, 1825, n. p.

2 leaves, both sides except verso of leaf 2 blank. 23 x 18.4 cm.

Pughe thanks Joanna's followers for choosing him to care for the sealed box.

263: SOUTHCOTT, JOANNA. A. L. (copy), n. p., February, 1802. To Mr. Charles Taylor, n. p.

2 leaves, both sides leaf 1, leaf 2 blank. 18.3 x 11.6 cm.

Explains Joanna's prophecy of her father's death and the fulfillment of the prophecy.

264: ————. A. L. S. (copy), n. p., February 28, 1802. To unknown recipient, n. p.

2 leaves, one side each. 22.2 x 18.3 cm.

A prophecy in couplets foretelling the death of a Mrs. Symonds. A note on the copy explains that the original was witnessed by Fanny Taylor, J. Jones, Mr. Symonds, and Eliz. Bolh.

265: ————. A. L. S., n. p., May 6, 1807. To Mr. Carder, n. p.

4 leaves, both sides. 18 x 11.4 cm.

Joanna reviews Carder's book, saying that he errs when he says that one can discern the promises of God by looking into her works. Rather, the scriptures also must be consulted.

266: ————. A. L. S. (extract), Paddington, December 21, 1802. To the King of England.

1 leaf, both sides. 30.4 x 18.7 cm.

Joanna aligns herself with Brothers as a prophetess by relying upon past prophecies as evidence. She then warns the king about a war with the Turks in which England will be victorious.

267: ————. A. L. S., n. p., January, 1804. To Mrs. Townley, London.

2 leaves, both sides. 18.5 x 11.2 cm.

An answer to Jane Townley's invitation for Joanna to come make her home in London. Joanna speaks of the evil in the city and God's promised punishment.

268: UNDERWOOD, ANN. A. L. (copy), "On Mrs. Robertshaw's Affliction," n. p., December 29, 1804. To "Dear Friend," n. p.

6 leaves, both sides. 17.9 x 11.3 cm.

A letter reporting a divine communication which asserts that a Mrs. Robertshaw's illness was inflicted because of divine love in order to cause humility rather than because of anger.

269: VINCENT, JOHN. A. L. S. (copy), Warrington, October 11, 1850. To "dear Friends," n. p.

4 leaves, both sides. 18 x 11.3 cm. Sewn.

Asserts that 1850 is the date of the second coming of the Shiloh who was born to Joanna in 1814 and caught up to heaven immediately. Vincent also discusses the reincarnation of Mr. [Stanhope?] Bruce in his own body as the embodiment of Christ.

270: ZEBULUN, JOSEPH. A. L. S., n. p., July 22, 1844. To Thomas Parsons, New Street, Stourbridge, Wocester-shire.

1 leaf, one side. 19 x 15.9 cm.

A letter which accompanied William Reuben's seal and which calls Parsons' attention to two evidently familiar songs.

271: ————. A. L. S., n. p., July 29, 1844. To Thomas Parsons, New Street, Stourbridge, Wocester-shire.

1 leaf, one side. 19.9 x 19.5 cm.

A letter which accompanied Mary Bird's seal and which calls Parsons' attention to an evidently familiar song.

272: ————. A. L. S., n. p. February 15, 1845. To Thomas Parsons, New Street, Stourbridge, Wocester-shire.

1 leaf, one side. 18.1 x 20.8 cm.

A letter which accompanied Elizah Bird's seal and which calls Parsons' attention to two evidently familiar songs.

273: [?]. A. L. (fragment), ". . . women at the last. . . ," with this addition on a separate page: "Ann Moore, May 12, 1813," n. p.

2 leaves. 18.7 x 12 cm. Text on two sides of leaf 1, inscription and date only on leaf 2.

Fragmentary remarks on several visions.

274: [?]. A. L. (fragment), "To the Friends of the church in Felker Lane," n. d.

2 leaves, both sides. 19 x 11.5 cm.

Written sometime after 1 January 1838 discussing the false prophecies of Jane Townley after Joanna's death.

275: [?] (The Panacea Society). T. L. S., Bedford, January 21st, 1966. To Eugene P. Wright, 1316-A Brackenridge Apts., Austin, Texas.

1 leaf, one side. 19 x 12.5 cm.

Signed letter on "The Panacea Society" stationery, but signature illegible. In answer to a letter requesting information on the Society, Joanna's box of Sealed Writings, and other Southcottian publications. The writer refuses to give the whereabouts of the box, although its availability to the bishops is assured. The writer suggests that Joanna's publications might be had by writing to Mr. Rosslyn E. Shumway, Star Route, Brown Valley, Yuba Co., California.

B : NOTES

276: [SOUTHCOTT, JOANNA]. A. N., n. d.

1 leaf, both sides. 7 x 9.9 cm. Irregular edges.

One side comments upon an attempted murder by and a suicide of a Mr. Peacock, and his wife's "pretended visitation." The other side comments upon the writer's health.

277: BENNETT, GEORGE. A. N. S., December, [18]89

1 leaf, one side. 10.8 x 17.2 cm.

A seven-line note which declares that when God establishes his earthly kingdom and man declares a new date, it will actually be the old date which God will follow.

278: [?]. A. N. (fragment), ". . . he began with reading one C—. . . ," n. d.

4 leaves, recto of 1 and 3, verso of 2 and 4 blank. The sheet is a printed "General Post Office Money Letter." 16.8 x 14 cm.

Part of a note reporting some man's observations about moral behavior for Christians.

C : SERMONS

279: INGALL, J[OHN]. Gloss on the scripture, "ii Philippians, v. 10-11," n. d.

1 leaf, one side. 8 x 18 cm.

Man and even Satan must bow to Christ.

280: [?]. (fragment), ". . . Believe my Gospel but deny the fulfillment," Saturday, April 1, no year.

8 leaves, both sides. 18.9 x 11.7 cm. Sewn.

Sermon discussing the civil punishment of "a woman," a follower of Joanna, who began her crimes against God and man in the spring of 1806, was taken into custody by civil authorities in October, 1808, and hanged in March, 1809. Though unnamed, the woman mentioned is most likely Mary Bateman (see Balleine, item 208, pp. 54-55).

281: [?]. "The Command to Prosecute," n. d.

6 leaves, both sides except last leaf blank. 22.7 x 19.8 cm. Sewn.

An answer to several prophecies by Richard Brothers and a warning that the end is near.

D: DIVINE COMMUNICATIONS

Those manuscripts here credited to Joanna Southcott are not in her hand. Soon after she began to experience the visitations, she received divine orders to dictate the communications to one or more of several secretaries, usually Ann Underwood or Jane Townley. It is fortunate that she did so, for as Joanna herself reports, her handwriting was so illegible that no one could read it. The fact that succeeding generations of believers have copied her manuscripts makes the discovery of original manuscripts difficult. And the fact that other "prophets," both in and out of the Southcottian Church, had visions of their own and recorded them with little provocation further complicates the picture.

The fact is, however, that Joanna is by far the most profuse contributor to the collection of manuscripts concerning divine communications. Matthews (see item 210) suggests that she "left behind sufficient manuscript material to have printed another 9,500 [pamphlets]." Those manuscripts listed below as author unknown, therefore, probably belong to Joanna, although at present no other evidence can be offered.

Further, not all of the divine communications in the collection are listed here. In the section of this listing titled NOTEBOOKS may be found a large number of communications, as well as poems, songs, letters, sermons, and prayers. The entries are listed according to date, the earliest first.

1: Given to Joanna Southcott

282: "I dreamed I was going along by a Church. . . ," July 2, 1796.

1 leaf, both sides. 34.9 x 25.2 cm.

The report of Joanna's dreams of her floating by a church from which came the sound of singing. Soon she lost sight of the church and came to a beautiful street. The "Answer of the Spirit" explains that Joanna will see heaven and return to report the scene.

283: "On the Pruning of the Trees, given in March 1799. . . ," n. d. (Copy signed by William Owen Pughe.)

2 leaves, both sides. 22.2 x 18.3 cm.

Compares the people of England first to one who climbs a tree cutting off the lower limbs (i.e. destroying the lower classes) as he climbs, thus leaving himself no way to get down when he must. Secondly, the people of England are compared to a young boy who, having got a few coins in his pocket (i.e. a few good men in the country), goes off thinking to buy everything at the fair (i.e. thinking to conquer the world).

284: "On the Last Day," March 8, 1797. (Copy in the hand of John Ingall.)

2 leaves, both sides. 30.6 x 19 cm.

Joanna's communication is an answer to a sermon by Mr. Pomeroy. It warns France of hard days because of the Godlessness of its leaders. England too is warned to be on guard.

285: "A communication given to Joanna Southcott 1801 concerning the Likenes [sic] of men to fallen Angels—when they wear [sic] cast out of heaven." (In the hand of Jane Townley.)

9 leaves, both sides. 20 x 16 cm.

The wars on earth involving France are compared to the "Tumult in the heaven." Those who oppose Joanna, such as Saunders and Thomas Moon, are identified as devils and damned to a life in Hell.

286: "In answer to a man who said the Bible would be no more Revealed than it was," July 7, 1802. With this: A. L. S., signed by T. Molineaux, dated August 24, 1900.

4 leaves, both sides except verso of leaf 4 blank. 17.2 x 11.1 cm.

Rebukes a Methodist who argued with Joanna about some of her conclusions. He is called Blind. Partly in poetic form. (See item 258.)

287: "Communication given to Joanna Southcott, Old Christmas Eve, 1802," n. d. (Copy, signed by Benjamin Howe.)

1 leaf, one side. 22.9 x 20.5 cm.

In poetic form comparing the Trinity to a cord between a chariot and horses, a cord which cannot be broken.

288: "Communication to Joanna upon One gaining the Prize," May 5, 1803. (Copy.)

2 leaves, both sides. 32.1 x 20.2 cm. Machine-made paper.

The "Prize" is God's gift of a peaceful earth to those who follow him. The seed which bruises the serpent's head is the word which flows from Joanna's mouth.

289: "Explanation of the Shadows . . . given to Joanna April 5, 1804."
Watermark reads 1818. (Copy.)

2 leaves both sides. 22.2 x 18.3 cm.

Exhorts believers to prepare for the end, which will come not
before the end of November [1804].

290: "Given to Joanna, April 6, 1804." Watermark reads 1803. (In
the hand of Jane Townley?)

2 leaves, both sides of leaf 2 blank. 31.8 x 19.3 cm.

Reports that "the Tryal" will come after May and before November of 1804. The spirit says that no one will be able to predict
the end of the world by the weather.

291: "A Communication concerning the progress of Judgments. . . ,"
Easter Sunday, 1804. Included with this: "The Answer of the
Spirit, Nov. 18, 1806." (In the hand of Jane Townley.)

12 leaves, both sides, except verso of leaf 12, blank. 18.4 x 11.8
cm. Sewn.

Both communications warn that the end is near and that the
Godly should look for signs and prepare.

292: "Given to Joanna Southcott Nov. 9th 1804," and "The words
spoken to Joanna in 1792. . . ," n. d. With this: A. L. S., signed
by T. Molineaux, n. d. (Copy, in the hand of T. Molineaux.)

6 leaves, both sides, except verso of leaf 5 and all of leaf 6 blank.
17.5 x 11.1 cm. Sewn at the tops of the sheets.

The first communication tells of the Judgment Day to come in
November, 1804. The second, earlier communication reassures
Joanna after her friends had scoffed at her.

293: "In Explanation to the 40 days mentioned to George Turner."
April 16, 1805. Copied September 1, 1813. Watermark reads
1812. (Copy by C. H. B[arnard].)

8 leaves, both sides, except verso of leaf 1 blank with title on
recto. 18.2 x 11.6 cm.

Foretells that England shall reap what it shall sow. If it spreads
death and war, then it will receive it also.

294: "Communication from Mrs. Southcott upon the present Harvest."
September 19, 1805. (Signed by "Jane Townly" [sic], but probably not her hand.)

1 leaf, both sides. 31.7 x 19.5 cm.

Tells of the reasons for the 3-year famine (from 1801-1803) and
warns that if the English people again turn from God the famine
will begin again.

295: "Communications." Old Swinford, November 9, 1805 [?]. (Copies, the last 14½ pp. in the hand of Rev. T. P. Foley.)

25 leaves, both sides, except leaf 25 blank. 22.5 x 17.8 cm.

Communications concerning Miss Harper's dream (March 6, 1802), a visit to a Mr. Halhed (December 17, 1804), "Explanation of the 12th Chapter of Revelations" (December 1, 1808), and "A Communication taken from the sealed writings, 1802."

296: "Communication given to Joanna Southcott, December 19, 1805 in answer to an inquiry. . . ," n. d. Also, a copy of a 1795 communication in answer to "the Methodiests [sic] saying the Lord was amongst them." N. d. (Copy signed by John Middleton.)

2 leaves with writing on verso of leaf 1 and recto of leaf 2. Double columns. 43.6 x 27 cm.

God promises punishment for the evil and reward for the faithful.

297: "Given October 2, 1809."

12 leaves, both sides. 18.8 x 11.9 cm.

Answers remarks made in a book by a Mr. Hann, who showed some of Joanna's prophecies to have proved false. Joanna answered the charge by saying that Mr. Hann had read her prophecies too literally. Although her father, for example, had not died in 1801 as she predicted, he did fall into a state like death as a warning of worse things to come.

298: Various communications from 1 January 1797 to December 1814. (Copies in the hand of Jane Townley.)

8 gatherings of 8 leaves each, both sides. Sewn separately. 20.9 x 13.9 cm.

Copies of several communications of various subjects: names of some of Joanna's followers, William Sharp perhaps the most famous. Interesting also is the dream allegory which depicts France as a cat which crawls down the throat of the dog England, scratching and destroying, but finally being consumed in the dog's "Bowells." Included also are the following: "Important Letter and communication sent by Joanna to a Friend in Contention being a warning to all the believers, that they shun strife and vain glory," a poem "Concerning Judas and Satan, and that her Father is compared to the Lord, the clergy & c," "Important communication given to Joanna on the man-child wherein Pomeroy is called the Shadow, the Spirit of God the Substance, and that it will when born be caught up to God," "Important Communication given to Joanna in answer to the Stumbles of the Sealed concerning the year 1807 and the 74 page of the warning to the world," "Communication given to Joanna on the White Horse in the 6 ch: Revelations," "The Conception Communication," and "An Important Communication given to Joanna from Priestley's wife being in Labour, which is said is a type of Joanna bringing forth the man-child, the 3 tables & c." The unfortunate parallel structure in the title of the last entry is typical of the prose style of Joanna.

299: Various communications from 1797 to 1814.

12 leaves, both sides plus writing on inside of back cover. 15.4 x 10 cm. Covered with marbled paper. "B 4" inscribed on front cover.

Includes "A Communication given to Joanna 1797 on Mr. Pomeroy's sermon," "The Answer of the Spirit to a false Prophet," "Part of a Communication given Joanna, December 1, 1804 concerning Pomeroy and Turner," "And now I shall show thee how the Shadow of men's Names. . . ," "I will give thee councell as my son Shiloh will shortly appear. . . ," and "A communication given in answer to the vision of Jedediah Holland."

300: ". . . Inhabitants of the earth . . . ," n. d. Watermark reads 1817. (Copies of a fragment.)

1 leaf, both sides. 36.6 x 22.8 cm.

Joanna laments the fact that man will not seek redemption although it is offered.

301: "Fragments from communications to Joanna related by Mrs. Taylor January 1833." On the same leaf, A. L. S., signed "Amey [?] Cocker." (Copies of fragments.)

2 leaves, both sides. 17.9 x 11.3 cm.

Includes a dream communication of a wheel full of cogs with every cog on fire. The spirit explained that the vision related to Ireland. The letter concerns Cocker's friendship with the Taylor family and also with a prophecy by Joanna that a certain plot of ground would be built on before her writings were proved.

302: "Part of a communication given from a ring . . . ," n. d. (Copy.)

2 leaves, both sides of leaf 1, leaf 2 blank. 23.1 x 19 cm.

Described symbolic qualities of the colors of the stones in a ring given to Joanna by "S. H. T." God promises to protect the giver from all harm.

303: "The Wonderful Woman," n. d.

3 leaves, both sides. 17.3 x 11.2 cm. Two leaves joined, one loose.

Comments upon God's use of Joanna to fulfill the prophecy of a "Wonderful Woman" found in the 12th Chapter of Revelation.

304: "That I've rocked first in thee. . . ." n. d. [1814].

1 leaf, both sides. 23.5 x 19 cm.

Unsigned communication referring to her "birth pangs." "This Communication was given about 8 o'clock at night at the Time Joanna was in great pain."

305: "In Answer to Mr. Wetherell respecting his and his children's Illness," n. d. (Copy.)

1 leaf, both sides. 19 x 25 cm.

Contains a verse of scripture (I Peter 4:17) copied from the King James version and rewritten in verse. The message is that infirmities must remain until Christ comes again and Satan is cast from the earth.

306: ". . . the blood dropped, and many strong hearts cried out. . . ," n. d. (Fragment.)

2 leaves, both sides except verso of leaf 2 blank. 20 x 16 cm.

Christ foretells the Turkish nation and others will bring destruction into the world. Christ's coming will, however, rid the world of hate and destruction. "Taken from Joanna's mouth by Ann Underwood."

2: *Given to Prophets Other Than Joanna*

307: TOWNLEY, JANE. "The awful stroke will be as great a blow to the King. . . ," London, August 6, 1824. (Signed by William Owen Pughe.)

2 leaves, both sides, except verso of leaf 2 blank. 22.2 x 18.5 cm.

Several communications "given to Jane Townley" and dated variously from July 14, 1824 to August 6, 1824. On the death of [William] Sharp, on Jane Townley's illness, and on the divine promise to Mr. Troop to restore his eyesight.

308: "Thou didst awake this morning," dated August 31, 1824 and August 16, 1824. (Signed by William Owen Pughe.)

2 leaves, both sides of leaf 1 and 1/3 page recto of leaf 2. 22.9 x 18.7 cm.

A communication on the subject of Jane Townley's illness.

309: TURNER, GEORGE. "Communication given to Mr. George Turner, April 23, 1815," n. d.

1 leaf, one side. 21.2 x 13 cm.

God will soon destroy the world and save the good.

310: ZEBULUN, JOSEPH. "Thus saith Christ. . . ," April 21, 1842.

1 leaf, one side. 24.3 x 19 cm.

There are 52 lines of iambic trimeter generally, riming abcb, defe, etc. Many misspelled words. Instructs Ann Bird, whose new name is Ann Reuben, to be faithful. The Birds were renamed Reuben after the tribe mentioned in Revelation as being "sealed of God."

311: "This seed is of me, saith the Lord. . . ," to Elizabeth Reuben, June 11, 1844.

1 leaf, one side. 38 x 23.8 cm. Attached with wax to Printed Broadside "The Seal of the Kingdom of Christ on Earth."

A poem in seven stanzas of eight lines each, uneven meter, riming abcb, defe, etc. Instructs the parents of the child Elizabeth Reuben to feed the child on God's word so that she might help fight Satan.

312: ————. "Come saith, Jah. Jehovah. . . ," July 22, 1844. To William Reuben, late Bird.

1 leaf, one side. 32.4 x 22 cm. Attached with wax to Printed Broadside "The Seal of the Kingdom of God on Earth."

A poem in seven stanzas of eight lines each, generally in iambic tetrameter, riming abcb, defe, etc. Admonishes William Reuben to be humble, and warns the devil to leave the sealed alone.

313: ————. "Christ, Jesus, is the Liveing [sic] vine. . . ," July 28, 1844. To Mary Reuben, late Bird.

1 leaf, one side. 32 x 22.5 cm.

A poem in seven stanzas of eight lines each, generally in iambic tretrameter, riming abcb, defe, etc. Instructs Mary Reuben to be wise and follow the teachings of God.

314: ————. "Thus saith the Lord, Creations [sic], God. . . ," August 29, 1844. To Joseph Reuben.

1 leaf, one side. 32.6 x 20 cm. Attached with wax to the Printed Broadside "The Seal of the Kingdom of Christ on Earth."

God promises to protect his "Babes in Christ" from Satan's power. A poem in seven stanzas of eight lines each, generally in iambic tetrameter, riming abcb, defe, etc.

315: [?]. "Now from the Kindred spirits I begin. . . ," Monday, September 10, 1804.

4 leaves, both sides. 32.2 x 20.4 cm.

Compares Christ's trials with Joanna's and comments upon "Mr. Pomproy's" [Pomeroy?] unsympathetic treatment of Joanna's cause. Part of this MS is in couplets.

316: [?]. "Gospel of the nine virgins. . . ." (Fragment, the second part of which is dated Sunday morning, February 16, no year.)

4 leaves, both sides, except last leaf blank. 19.2 x 12.1 cm.

A prophecy that God's enemies shall be overcome.

317: [?]. ". . . supposed the others could not be proper judges. . . ," n. d. (Fragment.)

8 leaves, both sides, except leaf 8 blank on recto; watercolor painting on verso of leaf 8. 16 x 10 cm.

Tells of the choosing of Pomeroy to recognize the holiness of Joanna's prophecies and his subsequent fall from favor. The painting is a landscape.

318: [?]. "I shall answer thee from his words," n. d.

8 leaves, both sides, except leaf 8, one side only. 19.2 x 12.3 cm.

Tells of the coming fulfillment of the scriptures.

319: [?]. ". . . own goodness for tho. . . ," watermark reads 1808. (Fragment.)

4 leaves, both sides, except leaves 3 and 4 blank. 18.7 x 11.7 cm.

Divine explanation of the likenesses and differences between God and man.

320: [?]. "Thee to search concerning the fruit. . . ," n. d. (Fragment.)

2 leaves, both sides. 16.3 x 10.3 cm.

Divine warning that the scriptures will be fulfilled.

321: [?]. "Therefore I could not. . . ," watermark reads 1807. (Fragment.)

8 leaves, both sides, except verso of leaf 4 and all of leaves 5, 6, 7, and 8 blank. 16 x 10 cm. Sewn.

Concerns the judging of Field.

322: [?]. "Continuation from the Second Book," n. d. (Fragment.)

8 leaves, both sides of leaves 1 and 2, the balance of the booklet blank. 19.3 x 12.2 cm. Sewn.

Part of a communication promising the fulfillment of the scriptures.

323: [?]. "A Prophecy Given in the 16th Century," n. d. (Copy.)

1 leaf, one side. 5.2 x 13.2 cm.

Foretells the birth of a "conqueror" to be born of a woman. The child will neither eat, sleep, nor remain with the mother.

E: NOTEBOOKS

These notebooks are generally conglomerations of manuscript material gathered at random and either bound together or copied in notebooks. The pieces of manuscripts collected by Lavinia E. C. Jones (see items 341 through 346) are of an almost infinite number of sizes, shapes, and subjects sewn together and covered with coarse cloth. Most of the material concerns communications given to Joanna, but letters, poems, sermons, prayers, lists of works, and essays from various people are included.

324: SOUTHCOTT, JOANNA, ET AL. Divine communications and letters on various subjects. "Glory to God Highest" and the figure "1" on front cover. "Vol. 1" inscribed on front flyleaf. Dates on copies range from 6 March 1802 to 21 July 1811. N. d. on the notebook. (Copies.)

66 leaves, both sides, except verso of leaf 1 and recto of leaf 2 blank. 22.4 x 18 cm. Boards.

Contains the following titles: "Joanna and her Sister. Type of the End," "Death of Mr. Joachim, Shot through the heart," "Com. in answer to Mary Bateman," "T. P. Foley to the Public-Advertisement," "Joanna to the Rev. T. P. Foley," "Com. on the Fake Charges agst. Joanna," "How the Sacrament is to be taken," "Answer to Mrs. Harpers Dread," "The Rotton Cucumbers & c.," "Banns of Marriage between the Church of Rome and the Protestant Church," "The Kingdom of God, what is it, Explained," "Comn. on the Ear of Corn," "The Peoples enquiry and no Communications," and "Comn. in Joannas own hand writing."

325: ———. Divine communications and letters on various subjects. "On Earth Peace Good will To Men" on front cover. Dates on copies range from 16 November 1802 to 20 October 1861. N. d. on the notebook. (Copies.)

86 leaves, both sides except verso of leaf 1, recto of leaf 2, and both sides of leaf 86 blank. 22.5 x 17.8 cm. Boards.

Contains the following titles: "Letter to the Rev. Mr. Bull," "The Comit [sic] of the year 1811," "Ordination," "The Spirit's answer to some events of 1811," "The Spirits answer to Peoples Unbelief of the Harvests," "Com. upon the Womans enmity against Satan," "The Mountains of Snow & c.," "Fake Charges brought by Hann," "Christs Birth, The Promise Pomeroy her Judge & c.," "The Spirit's answer to Foley's Sermon," "Foley's Sermon," "Com. on the Thanksgiving Day," "Com. upon Prayer & meeting together," "A Letter from G. B. to the Rev. J. Cunming," and "Upon Marriage." Most interesting is "The Spirit's answer to some events of 1811," in which Joanna discusses the wars of Spain and France and foretells England's future problems with both.

326: ————. Divine communications and letters on various subjects. "Alleluia Alleluia" and the figure "3" on front cover. Dates on copies range from 25 July 1802 to 24 December 1814. Printed article "our Colonial Empire" pasted on p. 84. N. d. on notebook. (Copies.)

94 leaves, both sides plus inside both covers. 23 x 18.1 cm. Boards.

Contains the following titles: "Satan's Host and Pharaoh host [sic]," "Letter to Daniel Roberts," "Answer to Baylee of Limerick," "Answer to announces [sic] Letter sent to Foley," "Joanna's Sufferings in Wilsons room," "Explanation of the 40 days (Turner)," "The Likeness of Joanna Southcott," "Letter from Joanna to George Turner," "Charity never Faileth," "Faith, a Gift of God," "Com. upon one gaining the Prize," "Com. upon the Awful Trial," "Floods at Weston Place, important," "Concerning the Methodists," "Important Comn. on the Birth of the Son, Shewing that It was only a Shadow that took place in the year 1814," and "The number created from Adam to the final Day of Judgment and the Crimes of Satan."

327: ————. Divine communications and letters on various subjects. "AΩ" in the Star of David and the figure "4" on front cover. "Vol. 4" inscribed on front flyleaf. Dates on copies range from 12 July 1802 to 31 August 1807. N. d. on notebook. (Copies.)

67 leaves, both sides, except verso of leaf 1, recto of leaf 2, and all of leaf 67 blank. 22.4 x 18.2 cm. Boards.

Contains the following titles: "Various Passages respecting the Messiah," "The Answer of the Spirit to the Judgment drawn by the Believers respecting Joanna's Trial Death & c.," "A com. in ans. to Joanna's Pondering thoughts of not having com's. while Dangers seem to Surround us," "Com. upon the Thunder, the Still Small Voice, and Blotting out Brother's Honour, and giving it to the Lord," "Comn. on the Boiling of the Bible," "Com. Respecting the Mail Coach, Pigeons, Owl, and Whistle," "Com. on the Sudden arrival in Leeds of Wilson & Carpenter, with Directions for the Sealed," "Joanna Sealed on a whole Sheet of paper," "Mr. John Wilson's Reproofs & c.," "The Vision seen at Medina," and "The Three Elect Children."

328: ————. Divine communications and letters on various subjects. A 6-pointed star with 4 leafy posts projecting from it on front cover. Inside the star are inscribed the letters "i h s." The figure "5" inscribed on front cover. "Vol. 5" inscribed on front flyleaf. Dates on copies range from 1 February 1802 to 25 November 1810. N. d. on notebook. With this glued to p. 99: A. N. S., "The Lord calls upon us to fulfill our Baptismal vows." Signed by G[eorge] Bennett. (Copies.)

87 leaves, both sides except leaves 1, 2, 86, 87, recto of leaf 3, and verso of leaf 85 blank. 22.5 x 18.1 cm. Boards.

Contains the following titles: "Joanna compared to Micaiah the true Prophet and the Shepherds to the false Prophets," "The Claiming of the Promise by the Women," "The Kingdom of God," "Answer to Mossop's question 'Whether It was a jesting Spirit that visited Joanna'," "Concerning Mrs. Wilmots sickness," "Death of Mrs. Bruce," "Patchwork Communication," "Letter from Joanna to Mr. Aked," "Service for the 12th of January," "Grand Dial & Sun Dial Com'n," "The old and young Prophet," "Concerning Satan being in the moon & c.," "Ans. to Mr. Hawes upon the Eleventh year," and "Comn. respecting our Saviour being very man." A very good example of Joanna's use of logic may be found in the letter to Mr. Sharp where she proves that Satan is in the moon.

329: ————. Divine communications and letters on various subjects. A 6-pointed star with the letters "I. H. E." inscribed on front cover. The figure "6" also inscribed inside the star. Dates on copies range from 1 January 1766 to 25 December 1814. Date "January 1, 1866" along with "THE STANDARD" seemingly cut from a newspaper and glued to p. 166. (Copies.)

136 leaves, both sides. 23.1 x 18.3 cm. Boards.

Contains the following titles: "Extracts from 1st Book of Sealed Prophecies explained," "Upon Joanna going to her Father's house," "Answer to important texts of Scripture," "The Recorder's visit to Joanna," "Ponderings of Joanna after leaving Bristol," "Com. in answer to Joanna's sister and her Husband," "Joanna's visit to Bath," "Comn. in answer to Sweedenbourg," "Joanna ordered to go to Tozers to receive the Sacrament," "Joanna's Prayer for Wilson," "Parable of an Highwayman," "Joanna's observations on Sweeden-bourg," "On our Departure and Flight," "Letter from G. Bennett to Charles Taylor," "The Standard," "Letter to Philip Norris of Liverpool," "A comn. on Joanna getting out of Bed & c.," "A comn. in ans. to a Lady who said the Prophecies failed," "April Fool communication," "Comn. Respecting Hann," "A comn. upon the Harvests of 1799 & 1800," "Answer to Prescott's Vision of Tree and Willows," "Spiritual Knowledge compared with Mechanism," "The church will awakened be," "The Spirits Answer to Hann's Book," "Upon the Secrets of the Lord to a Woman," "The Lords explanation of the 54th of Isaiah," "Joanna's Last Words."

The last entry, on "Joanna's Last Words," is a good review of Joanna's intent and belief in life.

Inside the front cover there is glued a black and white print depicting an ornate room with four figures. One figure, seated, draws a bow aimed out a window, while a companion looks on. The other two figures face each other. On the recto of the flyleaf there are glued 3 newspaper clippings: "Alleged Sentence of Christ," "Beautiful Aerial Spectacle," and "Now, one very remarkable thing revealed in Holy Scriptures."

330: ————. Divine communications, letters, and poems on various subjects. A wreath with a crown and the figure "7" inscribed in the wreath on front cover. Dates on copies range from 1652 to 30 October 1869. N. d. on notebook. (Copies.)

126 leaves plus verso and recto of back end papers plus 2 leaves (marked A, B: C, D), both sides sewn after p. 264. 23.3 x 19 cm. Boards.

Contains the following titles: "Concerning this being a Happy Land in 1807," "Mr. Hollond complains of Satan's temptations," "Joanna's Trial & Death & State of Believers & c.," "In answer to Mrs. Wilson about the Kingdom," "Joanna's Letter to the Revd. Basil Wood," "An Answer to the Above by the Spirit," "Explanation of St. Matthew 7th Chapter 1 & 2 verses," "Woolland Stung by a Bee—Vinegar & Honey," "Joanna's Private Marriage," "Stopping the Meetings till after the Birth," "Letter on the 2nd coming of Christ by G. Bennett," "The Fulness of the Time by G. Bennett," "The Midnight Cry & c.," "1st Kings 15 and John's Gospel 10—Ans'd," "Joanna & Brothers compared with Adam & Eve," "Sealing, Signing, and Thunder," "The Rising and Setting Sun," "Poetry by G. Bennett ('The Wise Virgins,' 'The Little Flock,' 'Future Happiness,' 'The Light of the World,' 'The Voice of the Spirit,' 'Creation and Redemption,' 'The Sealed of the Lord, Precious,' and 'The Church')," "An Address to the Bretherin by G. B.," "Comn upon Mockers and Unbelievers," "Comn upon Brothers & Turner," "Archbishop Usher's Prediction 1652," "Original Sin by G. Bennett," "Brothers compared to the Prophet Jonah," "The Labourers in the Vineyard," "The Comn. Old Fashions revived and music of this world," "Continuation of a comn on the Prophecies," and "Cain & his Wife going to the Land of Nod."

The entry "Joanna's Private Marriage" lists some very interesting visitors to Joanna during her "pregnancy": "Count Professor Arsolini, Accoucheur to the Empress of France at the Birth of the King of Rome," Count Lieven (Russian Ambassador), and General Count Orloff (Aid de Camp to the Emperor of Russia). These guests were to be kept secret to prevent "the abominable Caricatuers" in the newspapers.

On the front flyleaf there are glued two printed poems: "Faith in Heavenly Harmony" and "The Kingdom of Peace on Earth."

Inside the back cover are glued two printed works: "The Advent of Christ's Glorious Kingdom," a poem, and "Prayer for the Kingdom of God on Earth."

331: ————. Divine communications, letters, poems, and prayers on various subjects. "Vol. 8" on front flyleaf. Dates on copies range from 2 January 1802 to 15 February 1871. N. d. on notebook. (Copies.)

88 leaves, both sides plus verso of front and recto of back flyleaves. 23 x 18.8 cm. Boards.

Contains the following titles: "Prayer," "The Trinity," "Mrs. Buchan the Imposter & c.," "The Way to Happiness Described by Joanna," "Mr. & Mrs. Bateman applying for Seals," "Joanna's visit to Tozer's meeting unawares," "On the Death of Mrs. Bruce," "Letter to Turner with Comn's of Importance," "Will unbelievers be cut off by the year 1807," "Elder Brother brought on the Evil, Christ will bring the Good," "England, France, and the Sealed People," "Letter by G. Bennett to Rev. W. Hunt on the coming Rest," "Important Comn. upon the Trial & c.," "Comn. upon the Trial—Important," "Mutany in England to throw off the yoke," and "Wilson's Testimony of his Illness."

Most interesting are Joanna's poetic prophecy on p. 174 which foretells a civil war in England and her lament on pp. 146-147 that the world thinks her out of her senses.

332: ————. Divine communications, letters, poems, and prayers on various subjects. "Vol. 9" on front flyleaf. Dates on copies range from 7 December 1802 to 6 April 1877. N. d. on notebook. With this, glued inside front cover: a printed article "Examination of the Prophecies," n. d. Inside back cover, a printed article "Lord Redesdale on Disputed Points of Doctrine," n. d. (Copies.)

90 leaves, both sides plus verso of front and recto of back flyleaves. 22.7 x 18.8 cm. Boards.

Contains the following titles: "O Blessed Savior, God and King" (a poem by George Bennett), "Upon cutting the Communications," "Joanna's visit to Mr. Howes & the Death of her Brother," "Upon Joanna Southcott's History," "Letter from Joanna to Turner & His Daughter & c.," "Letter from Joanna upon Turner's Daughter," "The progress of Joanna's Journey to Exeter," "The Parable of the Shepherds and Sheep," "Strange Effects of Faith—Marriage Union," "There is scarce faith to believe the Promises," "The Sheep and the Lambs—A Dream," "The Kingdom of Christ, by G. Bennett," "Three Gardens, by G. Bennett," "The Sixth Hour to the Ninth, by G. Bennett," and "The True Vine, by G. Bennett."

The printed article which is attached inside the front cover lists the names of 23 persons, "Chosen by DIVINE command," to judge Joanna's words. She was given a unanimous approbation.

333: ————. Divine communications, letters, poems and printed articles on various subjects. "Vol. 10" inscribed on front cover. Dates on copies range from 1794 to 14 September 1814. Watermarks on sheets added to notebook read 1859. (Copies.)

186 leaves, both sides plus front and back flyleaves both sides plus inside front and back covers. The 143 pp. which make up the original notebook are 32 x 20 cm. Others vary from 22.1 x 14 to 31.5 x 19.5 cm. Boards.

Included are many printed articles (indicated by "p" in this description) glued to the leaves, often with autograph notes included on the same page. Contains the following works: "Sacred to the Memory of Joanna Southcott" (a copy of her epitaph), "The Three Visions on one paper," "The dream of a coach Stuck fast in wheel Ruts," "The Legend of St. Christopher" (p), "Curious Relic—Sentence on the Savior" (p), "On the Fast Day, 1797" (p), "The Destruction of the Nations," "Comn on the Bond" (p), "Paradise" (p), "St. Matthew 27/25" (p), "Belshazzar's Feast" (p), "The Holy Thorn" (p), "As the Days of Noah were" (p), "Carol" (p), "Comn in Answer to the Rev. Mr. Marshall" (p), "A Year's Troubles" (p), "Men wrangle about religion" (p), "Bethlehem" (p), "A Renovated Earth" (p), "The Law Against Satan" (p), "David" (p), "The Blessings and Comforts of Christianity" (p), "The Legend of Redbreast" (p), "Thoughts on the Coming of the Lord" (p), "Secret Prayer" (p), "Noah the Founder of the Chinese Empire" (p), "Diesire" (p), "Genesis" (p), "Future Existence" (p), "Comn. on Joanna taking Cold" (p), "The Shepherd" (p), "The Midnight Song of Bethlehem" (p), "The Lord's Sepulchre" (p), "Happiness! What is it?" (p), "The Mad Riders and Concerning Pomeroy & c." (p), "Mortality" (p), "For This is Not Your Rest" (p), "The Litany" (p), "The Contentions of the Nation," "Comn. on the Rose of Sharon" (p), "Joanna's Journay [sic] from Leeds to Stackton," "The Transfiguration" (p), "The Trial or Judgment of Satan" (p), "The Church Militant and Triumphant" (p), "Pray without Ceasing" (p), "Joanna's Prayer at her Departure," "Letter and comn. to Mrs. Townley," "Letter from Joanna to Mr. Wilson," "The Temporal and Spiritual Sword," "The Oath of Allegiance and the Sword of Gideon," "Com. in Answer to Mr. Crosley's dream," "The Com. on November Waiting to be Born," "Com. on the Harvest of the Year 1805," "Comn. on the first book of Wonders," "Com. on the Jubulee Church Bells & c.," "Com. on Mr. Spring's paper," "Com. on the Great Importance of the Trial in 1804," "Joanna writes to a friend about the Messiah," "The Purposes of God in the Creation of Man," "Comn. on Hanna's Prayer," "A Call to the Jews and all Nations," "A Letter to Mr. Field in answer to Mr. Finis," "Comn. in Answer to a Jew Respecting a Will," "Letter to Mr. Fisher—Scripture proofs for the Jews," "The Answer about the Books of Moses by the Spirit," "Com. for Mr. Fisher Concerning Mr. Fisher," "Com. on 12th of Revelations 1st verse," "The Children of this world, and the Children of Light," "Com. in Answer to Mr. Roberts—Mat. 11/28-29," "Com. About Mr. Priestley—About Astrology," "Com. on the Novel— The Romance of the Forest," "Dirge" (p), "Com. Respecting David's Throne," "The Tale of Agrippia, Adversity, and Prosperity," "A Warning to the different Sects," "On the death of Joseph Southcott's Son," "Letter from Joanna to Mr. Mansell— Token of Love," "Com. on the Fall and the Restoration," "The Doctrine of the Candles and Spacious room," "Joanna's Judgment and Sinking Faith," "On Some Calamities of the Holy Land" (p), "Fearful Earthquake in China" (p), "The Bahs of Persia" (p), "Ravages of Locusts" (p), "An Appeal to all Liberal-Minded Christians" (p), "The Doctrine of the Eucharist" (p), "The Conflagration at Santiago," "Eight Hundred Men Starving in the Snow" (p), "There is a limit to the feeling of horror" (p).

There is also a print of an engraving picturing 4 earthly and 6 heavenly angels with an A. N. "The Angels Rejoiced At her Birth 1.30—17, 20—19, 10."

334: ―――――. Divine communications, letters, poems, and printed articles on various subjects. "Vol. 11" on front flyleaf. Dates on copies range from 12 June 1796 to 12 July 1813. N. d. on notebook. Watermarks on notebook leaves read 1852 and on appended table of contents sheet, 1863. (Copies.)

113 leaves, both sides plus appended sheet glued inside front cover and recto of back flyleaf. 31.5 x 20.2 cm. 16 leaves cut out of the beginning of the notebook and unaccounted for in the table of contents.

Contains the following works: "Queen Mary and the Roman Powers & c.," "On the Illumination for Peace," "Upon the Oath taken to the Lord," "Answer to Halhed—National Judgment & c.," "Fox's Funeral," "Judgment begins at the house of God," "Joanna— the Judges, Jury and sudden death of Coy," "Coy's Funeral," "Dream of broken rings, Seals, Bonaparte & c.," "Concerning the Methodists," "The end of who reject the Visitation," "Burning ash faggots on Christmas eve," "Letter concerning Charles Abbott," "Letter concerning Joanna's suffering friends," "Joanna's Judgment upon the Bible & her writings," "Respecting faithful Labourers being sent out," "Mr. Brothers compared to Adam," "Judge, Jury, and Visitors at the trial," "The chain Communication," "Letters written by the Apostle Paul," "The Dream of the Diamond Ring," "Temporal and Spiritual things Compared," "Selection of passages concerning the Bride, Hell fire, the broken bottle of Wine, Blood of Christ & c.," "He Shall Rule whose blood was shed on Calvary's cross," "Christ's Reign on the earth as foretold & c.," "David's throne, Solomon's wisdom & c.," "Letter from Joanna to her Sister upon being deceived," "Letter to Hurst upon the Judgment of Believers," "Answers to a Dream of a Serpent in a man's pocket," and "Letter of Joanna's upon the Death of Mr. Cheese."

On the verso of leaf 113 and recto of the back fly sheet are two newspaper clippings: "The Writings of Joanna Southcote; Thornton V. Howe—Judgment" and a poem "Come, Holy Spirit, from above," and an epitaph: "On a Tomb Stone at Milton Church Yard, Kent."

335: ————. Divine communications, letters, and poems on various subjects. "Vol. 12" on front flyleaf. Dates on copies range from November 1799 to 10 May 1864. The names "B. B. Jones" and "Farleigh Dawn" inscribed in front cover along with the dates "1834 to 1846," but watermarks on the leaves read 1862. (Copies.)

56 leaves, both sides except recto of leaf 1, all of leaves 49 and 56, and verso of leaf 55 blank. 32.5 x 19.7 cm. Boards, but split at spine; leaves now loose.

Contains the following works: "The Trinity and National Judgments," "Priestly's Wife and the Man Child," "Conception Communication," "Discord among the Believers," "The Sacrament administered by Joanna," "Nutshell Communication," "A Letter by G. Bennett," "The Swerg. Communication," "A Communication upon the Scriptures," and "Important Comm. to George Turner."

336: ————. Divine communications, letters, and poems on various subjects. "Vol. 15" inscribed on front flyleaf. Dates on copies range from 1672 to 20 February 1881. N. d. on notebook. (Copies.)

138 leaves, both sides plus verso of front and recto of back flyleaf. 22.5 x 18.5 cm. Boards.

Contains the following works: "The First Resurrection by G. Bennett," "Com'n concerning the Judgment of the Wise Men," "A Letter from Joanna upon Mockery & c.," "The Answer to Senior's dream by the Spirit," "Concerning the Visions to Joseph Prescott," "Letter from Mr. Baylee to the Revd. Mr. Foley," "Respecting Mr. Senior's wrong Judgment," "Respecting Turner and Brother's being deceived," "Turner's Will and God's Will," "Turner's dream of the three Sheep," "Joanna's Vision of the Prince of Peace," "Joanna's Letter to Mr. Long, Priest Vicar, Devon," "Verses by G. Bennett upon Immorality," "Joanna's verses on the Creation (Answered)," "The Language of Joanna's heart," "An old Prophecy," "What is Abomination in the sight of God," "Announcement of Joanna's Death," "Copy of a Letter from T. P. Foley respecting the Box," "Letter from Joanna to Maria Bruce," "A Dream of the two Plows explained," and "Shewing how two men that are enemies to Joanna are like Bullocks that are yoked in and are unable to Hurt her."

Pp. 205-208 contain a revelation commenting upon the use of "high Language" and "Eloquence" in poetry as compared to "Simplicity and Innocence."

337: ————. Divine communications, letters, and poems on various subjects. "Vol. 16" and continuation "from End of Vol. 15" on flyleaf. Dates on copies range from September 1802 to April 1882. N. d. on notebook. Watermarks read 1828. (Copies.)

111 leaves, both sides. 22.8 x 18.7 cm.

Contains the following works: "The Revelations of St. John Explained by a Revelation from God," "His Malice must be Known," "Just as the Devil in Heaven begun, Just so on Earth, He now is come," "Lot's Daughters," "The Spirit of Truth," "The Lord's Prayer in Verse," "The Mysteries of the Fall."

Inside the front cover there is glued a coat of arms made up of a shield upon which appears a grating under a crown encircling three feathers.

338: ————. Divine communications, letters, and poems on various subjects. "Another duplicate copy of J. Southcott's Communications, Volume I, Volume II" inscribed on front cover. Dates on notebook range from 24 February [19]09 to 12 February [19]11. (Copies.)

114 leaves, both sides first 80 leaves, the balance blank. 22.8 x 17.7 cm.

Merely duplicates volume 1 and part of volume 2 described above (items 324 and 325).

339: ————. Divine communications, letters, and poems on various subjects. "Vol. 1" inscribed on recto of leaf 1. Dates on copies range from 1795 to 21 May 1813. N. d. on notebook. (Copies.)

172 leaves, both sides. 17.6 x 11 cm. Boards.

Not to be confused with item 324, also labeled "Vol. 1." Contains the following works: "On Speaking in an Empty House," "On the Prayer for the recovery of Mrs. Stanhope Bruce," "On the death of Miss Eveleigh and the happiness of the departed Spirits to meet each other in Glory," "On Queen Esther," "The Lord is not slack concerning his Promise," "The Justice of God in Creating Woman," "On Baptism," "On the Methodists saying the Lord was Among them," "On the death of Colonel Shadwell," "A Comn. sent to Pomeroy," "On the Fast day, Roman Power to be destroyed & c.," "On Joanna's Father being a Child with Old Age," "On the Illumination for Peace," "Answer to a Confusion in Joanna's Mind," "On Sealing up the Writings, Vision of Candles, Ten Years, & c.," "On too much oil putting out the Lamp," "On her Kinsman John," "On the Rising Sun," "Private Instructions by the Spirit of Joannas love, Pity, & c.," "A Root of Jesse, and Star of Jacob a light to the Gentiles," "On Hunters text," "On General Restoration," "On Adam's death and the Saint in the grave," "On the likeness of men to the fallen Angels," "A dream of her Elder Brothers taking of her Fathers Substance," "On Isaiah 52 Chr & Second Psalm,"

"On Pomeroy a type of the clergy," "On Bel and the Dragon," "On the Oath New-Created Being & c.," "On Burning Ashen faggots on Christmas Eve," "Concerning the first Sealing," "Copy of letter to Mrs. Bruce," and "On the Pearl of Great Price."

340: ————. Divine communications, letters, and poems on various subjects. "Vol. 2" inscribed on recto of leaf 1. Dates on copies range from 10 July 1795 to 10 May 1812. N. d. on notebook. (Copies.)

159 leaves, both sides. 17.5 x 11 cm.

Not to be confused with item 325, also labeled "Vol. 2." Contains, however, some duplication of other notebooks. Contains the following works: "Scriptures preceeding the Communication of the Comforter," "On David Being a Man after God's own heart," "On the Covering of Patchwork," "On the Progress of Judgments," "On Peter Launching into the great deep," "Instructions given to Joanna for Believers," "On the death of Joanna's Brother," "Mr. Southcotts death," "A Commn. given at various times, 1795, 1796, & c.," "On the 7 Men whose hands the Lord will Seal with Power," "On the disorder in the Eye, Explained," "On the Magistrats forbidding prayers in public," "An address to the Friends who are impatient with respect to the Birth of Shiloh," "On a dream of the Lambs in the Basket," "A letter to the Revd. Stanhope Bruce," "On Joannas Journey to Highgate," "On the Trinity," "On Joannas Dream of Sharp & Foley," "An Answer to Townley's will," "A Letter to the Bishop of London," "On Joannas pregnancy a *Shadow*," "On too much oil putting out the Lamp," "On her kinsman who lay 12 hours in Great Agonies," and "On the Methodists saying the Lord was among them."

341: ————. Divine communications, letters, notes, and poems in various hands on various subjects. Inscribed "L[avinia]. E[lizabeth]. C[hapman]. Jones, December 25, 1836." The date "1797" embroidered on cover.

90 leaves, both sides. Leaves vary from 8.5 x 12.4 to 22.2 x 14.2 cm. Sewn roughly and loosely bound in coarse cloth.

Communications and other miscellaneous MS material dated 1797 by and about Joanna.

342: ————. Divine communications, notes, letters, and poems in various hands on various subjects. Inscribed "L. E. C. Jones, December 25, 1836." Date "1798" embroidered on cover. (Copies.)

43 leaves, both sides. Leaves vary from 16 x 10.8 cm. to 22.2 x 14.5 cm. Sewn roughly and loosely bound in coarse cloth.

Communications and other miscellaneous MS material dated 1798 by and about Joanna.

343: ————. Divine communications, notes, letters, and poems in various hands on various subjects. Inscribed "L. E. C. Jones, December 25, 1836." Date "Febry. 1804" written on cover. (Copies.)

17 leaves, both sides. Leaves vary from 18.3 x 11.2 to 20.3 x 14.3 cm. Roughly sewn.

Communications and other miscellaneous MS material dated 1804 by and about Joanna.

344: ————. Divine communications, notes, letters, and poems in various hands on various subjects. Inscribed "L. E. C. Jones, December 25, 1836." Date "Octbr. 1804" written on cover. (Copies.)

34 leaves, both sides. Leaves vary from 18.3 x 11.3 to 21 x 13 cm. Roughly sewn.

Communications and other miscellaneous MS material dated 1804 by and about Joanna.

345: ————. Divine communications, notes, and poems in various hands on various subjects. Inscribed "L. E. C. Jones, December 25, 1836." Date "Decbr. 1804" written on cover. (Copies.)

52 leaves, both sides. Leaves vary from 18 x 10.5 to 20.8 x 13.4 cm. Roughly sewn.

Communications and other miscellaneous MS material dated 1804 by and about Joanna.

346: ————. Divine communications, notes, letters, and poems in various hands on various subjects. Inscribed "L. E. C. Jones, December 25, 1836." Date "1807" embroidered on cloth cover. (Copies.)

231 leaves, both sides. Leaves vary from 3.7 x 12.2 to 22.2 x 14 cm. Sewn roughly and loosely bound in coarse cloth.

Communications and other miscellaneous MS material dated 1807 concerning Joanna.

347: ————. Divine communications and notes on Joanna's health. Dated September 9, 1804 and September 10, 1804.

12 leaves, both sides plus inside front cover. 15.4 x 10.1 cm. Sewn and covered with paper marbled on outside.

Included is a note by Joanna in which she remarks that she would like to die.

348: ————. Divine communications, letters, sermons, newspaper reports, a drama (entitled "Montazamua"), and part of a folk tale ("Little Musgrave & Lady Barnaro"). Signed by "Chas. T. Barnard" inside front cover. (Copies.)

17 leaves, both sides except verso of leaf 6 and all of leaf 7 blank. 19.5 x 16.3 cm. Sewn and covered with paper marbled on one side.

The copies of Joanna's writings are separated from the non-Southcottian stories and reports by their being begun at the opposite end of the notebook and written with the book inverted.

The reports are copies from GENTLEMAN'S MAGAZINE, Vol. 66, p. 2, October 1796 and December 15, 1796. The drama "Montezamua" (elsewhere "Montezuma") is a tragedy.

349: INGALL, J[OHN]. "Wonderful Prop." Falsely dated 1805. Watermark reads 1818.

8 leaves, 4 of which are blank. Leaf 8 is torn to 1/3 size. 20 x 15.8 cm. Sewn.

Extracts from the works of Joanna Southcott.

350: ————. "The Marriage of the Lamb, both Spiritual and temporal: illustrated by Extracts from the writings of Joanna Southcott the Bride." January 18, 1814.

24 leaves, both sides. 19.6 x 12.9 cm. Covered and sewn.

The story of Joanna's marriage to an earthly bridegroom recorded totally by extracts from Joanna's published works.

351: TOWNLEY, JANE. "39th Book." Bristol, 1805.

16 sheets, both sides. 15.8 x 20.5 cm. Covered with heavy paper and sewn.

Reports on Joanna's mental and physical reactions to illness and the thwarting of her desires to set up a kingdom of God on earth.

352: WATSON, ELLEN. Poems and essays. December 25, 1891.

65 leaf notebook. 11.4 x 8.3 cm. Leather bound.

A present inscribed on end pages to Charlotte Kemble and signed by Ellen Watson. Contains "The Scripture Alphabet," "Comfort under affliction," "On the Uncertainty of Life," "An Affectionate Tribute to the memory of a Mother" (a poem of fifteen tercet stanzas, each of which concludes with the refrain "My Mother"), "Lines on Good Friday" (a poem of four 6-line stanzas in iambic tetrameter, riming every other line), "Hymn by the Reverend Mr. Medly" (a poem of eight 4-line stanzas, the last line of each always ending ". . . all for the best"), "Jesus, Justice, and the Sinner," (a short dramatic sketch), "A Communication given to Joanna Southcott July 22, 1806, called the Tale of Agrippa," and "An Extract from Mr. Sharps Letter to the Revd. T. P. Foley, London, Dec. 25, 1815."

F: PRAYERS

353: [SOUTHCOTT, JOANNA]. "The first Prayer of Joanna's, on Feb. 28, 1795," "On the 16th of January 1803," and "December 1804." N. d. (Copy.)

1 leaf, both sides. 31.8 x 20.1 cm.

Three prayers given publicly by Joanna on three different dates. All ask for forgiveness for man's sin and for divine help in destroying Satan.

354: [————]. "Joanna's Prayer at her departure from her Friend June 6, 1803," and "The Answer of the Lord to this Prayer." N. d.

1 leaf, both sides. 29.3 x 24 cm.

Joanna's prayer is that God will protect all believers and hasten the day when they can all live together without parting. The answer is that "be ye faithful unto death" and these things will be granted.

355: [————]. "Joanna's Prayer in Verse (S. A. Page 51)." Copied by T. Molineaux. N. d. (Copy.)

8 leaves, both sides, except verso of leaf 8 blank. 18.1 x 11.4 cm.

A poem in 57 stanzas of four lines each, riming abab usually in iambic tetrameter. The prayer asks for the swift return of Christ to earth.

356: [————]. "Thou who fillest the Heavens with Thy Majesty." N. d.

1 leaf, one side. 22.7 x 17.8 cm.

A request that Christ return quickly to defeat the devil. In the hand of T. P. Foley.

357: [?]. "Almighty God, unto whom all hearts be open." N. d.

1 leaf, one side. 32 x 20.1 cm.

A request for mercy.

G: POEMS AND SONGS

358: MESSENGER, RICHARD, ET AL. "Hymns Composed from the Writings of Joanna Southcott." N. d. Songs.

22 leaf notebook, partially filled. 18.7 x 16 cm. Paper bound.

Contains 6 hymns by Messenger: 1. "A Prayer for the Destruction of Satan," 2. "A Prayer for the Calling in of all Nations," 3. "A Prayer for the Salvation of our Country from all her Enemies," 4. "The Sealed Exhorted to Diligence from Faith in the New Jerusalem," 5. "Threatenings to the Lukewarm," and 6. "Ezekiel's dry Bones; or the Resurrection of the Faithful."

There are, in addition, four poems by various persons: two hymns written by Dr. [Isaac?] Watts and sung at Richard Messenger's funeral, December 30, 1810–1. "Hear What the Voice from Heaven Proclaimed" and 2. "When I can Read my Title Clear"; one anonymous poem in memory of Messenger; and one poem by a Mr. Pullen on the death of Mr. John Wilson on November 8, 1812, "Weep not, weep not, nor longer mourn." This last poem mentions Joanna's mystical powers.

359: SOUTHCOTT, JOANNA. "As Men did never see before." Included is A. N. dated January 22, 1802, in the same hand.

1 leaf 22.2 x 11.8 cm. attached to one side and 1 leaf 20.4 x 11.8 cm. attached to the other side of A. MS. (in French) 22.3 x 16.6 cm. with glue, covering the text of the original MS.

The poem in couplets is a divine warning that May will be a time of reckoning. The note concerns Joanna's troubles with a "violent horse" and her hearing "the Clashing of swords in the air."

360: WARDLE, JOHN POTTER. "Christian Warriors." Watermark reads 1844. Poem.

1 leaf, one side. 30.2 x 17 cm.

A poem in couplets ordering Christian Warriors to put on armour and go to fight Satan. In the same tradition as "Onward Christian Soldiers."

361: [?]. "Adam's Freehold." Copied by Major Eyre, 27 April 1812 Poem.

1 leaf, both sides. 22.4 x 18 cm.

36 lines, usually in rimed couplets and uneven meter. Following the poem are two A. N. S.: one by T. Molineaux and one signed by Colonel Lawley.

362: [?]. "For deep is the parable I tell you for all. . . ." N. d. Poem (fragment).

4 leaves, both sides. 18.5 x 11.7 cm.

Pp. 5-8 of a longer manuscript. A homily in rimed couplets and uneven meter, this poem warns of the danger of pride.

363: [?]. "Give me to see that spark of heavenly fire." N. d. Poem.

1 leaf, both sides. 11.2 x 18.5 cm.

Apparently two poems, the first of which is 10 lines of heroic couplets in uneven meter concerning the poet's desire for "heavenly fire." The second, four lines in rimed couplets, appears to be a personal attack upon "the reader."

364: [?]. "Oh! the flowers of summer." N. d. Song.

1 leaf, both sides. 20.5 x 16.3 cm.

A copy made on lined paper seemingly by some multi-copy process. The song praises nature as "Thoughts of God expressed."

365: [?]. "Prepare the way—Napolean comes!" A watermark on one leaf reads 1799. Poem.

32 leaves, with writing generally on only one side. Leaves vary from 14.5 x 23 cm. to 7.4 x 22.8 cm.

A vigorous moral, biting condemnation of Napoleon. In the course of this long poem the authoress comments upon Napoleon, his wife, his court, his expedition to Egypt, and the poet herself. The poem has 306 lines which are divided into stanzas only in so far as they are written on separate scraps of paper.

Napoleon is called "the Bully of the world" and compared to a mimicking monkey "Who one day seeing a man shave, / Lather'd his chops and cut his throat" in his attempt to ape the Monarchy.

That the poet is Joanna Southcott is doubtful, for she identifies herself with another sect, saying she wishes to die "a simple quaker."

Several times the pen has run out of ink and the words are missing.

366: [?]. "Prepare the Way—Napolean comes!" N. d. Poem (copy).

15 leaves, one side. 25.2 x 20 cm.

A typescript of the above. Where words are not legible, the typist has inserted dots.

H: SEALS

The exact purpose of the seals is not easy to determine, for the source of the term "seal" is vague. The book of Revelation, Joanna's favorite book, mentions "seals" and "sealing" several times, but just what the process is is not immediately apparent by the context in which the words appear. Chapter 7, verse 3 mentions "the seal of the living God," and several of the following verses mention "sealing" various tribes.

In books 19 and 48 Joanna discusses the meaning of her sealing people. She had found an unclaimed seal in the shop of a friend named Taylor. The seal consisted of the initials "I. C." (which Joanna took to be "J. C.," obviously suggesting Jesus Christ) and two stars. Joanna used this seal on a sheet of paper to "seal" her followers. She never claimed that the seals were a passport to heaven, although many of her followers took them as such. She further denied that she sold these seals as her critics charged. Lord Byron wrote in a letter to John Murray, "I should like to buy one of her seals. If salvation can be had for half a guinea, the landlord of the Crown and Anchor should be ashamed of charging double for a mere terrestrial banquet." But both Joanna and her closest followers insisted that the seals were issued only to those who strictly followed God's rules to show that they were among the elect, and that they were never sold for any price (see item 167). Balleine (item 208, p. 42) suggests that "The seal was a certificate that this renunciation [of Satan] had been made and this petition [to God to save the world] offered."

367: SOUTHCOTT, JOANNA. 52 seals of which 44 are unopened, being sealed with wax. Generally 18.1 x 18.8 cm.

The message "The Sealed of the Lord, the Elect, Precious, Man's redemption, to inherit the Tree of Life To be made Heirs of God, & Joint-Heirs with Jesus Christ." The person's name, the date, and Joanna's signature appear on one side of the paper with the message given above. All of the sheets are folded like a letter and the name of the "sealed" one appears on the outside.

The 44 which are unopened are sealed generàlly with two wax seals, the first, bearing the imprint of "I. C." with one star at the top and one at the bottom, always present and the second varying from one seal to another.

Those seals which are opened are listed first below, with the unopened seals following. The names appearing on the seals are as follows:

Opened: Elizabeth Bird (October, 1803), Elizabeth Hutchison (December, 1803), Ann Waldron (December, 1803), Henry Waldron (December, 1803), Samuel Wilson (July 21, 1806), Elizabeth Kindon (November, 1806), Jane Graystock (May, 1845), and Jane Bennett (n. d.).

Unopened: Alice Barras, George Bennett, Jane Bennett, Mary Bennett, Sarah Bennett, Techariah Broom, Caroline Eliza Campbell, Mary Carter, Mary Cooper, Rhoda Dabson, Thomas Eddison, Ann Gant, Betty Gant, Isaac Gant (3 seals), John Gant, Mary Gant (2 seals), Nancy Gant, Sarah Gant, Samuel Gant, John Glainsorth, Joseph Goldsmith, Sarah Goldsmith, Joseph Graystock, Elizabeth Griffin, Charles Heartley, Charlotte Kemble, William Lee, William Margrave, Rose Marshil, Benjamin Mirgetroyd, Deborah Murgatroyd, John Murgatroyed, Joseph Murgatroyed, Mary Murgatroyed, Neriah Murgatroyed, Sara Murgatroyed, Nehomiah Pearson, Barbary Ragner, Joseph Sourby, Mary Spencer, and Jane Wetherell.

I: SCROLLS

The scrolls have various purposes, but generally they can be taken as
rolls of the believers in England. The names on the rolls are usually
inscribed in one hand, probably that of a secretary of the local churches,
and most of the names on the rolls are of women.

368: ON TAKING THE OATH. Dated "commencing September 26, 1826"
and ending October 2, 1859.

1 sheet rolled on end boards. 83 x 53 cm. Parchment laid on
canvas with edges bound.

A list of people who have taken the following oath: "I * *. Swear,
by Him that Liveth, I will obey in all things, thy strict Commands
given thru thy Handmaid Joanna Southcott. And it is not all
The powers of Earth and Hell, shall make me turn to the Right,
or to the Left; but thy Commands the Living Lord of Heaven &
Earth, I will Obey." There are 182 names, with a note concerning
an error in entry signed by "I. I[ngall]."

369: PETITION OF JOANNA SOUTHCOTT. February 3, 1807. "C. S. 22 & 23
P 8" inscribed at the top.

1 sheet rolled on end boards. 95 x 34.8 cm. Laid on gauze with
edges bound.

Contains 123 names all inscribed by the same hand. The petition
is a prayer that death and hell "may be swollowed up in victory."

370: ROLL OF THE BELIEVERS IN LONDON. Dates range from 5 March
1809 to 23 October 1908.

Roll is made from 68 sheets of paper 40.3 x 32.5 cm. glued
together making a single strip some 2550 cm. long.

Contains 1571 signatures in various hands.

371: ROLL OF THE BELIEVERS. N. d. (watermark reads 1816).

Roll is made from 52 sheets of paper 40.5 x 31.5 cm. glued
together making a single strip some 1900 cm. long.

Contains 1291 names and addresses all in the same hand from the following places: London, Mansfield and Ackering, Stockport, Sheffield, Birmingham, Macclesfield, Gaddesden, Exeter, Bath, Bristol, Crediton, Charlestown, Manchester, Totnes, Plymouth Rock, Welford, Leichester, Bigbury, Brixham, Newark, Thorne, Netherwasdale, Gravesend, Chatham, Gosport, Noyna near Colne, Tiverton, Loughborough, Nottingham, Huddersfield, Crewekerne, Chesterfield, Idlethorpe, Pontefract, Wakefield, Staverton York, Ashburton, Gilling, and Tewksbury.

372: THE ROLL OF NAMES BY THE COMMAND OF THE LORD TO GEORGE TURNER WHO UNITE TO OBEY THE LORD AND ARE WAITING HIS APPEARING AND HIS SON SHILOH TO REIGN OVER US ON EARTH. N. d.

Roll is made from several sheets of vellum 59.5 cm. wide and of various lengths sewn together to make a single strip some 1320 cm. long.

Contains 4062 names from London and over forty other towns in England. Entry number 1707 is erased and the statement "This name is Struck out by the command of the Lord" appears in its place. Penned on vellum all in the same hand.

373: THE ROYAL PROCLAMATION. FOR THE CROWNING OF THE LORD JESUS CHRIST, KING OF KINGS, AND LORD OF LORDS, IN THE NAME OF THE FATHER, SON, AND HOLY GHOST, ON SUNDAY, DECEMBER 26, 1847, IN ALL THE CHURCHES OF THE TRUE ISRAEL, IN ENGLAND! A printed scroll.

1 sheet rolled on end boards. 150 x 50 cm. Laid on canvas, varnished, and edges bound.

Proclaims that the signees chose Christ as "Shepherd" and "King" and "proclaim Him to be the rightful Heir to the Crown." Signed by twelve of the "Council Chamber" and 173 believers.

374: SOUTHCOTTIAN CONSOLIDATED ROLL OF THE UNITED CHURCHES CONTAINING THE NAMES OF SUCH PERSONS WHO HAVE TAKING [sic] THE OATH AS COMMANDED BY THE LORD THRU JOANNA SOUTHCOTT: APPROVED BY CONFERENCE HOLDEN IN LONDON FOR SEVEN DAYS NOVEMBER 19th to the 26 1844.

1 sheet rolled on end boards. 100 x 65 cm. Laid on gauze with edges bound.

Contains 171 names in various hands.

J: MISCELLANEOUS MANUSCRIPT MATERIAL

375: [?]. "Sarah Bennett–Fredick Bennett." N. d. Birthdates.

1 leaf, one side. 18.5 x 12.3 cm. (irregular edges).

Records birthdates of Sarah Bennett (July 15, 1848) and Fredick Bennett (July 22, 1857).

376: [?]. "A personal interview took place between me and Field. . . ." 31 May 1810. Diary entry.

8 leaves, both sides. 16 x 10 cm. Sewn.

Recounts an interview between the author and a man named Field [E. J.?], who had committed some crime. The author condemns Field and reports that Joanna does the same.

377: [?]. "To the Memory of Joanna Southcott." N. d. Epitaph.

1 leaf, one side. 19 x 13.8 cm.

A manuscript draft of the epitaph on Joanna's tombstone.

378: [?]. "A Journal of the Trial and Proving of the writings of Joanna Southcott." N. d. Journal entry (fragment).

1 leaf, both sides. 28.6 x 19.2 cm.

Part of a journal concerning the meeting of clergymen who were to prove Joanna's writings. The meeting took place from December 5 to December 11, 1804. There were 48 plus an attorney present.

379: [?]. N. d. List of Joanna Southcott's communications.

A 66 leaf notebook mostly filled. 17.5 x 11 cm.

A listing by day, month, and year of Joanna's communications identified by subject.

380: [?]. N. d. Table of contents (fragment).

1 leaf, one side. 25.6 x 12.2 cm.

A table of contents from pp. 44-55 of some works, listing such subjects as "Answer to Brothers. Sep. 1806," and "Unitarians false Doctrine."

III. PAINTINGS

It can be assumed with some assurance that these are the paintings of Joseph Prescott mentioned by Joanna in her books 14, 15, and 16. Prescott is described by Joanna as a young orphan, a workhouse lad, who, when he was 18, began to have visions which he could not understand. Being able to draw reasonably well, Prescott painted his visions, and Joanna interpreted them.

The paintings are generally watercolors. The subjects are always visionary: angels, devils, crowns, jewels, clouds, fires, and mysterious figures floating in the heavens dominate the paintings. All show the results of some care in painting by the untrained Prescott.

The figures and letters which appear on the backs of many of the paintings refer to particular pages in certain of Joanna's books. The books referred to by the numbers may be ascertained by referring to Jones's CATALOGUE OF BOOKS PUBLISHED BY JOANNA SOUTHCOTT *(item 175) or to the first 65 items in this catalogue.*

381: Painting of a crown. "March 4th 1803, 15 B—6/19 P—, Expld. on Pa 114 1 Book Sd. P— & 15 B —Pa 11, 1st —" inscribed on back.

56.4 x 42.2 cm. Watercolor on white paper laid on gauze with edges bound.

Depicts a large crown set with red and blue stones in a network of pearls. Six smaller crowns are affixed to the larger. Above it all is an eye gazing on the crown.

382: Painting of a celestial figure on horseback. "No. 2nd, March 7, 1803, 15B—19P—" inscribed on back.

55.4 x 43.6 cm. Watercolor on white paper laid on gauze with edges bound.

Depicts a crowned celestial figure (Christ?) dressed in purple pantaloons and a scarlet robe, holding a curved sword, sitting astride a gray, spotted horse. He is surrounded by hundreds of winged cherubim. Below him is the starry dark sky with two planets visible, one seemingly being eclipsed.

383: "Behold the Glories of the Trinity." "No. 3, March 9, 1803, 15 B—23rd P." is inscribed on back.

55 x 42.2 cm. Watercolor on white paper laid on gauze with edges bound.

Depicts a large, jeweled crown with "God" inscribed on the front under a rainbow. The crown rests upon a tier inscribed "spirit," which in turn rests upon a tasseled pillow inscribed "Christ." The crown, tier, and pillow are all resting on a marble table.

384: "A Representation of the Knowledge of the Lord in Every Heart." The date "March 23, 1803" is inscribed on the front, and the same date, along with "No. 4, 15B—35P.," inscribed on back.

55 x 43.2 cm. Watercolor on white paper laid on gauze with edges bound.

Depicts an elaborately dressed male figure with arms outspread. He is flanked by two figures on the right and two on the left. Each of the attendant figures carries a flag (perhaps rough depictions of the English, Turkish, and American flags) and each has a musical instrument. One figure on the left is black-skinned, the others white. There appear to be many figures in the background.

385: Another watercolor of the above subject, but unfinished.

41.5 x 44.1 cm. Watercolor on white paper.

386: Painting of a celestial treasure chest. "No. 6, April 15, 1803, 16 B—7 P—" inscribed on back.

56.3 x 43.2 cm. Watercolor on white paper laid on gauze with edges bound.

Depicts a celestial eye shedding its rays on a bejeweled treasure chest being held by a hand emerging from the clouds. Inside the red-lined chest there are pieces of gold with promises of God inscribed on them. Beside the hand there is a bunch of grapes and a note, "See Dan. 5.5."

387: Painting of a crown. "No. 7, April 23, 1803, 16 B—9. P." inscribed on the back.

55.8 x 43.3 cm. Watercolor on white paper laid on gauze with edges bound.

Depicts an ornate crown on a marble table. The crown contains blue, red, and gold stones in a fragile, bead-like framework.

388: Painting of an angel leading a two-horse chariot toward heaven. The number "9" inscribed on front, and "B16—25P—" on back.

56.3 x 43.2 cm. Watercolor on white paper laid on gauze with edges bound.

Depicts an angel [Joanna?] leading a golden chariot drawn by two white horses toward heaven. On the chariot is a crown, and following it, as in a transparent sack, are seals of the Believers. Above are cherubim and below is a view of the coast, probably of England.

389: Painting of the "Celestial Tent" with angels. "No. 10, June 10, 1803, 16B— 37 P" inscribed on back. The number "12" inscribed on front.

56.5 x 43.5 cm. Watercolor on white paper laid on gauze with edges bound.

Colors are predominately green, white, gold, and black. The scene depicts a large white tent with two robed women, swords in hand, holding the door flaps apart to reveal a crown in the tent. Two other robed women with trumpets stand behind the tent, and a third woman, holding a spear, stands along side. On the back is an autograph summary of the scene entitled "Joseph [Prescott]'s description of this Vision, seen Friday Afternoon, June the 10th 1803."

390: Drawing of the "Celestial Tent" described above. Date entered in pencil on the back, "June 10, 1803."

18.3 x 14 cm. Watercolor and pencil drawing on white paper (one sheet made by splicing two smaller sheets together).

391: Painting of the "Rock of Ages." "No. 11, Decb. 15, 1803, 20 B—85 P" inscribed on back.

44.6 x 58.4 cm. Watercolor on white paper laid on gauze with edges bound.

Colors are predominately black, white, gold, red, green, and blue. Depicts the ship "Faith" transporting figures across a river to "The Rock of Ages" inhabited by hundreds of angelic figures. Angels also appear in the sky. The ship, a simple three-masted schooner with an elaborate gold stern, is loaded with hundreds of figures standing on the deck and standing and sitting on the mast spars.

392: Painting "Under his Wings shalt thou Trust." "March 4th 1803, 14 B 113 pa, Book 15 page 6" inscribed on back.

55.7 x 42.4 cm. Watercolor on white paper laid on gauze with edges bound.

Depicts an angel [Joanna?] in a long blue robe, jewels, crown, and wings holding a copy of the painting of a crown described above (see item 381).

393: Painting of the Last Day. "No. 9, June 3, 1803, 16—B—35p." inscribed on back.

56.3 x 43.5 cm. Watercolor on white paper laid on gauze with edges bound.

Depicts the day of judgment, with an angel robed in white [Joanna?] reclining in the middle of a large cloud beside a stack of bound volumes [perhaps her writings]. In her left hand she holds a scroll [perhaps of the believers]. Around her is a host of angels, and before her is a chained black figure being led to the angel by a knight in silver armor. Below the cloud is the earth, where hell's fires are burning, the lower regions being watched over by the black figure with a bow and arrow. Interesting is the fact that many in the heavenly host have brown skin.

394: Painting of Christ and angels. "Sept. 19, 1803, MS not in print" inscribed on back.

61.8 x 95.3 cm. Watercolor on white paper laid on gauze with edges bound.

Depicts Christ surrounded by angels near a grove of trees on the left of the paper. Before Christ stands a cherub with a scroll reading "Behold your Redeemer." On the right is a reclining robed figure with angels standing in back of her seemingly pleading her case to Christ. A dark-skinned man in a red toga leans against a tree observing. An angel floats in the heaven with a scroll reading "Have faith in the Son of God."

IV. ENGRAVINGS

Engravings included here are, with one exception, portraits of Joanna Southcott and Richard Brothers and, in one case, a follower of Brothers. The only non-portrait is a copy of a bookplate (item 397) and even it includes a small likeness of Joanna on it. Most of the portraits of Joanna show her to have very curly hair always worn under·a cap or hat. Also most show her to have a mole or mark of some kind in the lower left portion of her face. In none of them is she smiling, and in at least one she looks very morose.

Besides those listed below, five of the bound volumes in the collection include reproductions of the Sharp portrait (item 396) as a frontispiece. (See SOUTHCOTT'S PROPHECIES, *Texas accession nos. 195-7, 199-200. Volume 4 (198) has the front cover missing.)*

A: PORTRAITS OF JOANNA SOUTHCOTT

395: COOPER, R[ICHARD]. "Joanna Southcott, An Extraordinary Fanatic." London, 1822. Published by J. Robins and Company.

13.5 X 10 cm.

A half-length portrait of Joanna in a bonnet. The engraver is probably the younger Richard Cooper.

396(1): SHARP, WILLIAM. "Drawn and Engraved from life." January, 1812. Published by Jane Townley.

Portrait printed on a larger sheet of paper measures 23.6 x 18.7 cm. The whole unit, which includes a paper mat glued to the back of the portrait, measures 38.5 x 30 cm. Framed in a heavy wooden frame painted gold and black.

The most famous engraving of Joanna. Inscribed below the portrait are several verses of scripture concerning prophecy and salvation.

(2): Another copy. Unframed.

(3): Another copy. Reduced to carte-de-visite size.

10.5 x 8.1 cm.

397: W[HITE], T[HOMAS]. J[ESSON]. "Ex-Bibliotheca THOMAS JESSON WHITE MF 1894." Includes a portrait of Joanna.

14 x 11 cm.

Around the borders of the portrait are printed the words "If I have been misled, it has been by some spirit good or evil."

398: [?]. Engraved copper plate. November, 1814. Published by T. W. H. Payne.

16.5 x 11.5 cm.

A mezzotint portrait of head and shoulders to waist.

399: A print from the above plate.

400: [?]. 21 October 1814. Published by John Bell.

10.5 x 8.5 cm.

Seemingly by the same artist as item 398, but from another plate. Shows Joanna leaning on a table with an open book.

401: [?]. "Johanna Southcote." N. d.

15.7 x 10.6 cm.

Shows Joanna seated at a fireside by a writing table. In her left hand she holds a book "Divine Hyms" [sic]. An oval portrait of Christ is above the mantel.

402: [?]. N. d.

9.6 x 7.9 cm.

Head and shoulders of Joanna in a mob cap.

403: [?]. N. d.

13.6 x 9.3 cm.

A rough engraving showing Joanna wearing a mob cap and seated. The portrait is glued to another sheet, but portions of an un-sympathetic account of her life are discernible on the back of the portrait.

B: PORTRAITS OF RICHARD BROTHERS

404(1): CHAPMAN, J. Oval portrait. N. d.

10.7 x 8.2 cm. (oval).

Engraver not listed in DNB, Bryan, or Thieme-Becker.

(2): Another copy. June 1, 1795.

405: CROSBY, B., publisher. March 11, 1795.

9 x 7 cm. (oval).

Brothers is engraved holding a volume entitled "Divine Revelations of. . . Prophet." A short biographical note on Brothers inscribed on the back with this note: "This particular print not in Brit. Mus. Catl. of portraits Vol I–1908."

406: CRUIKSHANK, J. "Rd. Brothers, The Pretended Prophet." N. d.

5.2 x 3.8 cm.

Engraver not listed in DNB, Bryan, or Thieme-Becker.

407: MONK. August 1, 1795.

6 x 4 cm. (oval).

Engraver not listed in DNB, Bryan, or Thieme-Becker.

408: SHARP, WILLIAM. April 16, 1795.

14.7 x 14 cm.

Across the title at the foot of the portrait is a poem condemning Brothers for deceiving men. At the top is a quotation from Jonah 4:9.

C: PORTRAIT OF JOHN FINLAYSON

409: KAY, I. [JOHN?]. 1797.

9 x 615 cm. (oval).

Note under the portrait: "Author of the ADMONITIONS TO ALL COUNTRIES and a believer in Mr. Brothers."

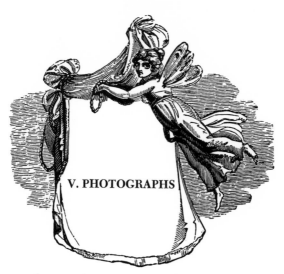

V. PHOTOGRAPHS

410: WATSON, W. Photograph of Joanna's grave. N. d.

6.3 x 10.5 cm.

Shows the grave surrounded by an ornamental metal fence.

411: [?]. Photograph of Joanna's tombstone, erected in 1828. "Sacred to the Memory of Joanna Southcott."

14 x 8.8 cm. mounted on cardboard 16.4 x 10 cm.

Erected "By the sincere friends of the above." Contains date of death (December 27, 1814) and several verses of scripture.

INDEX

(Items are referred to by page rather than by item numbers.)

Abbott, Charles 23, 58, 60, 88
"Abounding in Hope" 65
Abraham 51
ACCOUNT OF THE TRIALS ON BILLS OF EXCHANGE WHEREIN THE DECEIT OF MR. JOHN KING AND HIS CONFEDERATES, UNDER THE PRETENSE OF LENDING MONEY IS EXPOSED, AND THEIR ARTS BROUGHT TO LIGHT 29
Adam 85, 88, 90, 96
"Adam's Freehold" 96
"An Address to the Bretherin" 85
"AN ADDRESS TO THE CLERGY, PARTICULARLY THE BENCH OF BISHOPS; CONTAINING SOME IMPORTANT FACTS WORTHY OF THE CONSIDERATION OF ALL RANKS AND DENOMINATIONS AT THE DANGEROUS CRISIS" 48
"An address to the friends who are impatient with respect to the Birth of Shiloh" 91
"An Address to the Protestants of England, Especially the Queen, the archbishops, bishops, and clergy, to every sect of professing Christians, and every one who believes the Bible to be the true Word of God" 45
"The Advent of Christ's Glorious Kingdom" 85
"An Affectionate Tribute to the memory of a Mother" 93
AGE OF REASON 31
Agrippa 88
Aded, J. 50, 84
Albert, Prince 46
"Alleged Sentence of Christ" 85
Allen, W. W. 68
"Almighty God, unto Whom all hearts be open" 94
"Amraphel" 42
"Announcement of Joanna's Death" 89
"The Answer about the Books of Moses by the Spirit" 87
THE ANSWER OF THE LORD TO THE POWERS OF DARKNESS 15
THE ANSWER OF THE REVEREND THOMAS P. FOLEY TO THE WORLD, WHO

HATH BLAMED HIS FAITH IN BELIEVING IT WAS A COMMAND TO THE LORD TO PUT IN PRINT SUCH PARABLES, AS HE PRINTED LAST YEAR AT STOUR-BRIDGE UNDER THE TITLE "WHAT MANNER OF COMMUNICATIONS ARE THESE?" 26

"The Answer of the Spirit, November 18, 1806" 76

"The Answer of the Spirit to the Judgment drawn by the Believers respecting Joanna's Trial Death and c." 83

"Answer to announces Letter sent to Foley" 83

"Answer to Baylee of Limerick" 92

"Answer to a Confusion in Joanna's mind" 90

"Answers to a Dream of a Serpent in a man's pocket" 88

"Answer to false doctrines, and the crying sins of the nation" 30

"Answer to Halked—National Judgments and c." 88

"Answer to important texts of Scripture" 84

"Answer to Mossop's question 'Whether It was a jesting Spirit that visited Joanna' " 84

ANSWER TO MR. BROTHER'S BOOK, PUBLISHED IN SEPTEMBER 1806, AND OBSERVATIONS ON HIS FORMER WRITINGS; ALSO, A LETTER SENT TO MR. HUNTINGTON WITH REMARKS ON THE CALVINIST AND ROMAN CATHOLIC DOCTRINES, AND C. AND C. AND THE UNBELIEF OF THE JEWS AT THE DESTRUCTION OF JERUSALEM 29

"Answer to Mr. Carpenter's Letters, and the Chapters in the Bible, Which He Sent to Joanna" 39

"Answer to Mr. Hawes upon the Eleventh year" 84

"Answer to Mr. W. Ingall" 39

"Answer to Mrs. Harper's Dread" 82

"Answer to Prescott's Vision of Tree and Willows" 84

"Answer to Senior's dream by the Spirit" 89

"Answer to a Sermon published and preached by Mr. Smith on Tuesday evening, March 15, 1808, at Beersheba-Chapel, Prospect-Place, St. George's Field" 29, 30

"Answer to the False Reports Concerning the Sealing of the People" 17

"Answer to the Leeds Charges" 51

AN ANSWER TO THE WORLD, FOR PUTTING IN PRINT A BOOK IN 1804, CALLED "COPIES AND PARTS OF COPIES OF LETTERS AND COMMUNICATIONS WRITTEN FROM JOANNA SOUTHCOTT," AND TRANSMITTED BY MISS TOWNLEY TO MR. SHARP IN LONDON 27, 28

AN ANSWER TO THOMAS PAINE'S THIRD PART OF THE AGE OF REASON PUBLISHED BY D. I. EATON; LIKEWISE TO S. LANE, A CALVINISTIC PREACHER, AT YEOVIL, IN SOMERSETSHIRE; AND TO HEWSON CLARKE, EDITOR OF "THE SCOURGE," AND LATE OF EMANUEL COLLEGE, CAMBRIDGE 31

"Answer to Townley's will" 91

"Anti-Corn Law Conference" 45

"An Appeal to all Liberal-Minded Christians" 88

"An Appeal to the Believers in the Divine Mission of Joanna Southcott" 43

"April Fool communication" 84

"Archbishop Usher's Prediction 1652" 85

"Are these things so? Being remarks on 'Demonocracy Detected': shewing the erroneous statements of that author, and proving the scriptural opinions of Joanna Southcott, and those in faith united with her" 43

Arians 24

Arsolini, Count Professor 85

"As Men did never see before" 95

"As the Days of Noah were" 87
"Astrology and Witchcraft" 36
"Author of the Admonition to All Countries and a believer in Mr. Brothers" 109

"The Bahs of Persia" 88
Balleine, G.R. 1, 3, 6, 55, 62, 73, 97
"Banns of Marriage between the Church of Rome and the Protestant Church" 82
Barnard, Charles T. 92
Barltrop, Mabel 4
Barras, Alice 98
Bateman, Mary 5, 73, 82, 86
Bateman, Mr. 86
Bateman, Mr. and Mrs. 86
Baylee, Mr. 89
Beaumont, G. 42
"Beautiful Aerial Spectacle" 85
Bede 64
"Behold the Glories of the Trinity" 104
"Behold the tent!" 46
"Behold your Redeemer" 106
"Bel and the Dragon" 36, 91
Belk, William 58
BELL'S WEEKLY MESSENGER, September 4, 1814 57
"Belshazzar's Feast" 87
Bennett, Frederick 101
Bennett, George 1, 42, 44, 45, 52, 68, 72, 84, 85, 86, 89, 98
Bennett, Jane 98
Bennett, John 45
Bennett, Sarah 101
"Bethlehem" 87
"B.H., a Mechanic" 24
"The Bible—The Dial" 58
Bishop, Mr. Alfred 48
"Bishops on the Box" 61
Bird, Daniel 68
Bird, Elizabeth 98
Bird, Mary 70, 80
Bird, William 80
Blake, William 2, 4, 5
"The Blessings and Comforts of Christianity" 87
". . . the blood dropped, and many strong hearts cried out . . ." 79
Bockholt 57
Bolh, Elizabeth 69
Bonaparte 52, 89
THE BOOK OF WONDERFUL CHARACTERS: MEMOIRS AND ANECDOTES OF RE-MARKABLE AND ECCENTRIC PERSONS IN ALL AGES AND COUNTRIES 56
THE BOOK OF WONDERS, MARVELLOUS AND TRUE 31
Bowman, Mr. 50
Box of Sealed Writings 1, 4, 89
Bradbury, John 38
Bridge, Stone 68
Brothers, Richard 29, 39, 40, 47, 48, 50, 55, 56, 62, 64, 70, 73, 83, 85,

88, 89, 90, 101, 107, 109
Bruce, Basil, Esq. 14, 62
Bruce, Maria 89
Bruce, Mrs. 84, 86, 91
Bruce, Stanhope 14, 23, 58, 62, 63, 70
Buchan, Mrs. 57, 86
Bull, Rev. Mr. 82
"Burning ash faggots on Xmas Eve" 88
Byron, Lord 5, 97

Cain 37, 85
"Cain and His Wife going to the Land of Nod" 85
"A Call for Revival" 65
"A Call from the Most High God, the God of Abraham, the God of
    Jacob, to his Ancient People the Jews, Scattered throughout the earth,
    by his Holy Spirit to the Bride, as Promised through the prophets, the
    Gospel and Apostles, to the Gentile Church" 51
"A Call to the Believers in the Divine Mission of Lord of J.S., stimulating
    them to do their duty to their God, their King, their Country, their
    families, and theirselves" 44
"A Call to the Jews and all Nations" 87
Calvinists 24, 29, 31
Campbell, Caroline Eliza 98
"Carol" 87
Carpenter, Elias 23, 27, 39, 43, 58, 83
Carter, Mary 98
Carter, Mr. 69
"Catalogue of Books Published by Joanna Southcott" 9, 34, 47, 49, 103
Caulfield, James 56
A CAUTION AND INSTRUCTION TO THE SEALED THAT THEY MAY, THAT THEY
    MAY KNOW FOR WHAT THEY ARE SEALED 29
"Celestial Tent" 105
The "Chain Communication" 88
Chapman, J. 109
"Charity never faileth" 83
Cheese, Mr. 88
"The Children of this world and the children of Light" 88, 89
"Christ, Jesus, is the Liveing vine . . ." 80
"Christian Warriors" 95
"Christs Birth, The Promise Pomeroy her Judge and c." 83
"Christ's Reign on the Earth as foretold and c." 88
"Christ's Spirit, The Heir of the Promised Land" 59
"The Church" 85
"The Church Militant and Triumphant" 87
"The church will awakened be" 84
"A Circular addressed to all the Believers in the Divine Mission of the
    Lord to Joanna Southcott" 50
"The Claiming of the Promise by the Women" 84
Clarke, Hewson 31
"Close the Box!" 61
Cocker, Amey 78
Cockin, Rev. I. 28
Coleridge, Samuel Taylor 2, 5
"Come saith, Jah. Jehovah . . ." 80

"Comfort under affliction" 93

"The Comit of the year 1811" 83

"The Command to Prosecute" 73

"Commentary upon the prayers and ordinances of the Eng. Protestant Church, Extracted from revelations given by the small still voice in London, during the years 1801 to 1814" 47

"Communications" 77

"Communication: An Extract upon Thunder and Lightning" 36

"Communication: How to Contend with Evil Spirits, an Extraction" 40

"Communication: Love and Anger" 40

"The Communication: Old Fashions revived and the Music of this world" 85

"Communication: Prophecy upon the French Nation" 36

"Communication about Mr. Priestley—About Astrology" 88

"Communication by the Small Still Voice in Explanation of many Scriptures, Especially on the Subject of the Mighty Counselor" 39

"Communication by the Small Still Voice on the History of Josephus" 39

"Communication by the Small Still Voice on the Meaning of the Stone Cut without hands" 41

"Communication by the Small Still Voice, on Monarchy in France" 35

"Communication by the Small Still Voice on Psalm XCII" 40

"Communication concerning Ordination" 35

"Communication concerning the Judgment of the Wise Men" 89

"A Communication concerning the progress of Judgments . . ." 76

"A Communication given at various times" 91

"Communication given by the Small Still Voice on the Cot" 41

"Communication given by the Small Still Voice on the 7th Angel Sound" 41

"Communication given by the Small Still Voice Upon 'To-morrow is a Day Unknown'" 39

"Communication given by the Spirit on the Vision of the Candle, Also an Explanation of Joanna's Illness" 41

"Communication given Good-Friday" 35

"Communication given in Answer to a Believer being Bound for a friend, and who was called upon to pay the bond" 40

"A Communication given to Joanna Southcott 1801 concerning the Likenes of men to fallen Angels—when they wear cast out of heaven" 75

"Communication given to Joanna Southcott, Dec. 19, 1805 in answer to an inquiry" 77

COMMUNICATION GIVEN TO JOANNA, IN ANSWER TO MR. BROTHERS' LAST BOOK, PUBLISHED THE END OF THIS YEAR 16

"A Communication to Joanna Southcott July 22, 1806, called the Tale of Agrippa" 93

"Communication given to Joanna Southcott, Old Christmas Eve, 1802" 93

"Communication given to Mr. George Turner, April 23, 1815" 79

"Communication for Mr. Fisher Concerning Mr. Fisher" 87

"Communication from Mrs. Southcott upon the present Harvest" 76

"Communication from the Small Still Voice in Explanation of a Dream upon Wax Work" 41

"Communication from the Spirit of Christ. Small Still Voice, — Joanna Southcott on the Jubilee" 35

"Communication from the Spirit of the Small Still Voice on Protection from Every Danger" 39

"Communication in answer to a Circumstance Which caused some Dispute" 40

"Communication in answer to a Jew Respecting a Will" 87

"A Communication in answer to a Lady who said the Prophecies failed" 84

"Communication in answer to an enquiry concerning Matthew XXV—41 to 46. on the word 'Everlasting' " 35

"Communication in answer to Baron Swedenborg's Description of Heaven" 39

"A Communication in answer to Joanna's Pondering thoughts of not having communications while Dangers seem to Surround us" 83

"Communication in answer to Joanna's sister and her Husband" 84

"Communication in answer to Mary Bateman" 82

"Communication in answer to Mr. Brothers' book and a Vision he had of two Suns" 40

"Communication in answer to Mr. Crosley's dream" 87

"Communication in answer to Mr. Robert—Mat. 11/28-29" 88

"Communication in answer to Sweedenbourg" 84

"Communication in answer to the Judgment of friends at Birmingham" 37

"Communication in answer to the people at Birmingham, who made Great Disturbance by Throwing Blood and Grains into the meetings, and other Annoyances" 41

"Communication in answer to the Rev. Mr. Marshall" 87

"Communication in Joanna's own hand writing" 82

"Communication in Explanation of the Conception" 38

"Communication of the Parable of 'The Highwayman' " 36

"Communication on Charges" 37

"Communication on Charity" 39

"Communication on Coming in a Cloud, Continued" 36

"Communication on Esdras" 37

"Communication on Hanna's Prayer" 87

"Communication on 'Jesus Christ to be seen three days and three nights in the Centre of the Earth' " 38

"Communication on Joanna getting out of Bed and c." 84

"Communication on Joanna taking Cold" 87

"Communication on Joanna's being misled" 36

"Communication on Joanna's Persecution" 36

"Communication on Joanna's Death: She Being the Rising and Setting Sun" 41

"Communication on Mr. Spring's paper" 87

"Communication on November Waiting to be Born" 87

"Communication on Prayer" 36

"Communication on Queen Esther" 38

"Communication on Spirits in Prison" 38

"Communication on Spiritual and Temporal Builders" 37

"Communication on the Boiling of the Bible" 83

"Communication on the Bond" 87

"Communication on the Children of this World are Wiser in their generation than the Children of Light" 37

"Communication on the Comet" 40

"Communication on the Ear of Corn" 82

"Communication on the Fake Charges agst. Joanna" 82

"Communication on the Fall and the Restoration" 88

"Communication on the first book of Wonders" 87
"Communication on the Folly of Deception" 39
"Communication on the Great Importance of the Trial in 1804" 87
"Communication on the Harvest of the Year 1805" 87
"Communication on the Jubulee Church Bells and c." 87
"Communication on the Law against Satan" 36
"Communication on the Likeness of Men to the Fallen Angels when they
    were cast out of Heaven" 35
"Communication on the Novel—THE ROMANCE OF THE FOREST" 88
"Communication on the Oath" 36
"Communication on the Oath of Allegiance" 36
"Communication on the Oath of Swearing Allegiance" 36
"Communication on the Persecution Caused by the Devil and the Possi-
    bility of his Visible Appearance" 40
"Communication on the Second Sealing" 40
"Communication on the Rose of Sharon" 87
"Communication on the Sacrament to be Received at the Church" 38
"Communication on the Sudden arrival in Leeds of Wilson and Carpenter
    with Directions for the Sealed" 83
"Communication on the Sun Dial and Grand Dial" 39
"Communication on the Temporal and Spiritual Sword" 35
"Communication on the Thanksgiving Day" 83
"Communication on Troubles on England" 30
"Communication on 12th of Revelations, 1st verse" 87
"Communication respecting David's Throne" 88
"Communication respecting Hann" 84
"Communication respecting our Savior being very man" 84
"Communication sent in a Letter to the Reverend Mr. P. in 1797, with
    an Explanation Thereon Now Given" 33
"Communication sent to Mr. Pomeroy" 37, 90
"Communication taken out of Sealed Writings" 38
"Communication to Joanna upon One gaining the Prize, May 5, 1803"
    75
"Communication to the Old and Young Prophet" 39
"Communication upon Baptism" 35
"Communication upon Brothers and Turner" 85
"Communication upon Cain's Madness Possessing ¾'s of the Habitable
    Globe" 37
"Communication upon Mockers and Unbelievers" 85
"Communication upon one gaining the Prize" 83
"Communication upon Parables" 39
"Communication upon Prayer and meeting together" 83
"Communication upon the Awful Trial" 83
"Communication upon the Bible Society and Upon 'The Infant of Days' "
    41
"Communication upon the Duty of the Jews" 37
"Communication upon the Harvests of 1799 and 1800" 84
"Communication upon the Propriety of the Friends meeting together" 40
"Communication upon the Scriptures" 89
"Communication upon the Teachings of Baron Swedenborg" 39
"Communication upon the Thunder, the Still Small Voice, and Blotting
    out Brother's Honour, and giving in to the Lord" 83
"Communication upon the Trial—Important" 86
"Communication upon the Two Witnesses" 35

"Communication upon the Womans enmity against Satan" 83

"Communication wherein it is ascertained that it is the spirit, and not the body of the wicked which goeth to Hell" 35

"Conception Communication" 89

"Concerning Mrs. Wilmot's sickness" 84

"Concerning Satan being in the moon and c." 84

"Concerning the first Sealing" 91

"Concerning the Methodists" 83, 88

"Concerning the Visions to Joseph Prescott" 89

"Concerning this being a Happy Land in 1807" 85

"Conflagration at Santiago" 88

"Contentions of the Nation" 87

"Continuation and Further Opening of the Subject of the Two Witnesses" 36

"Continuation from the Second Book" 81

"Continuation of a communication on the Prophecies" 85

"Continuation of Joanna's History" 21

"Continuation of Prophecies" 14

"Continuation of the Controversy with the worldly wise" 30, 31

"Continuation of the Prophecies of Joanna Southcott. A Word in Season to a Sinking Kingdom" 17

CONTROVERSY BETWEEN JOANNA SOUTHCOTT AND ELIAS CARPENTER, PART I 27; PART II 27; PART III 27; PART IV 27; PART V 27

CONTROVERSY OF THE SPIRIT WITH THE WORLDLY WISE, AS GIVEN THROUGH JOANNA SOUTHCOTT 30

Cooper, Mary 98

Copas, Thomas 43, 45, 47

COPIES AND PARTS OF COPIES OF LETTERS AND COMMUNICATION WRITTEN FROM JOANNA SOUTHCOTT, AND TRANSMITTED BY MISS TOWNLEY TO MR. W. SHARP IN LONDON 20, 21, 43, 44

COPIES OF DEEP AND IMPORTANT LETTERS, ADDRESSED TO THE QUEEN, PRINCE ALBERT, THE QUEEN DOWAGER, THE ARCHBISHOP OF CANTERBURY, AND OTHERS, ON THE CAUSE OF ENGLAND'S DISTRESS, AND THE REMEDY 46

COPIES OF LETTERS SENT TO THE CLERGY OF EXETER, FROM 1796-1800, WITH COMMUNICATION AND PROPHECIES PUT IN THE NEWSPAPERS IN 1813 31, 32

"Copy of a Letter: Eng. May be a Happy Land; Also the Warning given by Mr. Brothers" 39

"Copy of a Letter from T.P. Foley respecting the Box" 89

"Copy of an address to the Chairman of the anti-corn law conference in London giving the cause, and shewing the remedy for the present evils and distresses, as proved from the prophetic writings of the late Joanna Southcott" 45

"Copy of an epistle of the most extraordinary nature; sent to the right honorable Henry Addington, Prime Minister of the United Kingdoms, on Affairs of the Utmost Importance" 48

"Copy of an Epistle, with a few alterations, addressed to the Rev. Mr. Vice-Chancellors of Cambridge and Oxford, being a plain and honest statement of the chief and leading events which took place during the years 1801, 1802, and 1803, respecting J.S. and the Believers in her divine mission" 44

A CORRECT ACCOUNT OF THE INVASION AND CONQUEST OF THE ROMAN COLONY OF AILBANE, OR BRITAIN, BY THE SAXONS, NEVER PUBLISHED

BEFORE: AND WHICH IS VERY INTERESTING TO THE PRESENT ENGLISH, WHO ARE DESCENDED FROM THOSE GREAT AND BRAVE MEN 64

"Correspondence of the Southcottian Church" 51

Cowper, William 52

Coy, William 88

"Coy's Funeral" 88

"Creation and Redemption" 85

Crosby, B. 109

Crossley, John 44, 87

Cruikshank, J. 109

Cunming, Rev. J. 83

"Curious Relic—Sentence on the Savior" 87

Dabson, Rhoda 98

DAILY NEWS 61

DALLAS MORNING NEWS 61

Daniel 36

David 88, 91

"David's throne, Solomon's wisdom and c." 88

Davis, Geo. 45

"Death of Mr. Joachim, Shot through the heart" 82

"Death of Mrs. Bruce" 84

Decker, J. 52

DEMOCRACY DETECTED—VISIONARY ENTHUSIASM CORRECTED; OR, SIX PENNY-WORTH OF GOOD ADVICE SELECTED FROM THE SCRIPTURES OF TRUTH 22, 43

DESCRIPTION OF JERUSALEM, ACCORDING TO THE SCRIPTURE; PUBLISHED IN SUPPORT OF THE BIBLE, AND THE DIVINE REVELATION IT CONTAINS, FOR THE BENEFIT OF ALL DENOMINATIONS AND DISTINCTIONS OF PEOPLE ON EARTH 64

A DESCRIPTION OF JERUSALEM; ITS HOUSES AND STREETS, SQUARES, COL-LEGES, MARKETS, AND CATHEDRALS, THE ROYAL AND PRIVATE PALACES, WITH THE GARDEN OF EDEN IN THE CENTER, AS LAID DOWN IN THE LAST CHAPTERS OF EZEKIEL. ALSO THE FIRST CHAPTER OF GENESIS VERI-FIED, AS STRICTLY DIVINE AND TRUE. AND THE SOLAR SYSTEM, WITH ALL ITS PLURALITY OF INHABITED WORLDS, AND MILLIONS OF SUNS, AS POSI-TIVELY PROVED TO BE DELUSIVE AND FALSE 63

"Destruction of the Nations" 87

"Dictionary of Christ and the Gospels" 61

"Diesire" 87

"Dirge" 88

"Discord Among the Believers" 89

DISPUTE BETWEEN THE WOMAN AND THE POWERS OF DARKNESS 15

DIVINE AND SPIRITUAL COMMUNICATION WRITTEN BY JOANNA SOUTHCOTT; ON THE PRAYERS OF THE CHURCH OF ENGLAND; THE CONDUCT OF THE CLERGY, AND CALVANISTIC METHODS, WITH OTHER PARTICULARS 18

DIVINE AND SPIRITUAL LETTERS OF PROPHECIES 14, 15

DIVINE AND SPIRITUAL LETTERS OF PROPHECIES SENT TO REVEREND DIVINES, AND OTHER SPIRITUAL GOOD MEN AND WOMEN, THAT ARE NOW ORDERED TO BE PUT IN PRINT BY DIVINE COMMAND FOR THE GOOD OF THE PUBLIC, AND TO TRY THE WISDOM OF MANKIND TO WHAT SPIRIT THEY WILL ALLUDE THIS STRANGE REVELATION 15

"Divine Hyms" 108

"Divine Revelations of . . . Prophet" 109
Divines, Reverend 14, 15
"Doctrine of the Eucharist" 88
"The Doctrine of the Candles and Spacious room" 88
DON JUAN 5
"Dream of a coach Stuck fast in wheel Ruts" 87
"Dream of broken rings, Seals, Bonaparte and c." 88
"Dream of her Elder Brothers taking of her Fathers Substance" 90
"Dream of the Diamond Ring" 88
"Dream of the Two Plows explained" 89

Eaton, D.I. 31
Eddison, Thomas 98
"Eight Hundred Men Starving in the Snow" 88
"Elder Brother brought on the Evil, Christ will bring the Good" 86
"The End of who reject the Visitation" 88
"England, France, and the Sealed People" 86
ENGLISH MESSIAHS: STUDIES OF SIX ENGLISH RELIGIOUS PRETENDERS, 1656-
    1927 55
ENGLISH ECCENTRICS AND ECCENTRICITIES 56
Engravings 107-109
EPHESIANS 25
Esther Queen 38, 90
Eve 85
Eveleigh, Miss 90
EVENING STANDARD 59
"Everlasting Gospel Satan's ten plagues" 47
"Everyday Religion" 65
"Examination of Prophecies" 44, 86
Exeter, Helen 4
"Explanation of St. Matthew 7th Chapter 1 and 2 verses 85
"Explanation of the Forty Days (Turner) 83
EXPLANATION OF THE PARABLES PUBLISHED IN 1804 25
"Explanation of the Shadows . . . given to Joanna April 5, 1804 76
"An Explanation of the Visitation of the Spirit to Joanna Southcott" 38
THE EXPRESS 49, 50, 56, 59
"Extracts from FIRST BOOK OF SEALED PROPHECIES explained" 84
Eyre, Major 96
EZEKIEL 63
"Ezekiel's dry Bones; or the Resurrection of the Faithful" 95

"Fake Charges brought by Hann" 83
Faith 106
"Faith, a Gift of God" 83
"Faith in Heavenly Harmony" 85
"Far-fetched Fun" 14
Farleigh Dawn 89
"Fearful Earthquake in China" 88
Field, Elias Jameson 23, 58, 81, 87, 101
FIFTH BOOK OF WONDERS, ANNOUNCING THE EVENT HAVING TAKEN PLACE,
    WHICH WAS PROMISED IN THE FOURTH BOOK SHOULD BE IN MAY. WITH
    A FURTHER EXPLANATION OF THE FOUR FORMER BOOKS; ALSO AN ANSWER
    TO THE ADDRESS OF THE REV. JAMES HEARN, CURATE OF BRIXHAM, DEVON;
    AND TO THE MOCKERY OF OTHERS 32

Finis, Mr. 87
"First and Second Coming of Christ" 51
FIRST BOOK OF SEALED PROPHECIES 16, 17, 85
THE FIRST BOOK OF VISIONS 16
"FIRST KINGS 15 and JOHN'S GOSPEL 10—Ans'd" 85
"First Prayer of Joanna's on February 28, 1795, on the 16th of Jan. 1803, and Dec. 1804" 94
"The First Resurrection by G. Bennett" 89
Fisher, Mr. 87
FIXED STARS; OR, AN ANALYZATION AND REFUTATION OF ASTROLOGY: THE PRINCIPLES OF THIS SCIENCE BEING PLAINLY LAID OPEN, AND THEIR ABSURDITY AND WICKEDNESS DEMONSTRATED. TO WHICH IS ADDED, THE TESTIMONIES OF MANY LEARNED MEN AGAINST THE SCIENCE OF ASTROLOGY 42
"Floods at Weston Place" 83
Foley, Rev. T.P. 21, 23, 26, 44, 58, 62, 77, 82, 83, 89, 91, 93, 94
"Foley's Sermon" 83
"The Folly of the Times Exemplified in the Attentions Obtained by Joanna Southcott" 57
"For deep is the parable I tell you for all . . ." 96
"For This is Not Your Rest" 87
FOURTH BOOK OF WONDERS BEING THE ANSWER OF THE LORD TO THE HEBREWS 32
Fox, Mrs. Rachel 58
Fox 88
"Fox's Funeral" 88
FULL ASSURANCE THAT THE KINGDOM OF CHRIST IS AT HAND FROM THE SIGNS OF THE TIMES 28
"Fulness of the Time" 85
"Future Happiness" 55
"Future Existence" 87

Galpin, Elias 31
Gant, Ann 98
Gant, Betty 98
Gant, Isaac 98
Gant, John 98
Gant, Mary 98
Gant, Nancy 98
Gant, Samuel 98
Gant, Sarah 98
Garrett, Rev. Jeremiah Learnoult 22, 24
GENERAL INDEX TO THE WRITINGS OF JOANNA SOUTHCOTT, THE PROPHETESS 49, 51
General Post Office Money Letter 72
GENESIS 63, 87
GENTLEMAN'S MAGAZINE 93
George III 62, 70
"Give me to see that spark of Heavenly fire" 96
"Given October 2, 1809" 77
"Given to Joanna, April 6, 1804" 76
"Given to Joanna Southcott November 9th 1804, and The words spoken to Joanna in 1792 . . ." 76
Glainsorth, John 98

"Glorious Predestination" 65
"Go on Your Way Rejoicing" 61
Goldsmith, Joseph 98
Goldsmith, Sarah 98
"Gospel of the Nine Virgins" 81
Grabianka, Tadeus 62
Graystock, Jane 98
Graystock, Joseph 98
"Grand Dial and Sun Dial Com'n" 84
"A Greater Solomon" 66
Griffin, Elizabeth 98

Hagger, John 44, 45, 50
Halked, M.P. 62, 88
Hann 33, 77, 83, 84
Hanna 87
"Happiness! What is it?" 87
Harper, Miss 76, 82
Harrison, W.B. 45, 46, 51
Harwood, William 23
"Hastening on" 14
"Have faith in the Son of God" 106
Headby-ashe, Robert 30
Hearn, Rev. James 32
Heartley, Charles 98
"Hear What the Voice from Heaven Proclaimed" 95
HEBREWS 63
"He Shall Rule Whose Blood was Shed on Calvary's Cross" 88
"Hierogliphic as appeared in Moore's Almanak A.D. 1779" 10
"The Highwayman" 36
Hinds, George 45
"His Malice Must be known" 90
"Holland complains of Satan's temptations" 85
Holland, Jedediah 78, 85
"Holy Thorn" 87
House of David 4
Howe, Benjamin 45, 75, 86
Howe, Thornton V. 89
"How the Sacrament is to be taken" 82
Hows, John 23
Hudson, Thomas P. 46
Hunt, Rev. W. 86
Hunter 90
Hurst 88
Hutchison, Elizabeth 98
Hutchinson, W.H. 65
"Hymn by the Reverend Mr. Medly" 93
"Hymns, or spiritual songs, composed from the prophetic writings of Joanna Southcott" 49

"I dreamed I was going along by a Church . . ." 74
"I shall answer thee from his words" 81
I.H.E. 84
I.H.S. 84

"Important Communication on the Birth the Son, Shewing that It was only a Shadow that took place in the year 1814" 83
"Important Communication to George Turner" 89
"Important Communication upon the Trial and c." 86
"In answer to a man who said the Bible would be no more Revealed than it was, July 7, 1802" 75
"In answer to Mrs. Wilson about the Kingdom" 85
"In Answer to Mr. Wetherell respecting his and his Children's Illness" 79
INDEX TO THE DIVINE AND SPIRITUAL WRITINGS OF JOANNA SOUTHCOTT 49, 51
INDICTMENT, AGAINST THAT TYRANNICAL, CRUEL, AND BLOODY MONARCH, SATAN, THE GOD OF THIS WORLD; WHOM THE CREATED CREATURES OF GOD INTEND, BY GOD'S DIRECTIONS, TO BRING TO CONDIGN PUNISHMENT. ALSO, THE MINUTES OF THE MEMBERS OF THE SOUTHCOTTIAN CHURCH IN LONDON, FOR & DAYS, FROM THE 19TH TO THE 25TH OF NOVEMBER, 1844 52
"In Explanation to the 40 days mentioned to George Turner" 76
Ingall, John 46, 73, 75, 93
Ingall, W. 39
"Inhabitants of the Earth . . ." 78
"Instructions given to Joanna for Believers" 91
ISAIAH 84, 90

Jacob 90
"Jesus, Justice, and the Sinner" 93
Jezreel, James (See White, James)
Joachim, Mr. 82
"Joanna and Brothers compared with Adam and Eve" 85
"Joanna and her Sister, Type of the End" 82
"Joanna compared to Micaiah the true Prophet and the Shepherds to the false Prophets" 84
"Joanna ordered to go to Tozers to receive the Sacrament" 84
"Joanna Sealed on a whole sheet of paper" 83
"Joanna—the Judges, Jury, and Sudden death of Coy" 88
"Joanna to the Reverend T.P. Foley" 82
"Joanna writes to a friend about the Importance of the Trial-1804" 87
"Joanna's Journay from Leeds to Stackton" 87
"Joanna's Judgment and Sinking Faith" 88
"Joanna's Judgment on the Bible and her writers" 88
"Joanna's Last Words" 84, 85
"Joanna's Letter to Mr. Long, Priest Vicar, Devon" 89
"Joanna's Letter to the Reverend Basil Wood" 85
"Joanna's observations on Sweedenbourg" 84
"Joanna's Prayer at her Departure" 87
"Joanna's Prayer at her departure from her friends June 6, 1803, and 'The Answer of the Lord to this Prayer'" 94
"Joanna's Prayer in Verse" 94
"Joanna's Prayer for Wilson" 84
"Joanna's Private Marriage" 85
"Joanna's Sufferings in Wilsons room" 83
"Joanna's Trial and Death and State of Believers and c." 85
"Joanna's verses on the Creation (Answered)" 89
"Joanna's Vision of the Prince of Peace" 89
"Joanna's Visit to Bath" 84

"Joanna's Visit to Mr. Howes and the Death of her Brother" 86
"Joanna's visit to Tozer's meeting unawares" 86
JOANNA SOUTHCOTT'S ANSWER TO GARRETT'S BOOK 22
JOANNA SOUTHCOTT'S ANSWER TO THE FIVE CHARGES IN THE "LEEDS MER-
CURY" 22, 23
Jonah 85
Jones, B.B. 89
Jones, Daniel 2, 9, 20, 28, 30, 34, 46, 58
Jones, J. 69
Jones, Lavinia Elizabeth Chapman 1, 2, 34, 47, 58, 59, 82, 91, 92
MR. JOSEPH SOUTHCOTT, THE BROTHER OF JOANNA SOUTHCOTT, WILL NOW
COME FORWARD AS DINAH'S BRETHREN DID; THAT THEY SHALL NOT DEAL
WITH HIS SISTER, AS THEY WOULD WITH A HARLOT; FOR SO THEY ARE
NOW DEALING WITH HER 21
Josephus 38
"A Journal of the Trial and Proving of the writings of Joanna Southcott"
101
Jowett, Samuel 47
Jowett, William 23, 44, 58
"Judge, Jury, and Visitors at the Trial" 88
"Judgment Begins at the House of God" 88
"Judgment Day" 13
"Just as the Devil in Heaven begun, Just so on Earth, He now is come"
90
"The Justice, of God in Creating Woman" 91

Kay, I. 109
Keats, John 4
Kemble, Charlotte 93, 98
"Key to Happiness" 58
Kindon, Elizabeth 98
King, John 29
"The Kingdom of Christ" 86
THE KINGDOM OF CHRIST IS AT HAND 20, 25
"The Kingdom of God" 84
"The Kingdom of God what is it Explained" 82
"The Kingdom of Peace on Earth" 85
Kinsman, John 90
Kirby, R. S. 55
KIRBY'S WONDERFUL AND ECCENTRIC MUSEUM; OR MAGAZINE OF REMARK-
ABLE CHARACTERS. INCLUDING ALL THE CURIOSITIES OF NATURE AND ART,
FROM THE REMOTEST PERIOD TO THE PRESENT TIME, DRAWN FROM EVERY
AUTHENTIC SOURCE 55

"The Laborers, in the Vineyard" 85
Lane, S. 31
"Language of Joanna's heart" 89
Law, Richard 23, 47, 58
"The Law Against Satan" 87
Lawley, Colonel 96
Lee, Ann 57
Lee, William 98
LEEDS MERCURY 42
Lees, G. Frederic 59

"Legend of Redbreast" 87
"Legend of St. Christopher" 87
"Let these words go forth to the ends of the earth" 59
"Letter addressed to an Eminent Clergyman of the Established Church of England Explaining the nature and object of the divine mission of the Late Joanna Southcott" 46
"A letter addressed to a friend proving from reason and scripture, that a further Divine revelation will be given for the instruction and direction of mankind, previous to the establishment of Christ's Kingdom on earth" 45
"Letter and Communication to Mrs. Townley" 87
"Letter by G. Bennett" 89
"Letter by G. Bennett to Rev. W. Hunt on the Coming Rest" 86
"Letter concerning Charles Abbott" 88
"Letter concerning Joanna's suffering friends" 88
"Letter from G. Bennett to Charles Taylor" 84
"A Letter from G. B. to the Rev. J. Cunming" 83
"Letter from Joanna to George Turner" 83
"Letter from Joanna to her Sister upon being deceived" 88
"Letter from Joanna to Maria Bruce" 89
"Letter from Joanna to Mr. Aked" 84
"Letter from Joanna to Mr. Mansell—Token of Love" 88
"Letter from Joanna to Turner and His Daughter and c." 86
"Letter from Joanna to Mr. Wilson" 87
"A Letter from Joanna upon Mockery and c." 89
"Letter from Mr. Baylee to the Rev. Mr. Foley" 89
"Letter of Joanna's upon the Death of Mr. Cheese" 88
"Letter on the second coming of Christ by G. Bennett" 85
"Letter to Daniel Roberts" 83
"Letter to Hurst upon the Judgment of Believers" 88
"A Letter to Mr. Field in answer to Mr. Finis" 87
"Letter to Mr. Fisher—Scripture proofs for the Jews" 87
"Letter to Turner with Comments of Importance" 86
"Letter to Mr. Wadman, Respecting the Duty of Warning the People" 40
"Letter to Philip Norris of Liverpool" 84
"A Letter to the Bishop of London" 91
"Letter to the Rev. Mr. Bull" 82
"A Letter to the Revd. Stanhope Bruce" 91
A LETTER TO THE SUBSCRIBERS FOR ENGRAVING THE PLANS OF JERUSALEM, THE KING'S PALACE, THE PRIVATE PALACES, COLLEGE-HALLS, CATHE-DRALS, AND PARLIAMENT-HOUSES 63
LETTERS AND COMMUNICATION OF JOANNA SOUTHCOTT. THE PROPHETESS OF EXETER: LATELY WRITTEN TO JANE TOWNLEY 21
"Letters, and Observations to Ministers" 44
"Letters on the signs of the Times" 50
LETTERS ON VARIOUS SUBJECTS, FROM MRS. JOANNA SOUTHCOTT TO MISS TOWNLEY 20
"Letters to the Believers in the Divine Mission to Joanna Southcott, in reply to the Various letters received in connection with their Second Circular" 45, 47, 48
"Letters written by the Apostle Paul" 88
Lewick, Mr. 23
Lewis, F. 48

Ley, John 45
Lieven, Count 85
"The Light of the World" 85
"The Likeness of Joanna Southcott" 83
"Lines on Good Friday" 93
"The Litany" 87
"The Little Flock" 85
"Little Flock of Sheep" 20, 28
"Little Musgrave and Lady Barnaro" 93
"Locust of Abaddon" 3
THE (LONDON?) DAILY NEWS 61
(LONDON) TIMES 59
Long, Mr. 89
LONG-WISHED-FOR REVOLUTION ANNOUNCED TO BE AT HAND IN A BOOK
    LATELY PUBLISHED BY L. MAYER, WHEN, AS HE SAYS, "GOD WILL CLEANSE
    THE EARTH BY HIS JUDGEMENTS, AND WHEN ALL DOMINIONS SHALL SERVE
    THE MOST HIGH." EXPLAINED BY JOANNA SOUTHCOTT; WITH LETTERS TO
    HER FROM THE AUTHOR OF THAT BOOK AND HER ANSWERS; TO WHICH
    ARE ADDED OBSERVATIONS UPON HIS WRONG APPLICATION OF THE SCRIP-
    TURE PROPHECIES IN GENERAL, AND HIS IGNORANCE, PARTICULARLY IN
    WISHING FOR A PERIOD OF JUDGMENTS, WITHOUT EXPLAINING WHAT WILL
    BRING THIS HAPPY DELIVERANCE IN THE END, WHICH SHALL BE TO THE
    GLORY OF GOD, AND TO THE GOOD OF THE WHOLE HUMAN RACE, BY
    BEING UNITED TO HIS SPIRIT, AND BEARING HIS IMAGE, AND SATAN CAST
    OUT, SO THAT THE EARTH MAY BE AT REST FOR ONE THOUSAND YEARS 29
"The Lord is not slack concerning his promise" 90
"The Lord's explanation of the 54th of Isaiah" 84
"The Lord's Prayer" 61
"The Lord's Prayer in Verse" 90
"The Lord's Sepulchre" 87
Lot 90
"Lot's Daughters" 90
"Lycidas" 26
"Lying Prophetess Detected" 30

"The Mad Riders and Concerning Pomeroy and c." 87
Malby, Thos. 44, 45, 47, 48
"Malice in Men" 38
Mansell, Mr. 88
Margrave, William 98
Markett, Rhy 68
"The Marriage of the Lamb, both Spiritual and temporal: illustrated by
    Extracts from the writings of Joanna Southcott the Bride" 93
Marshall, Mr. 87
Marshil, Rose 98
Mary, Queen 87
Maskell, Rev. William, M.A. 48
Matthews, Robert 57
Matthews, Ronald 6, 55
Mayer, Lewis 29, 49
"The Meaning of the word 'Rulers'" 37
Medly, Mr. 93
"Men wrangle about religion" 87
Messenger, Richard, 95

MICAIAH 84
Middleton, John 77
"The Midnight Cry and c." 85
"The Midnight Song of Bethlehem" 87
"The Millennium" 55
Milton, John 26
Mirgetroyd, Benjamin 98
MODERN REALITIES; OR, THE SUBSTANCE FOLLOWING THE SHADOW: BEING
    A REPLY TO "MODERN VISIONARIES," BY J. T. WHEREIN ARE DISPLAYED
    THE FALLACY OF JUDGING WITHOUT INQUIRY, AND THE INJUSTICE OF
    CONDEMNING CHARACTERS ON MERE REPORT; SHEWING THAT THE SYSTEM
    IN WHICH WE ARE ENGAGED, HAS NO OTHER OBJECT THAN THE PREPARING
    MEN'S MINDS FOR THE GLORIOUS PERIOD THE POET HAD IN VIEW 43
Molineaux, T. and S. 69, 75, 76, 94, 96
Molyneux, Rev. Capel, B.A. 65
Monk 109
"Montazamua (Montezuma)" 92, 93
Moon, Thos. 75
Moore, Ann 30, 71
Morison, Peter 23, 58
Morris, John 23, 58
"Mortality" 87
Mossop 84
"The Mountains of Snow and c." 83
Munzer 57
Murgatroyed, Deborah 98
Murgatroyed, John 98
Murgatroyed, Joseph 98
Murgatroyed, Mary 98
Murgatroyed, Neriah 98
Murgatroyed, Sarah 98
Murray, John 97
"Mutany in England to throw off the Yoke" 86
"The Mysteries of the Fall" 90
Mysticism 6

Napoleon 48, 96
Nayler, James 55
Neckinger House 22
Neilson, Mr. and Mrs. 69
Newton, Sir Isaac 18
Noah 87
"Noah the Founder of the Chinese Empire" 87
NOCTURNAL ALARM; BEING AN ESSAY ON PROPHECY AND VISION: OR A BRIEF
    EXAMINATION OF SOME REMARKABLE THINGS UNDER THOSE HEADS WHICH
    HAVE RECENTLY APPEARED ON THE WORLD: AND WHICH, FROM THEIR
    EXTRAORDINARY IMPORT, SEEM WORTHY OF THE ENQUIRY AND CONSID-
    ERATION OF ALL SERIOUS AND WELL-DISPOSED CHRISTIANS 43
"No Deliverance from Present World Conditions Until the Bishops Act"
    59
Norris, Phillip 84
"Now from the Kindred spirits I begin" 80
"Now, one very remarkable thing revealed in Holy Scriptures" 85
Nyland, Joanna 69

"O Blessed Savior, God and King" 86
"The Oath of Allegiance and the Sword of Gideon" 87
"Octavia" (See Barltrop, Mabel)
"Oh! the flowers of summer" 96
OLD AND NEW LONDON: A NARRATIVE OF ITS HISTORY, ITS PEOPLE, AND ITS
    PLACES 56
"The old and young Prophet" 84
"An old Prophecy" 89
"On a dream of the Lambs in the Basket" 91
"On Baptism" 90
"On Bel and the Dragon" 91
"On Burning Ashen faggots on Christmas Eve" 91
"On David Being a Man after God's own heart" 91
"On Earth Peace Good will To Men" 82
"On General Restoration" 90
"On her Kinsman John" 90
"On her Kinsman who lay 12 hours in Great Agonies" 91
"On Hunters text" 90
"On ISAIAH 52 Chr and Second PSALM" 91
"On Joanna's Dream of Sharp and Foley" 91
"On Joanna's Father being a Child with Old Age" 90
"On Joanna's Journey to Highgate" 91
"On Joanna's pregnancy a *Shadow*" 91
"On our Departure and Flight" 84
"On Peter Launching into the Great deep" 91
"On Pomeroy a type of the clergy" 91
"On Sealing up the Writings, Vision of Candles, Ten Years, and c." 90
"On some Calamities of the Holy Land" 88
"On Speaking in an Empty House" 90
"On taking the Oath" 99
"On Temptations" 37
"On the Covering of the Patchwork" 91
"On the death of Colonel Shadwell" 90
"On the death of Joseph Southcott's Son" 88
"On the death of Joanna's Brother" 91
"On the death of Miss Eveleigh and the Happiness of the departed Spirits
    to meet each other in Glory" 90
"On the Death of Mrs. Bruce" 86
"On the disorder in the Eye, Explained" 91
"On the Fast Day, 1797" 87
"On the Fast day, Roman Power to be destroyed and c." 90
"On the Fast Day, 1797, the following was given to Joanna Southcott,
    in answer to the Rev. J. Pomeroy, saying, 'That there were more than
    50 Righteous to Save the Nation from God's Judgments'" 34
"On the Illumination for Peace" 88, 90
"On the Last Day, March 8, 1797" 75
"On the likeness of men to the fallen Angels" 90
"On the Magistrates forbidding prayers in public" 91
"On the Methodists saying the Lord was among them" 91
"On the Millennium" 61
"On the Oath New—Created Being and c." 91
"On the Pearl of Great Price" 91
"On the Prayer for the recovery of Mrs. Stanhope Bruce" 90
"On the Prayers for Fast Day" 20

"On the Progress of Judgments" 91
"On the Pruning of the Trees given in March 1759" 75
"On the Rising Sun" 90
"On the Seven Men whose hands the Lord will Seal with Power" 91
"On the Trinity" 91
"On the Uncertainty of Life" 93
"On too much oil putting out the Lamp" 90, 91
"Open Vision" 12
"Orders about Believers Going to Church" 38
"Ordination" 82
"Original Sin" 85
Orloff, General Count 85
"Our Lord's Question to the Blind Men" 65
Owen, William 23
". . . own goodness for tho . . ." 81

P., Reverend Mr. 33
Paine, Thomas 31
Panacea Society 4, 6, 59, 71
"Parable of an Highwayman" 84
"The Parable of the Hermit" 20, 21
"Parable of the Shepherds and Sheep" 86
"Paradise" 87
Parker, William 44, 45, 48, 50
Parsons, Thomas 70
"Part of a communication given from a ring . . ." 78
PAST FINDING OUT 55, 56
"Patchwork Communication" 84
Peacock, Mr. 72
Peason, Nehomiah 98
"The Peoples enquiry and no Communications" 82
"The Period of the Redemption of Man illustrated" 52
Perkins 10, 11, 12, 13, 14, 15
"A personal interview took place between me and Field . . ." 101
Peter 91
"Petition of Joanna Southcott" 99
Pitt, Mr. 63
Poems 65
"Poetry by G. Bennett" 85
Pomeroy, Rev. Mr. 23, 34, 37, 75, 78, 80, 81, 83, 87, 91
"Ponderings of Joanna after leaving Bristol" 84
Portrait of John Finlayson 109
Portraits of Joanna Southcott 107, 108
Portraits of Richard Brothers 109
Pratt, Willis W. 6
"Pray without Ceasing" 87
"Prayer" 86
"Prayer for Absent friends" 61
"Prayer for the Calling in of all Nations" 95
"Prayer for the Destruction of Satan" 95
"Prayer for the Kingdom of God on Earth" 86
"Prayer for the Salvation of our Country from all her Enemies" 95
"Prayer for this Present Time" 40
"Prepare the way—Napolean comes" 96

Prescot, Bar 63, 64
Prescott, Joseph 2, 16, 17, 27, 47, 84, 89, 103
Priestly, Mr. 36, 87, 89
"Priestly's Wife and the Man Child" 89
Prince, Henry James 55
"Private Instructions by the Spirit to Joanna's love, Pity, and c." 90
"The progress, of Joanna's Journey to Exeter" 86
PROPHECIES. A WARNING TO THE WHOLE WORLD, FROM THE SEALED PROPH-
ECIES OF JOANNA SOUTHCOTT, AND OTHER OPEN COMMUNICATIONS GIVEN
SINCE THE WRITINGS WERE OPENED ON THE 12TH OF JANUARY, 1803 16
PROPHECIES ANNOUNCING THE BIRTH OF THE PRINCE OF PEACE, EXTRACTED
FROM WORKS OF JOANNA SOUTHCOTT; TO WHICH ARE ADDED A FEW RE-
MARKS THEREON MADE BY HER 33
"Prophecies of Joanna Southcott" 60
"The Prophecies of Joanna Southcott are Proved Undeniably True by
Their Fulfilment" 60
"Prophecy Given in the 16th Century" 81
PSALM XCII 40
Pughe, William Owen 69, 79
Pullen, Philip 49, 51, 95
"The Purposes of God in the Creation of Man" 87
Pye, John Jr. 45
Pye, John Sr. 44, 45, 47, 48

"Queen Mary and the Roman Powers and c." 88
"Queries and remarks upon a late pamphlet entitled, 'The Question
Answered,' by Mr. Alfred Bishop" 48
"Question Answered" 48

Ragner, Barbarry 98
"Ravages of Locusts" 88
"Rays of Everlasting Light" 22
"Reasons for the Fall of Man" 51
"The Recorder's visit to Joanna" 84
Redesdale, Lord 86
RELIGIOUS IMPOSTERS 57
REMARKS AND INQUIRIES ON THE REV. I. COCKIN'S SERMON 28
"Renovated Earth" 87
"A Representation of the Knowledge of the Lord in Every Heart" 104
"Respecting faithful Labourers being sent out" 88
"Respecting Mr. Senior's wrong Judgment" 89
"Respecting the Seals being put into the Coffin with the Individual who
leaves the Earth" 38
"Respecting Turner and Brother's being deceived" 89
RETREAT OF THE FRENCH ARMY FROM RUSSIA; BEING A MOST INTERESTING
DETAIL OF THE IMPORTANT EVENTS AND DREADFUL SUFFERINGS OF THE
ALLIED FORCES, COMMANDED BY BONAPARTE, DURING THEIR RETREAT
FROM MOSCOW 52
A REVEALED KNOWLEDGE OF THE PROPHECIES AND TIMES, BOOK THE FIRST.
WROTE UNDER THE DIRECTION OF THE LORD GOD, AND PUBLISHED BY HIS
SACRED COMMAND; IT BEING THE FIRST SIGN OF WARNING FOR THE
BENEFIT OF ALL NATIONS. CONTAINING, WITH OTHER GREAT AND RE-
MARKABLE THINGS, NOT REVEALED TO ANY OTHER PERSON ON EARTH,
THE RESTORATION OF THE HEBREW TO JERUSALEM BY THE YEAR OF
1798: UNDER THEIR REVEALED PRINCE AND PROPHET 62, 64

A REVEALED KNOWLEDGE OF THE PROPHECIES AND TIMES. PARTICULARLY OF THE PRESENT TIME, THE PRESENT WAR AND THE PROPHECY NOW FULFILLING. THE YEAR OF THE WORLD 1513. BOOK THE SECOND. CONTAINING OTHER GREAT AND REMARKABLE THINGS, NOT REVEALED TO ANY OTHER PERSON ON EARTH, THE SUDDEN AND PERPETUAL FALL OF THE TURKISH, GERMAN, AND RUSSIAN EMPIRES, WROTE UNDER THE DIRECTION OF THE LORD GOD, AND PUBLISHED BY HIS SACRED COMMAND; IT BEING A SECOND SIGN OF WARNING FOR THE BENEFIT OF ALL NATIONS. BY THE MAN THAT WILL BE REVEALED TO THE HEBREWS AS THEIR PRINCE AND PROPHET 63

REVELATION 97

"Revelation of Jesus Christ to John at Patmos" 47

"The Revelations of St. John Explained by a Revelation from God" 90

"Rd. Brothers, the Pretended Prophet" 109

Reuben, Ann 60, 80

Reuben, Elizabeth 60, 80

Reuben, Joseph 61, 80

Reuben, Mary 61, 80

Reuben, William 60, 70, 80

"The Rising and Setting Sun" 85

Roberts, Daniel 83, 88

Robertshaw, Mrs. 70

Robinson, Henry Crabb 4

"Rock of Ages" 106

"The Roll of Names by the Command of the Lord to Geo. Turner who unite to obey the Lord and are waiting his appearing and his son Shiloh to Reign over us on Earth" 100

"Roll of the Believers" 99, 100

"Roll of the Believers in London" 99

"A root of Jesse, and Star of Jacob a light to the Gentiles" 90

"The Rotton Cucumbers and c." 82

"Royal Proclamation. For the Crowning of the Lord Jesus Christ, King of Kings, and Lord of Lords, in the name of the Father, Son, and Holy Ghost, on Sunday, Dec. 26, 1847, in all the Churches of the True Israel, in England!" 100

"The Royal Proclamation for the Crowning of the Lord Jesus Christ, King of Kings and, Lord of Lords, in the name of the father, son, and holy ghost, on Sunday, December 26, 1841, in all the churches of the true Israel, in England. With the form of service for such important proclamation, as decided on by the cabinet council, in London, Dec. 7, 1847" 46

THE RUINS OF BALBEC AND PALMYRA, IN THEIR PRESENT STATE, DESCRIBED AND EXPLAINED FROM THE PLATES OF ROBERT WOOD, ESQ. UNDER SECRETARY OF STATE TO HIS BRITANIC MAJESTY, PROVED TO BE LEBANON HOUSE AND TADMOR IN THE DESERT, THE PALACES OF SOLOMON, KING OF ISRAEL 64

"The Sacrament administered by Joanna" 89

"Sacred to the Memory of Joanna Southcott" 87, 111

St. Christopher 87

St. Joan 5

St. John 90

St. Theresa 5

Saunders 75

Saxons 64
"The Scourge" 31
"The Scripture Alphabet" 93
"The Scriptures of the Holy Trinity" 34, 46, 47
"The Scriptures of the Holy Trinity. The new testament explained in England by the Voice of the Spirit of Christ. Part IV. Hebrews to Timothy" 34
"Scriptures Which Shew for What Christ died; Also which Shew His Second Coming, to Bruise Satan's Head, and to Establish His Peaceable Kingdom on Earth. The Difference of the First Resurrection and the General Resurrection. Likewise the Remarkable events of 1811, selected from the newspapers" 52
Seals 38, 97-98
"The Seal of the Kingdom of Christ on Earth" 60, 61, 80
"The Sealed Exhorted to Diligence in the New Jerusalem" 95
"The Sealed of the Lord Precious" 85
"Sealing Signing, and Thunder" 85
SECOND BOOK OF SEALED PROPHECIES 26
SECOND BOOK OF VISIONS 17
SECOND BOOK OF WONDERS MORE MARVELLOUS THAN THE FIRST 31
"Second Circular. To the Believers in the Divine Mission to Joanna Southcott" 50
"Secret Prayer" 87
"Selection of passages concerning the Bride, Hell fire, the broken bottle of Wine, Blood of Christ and c." 88
Senior 89
"Service for the 12th of January" 84
Seymour, Alice 6, 49, 56
Shadwell, Colonel 90
Sharp, William 4, 14, 16, 18, 20, 23, 28, 58, 62, 76, 79, 83, 88, 93, 107, 108, 109
Shaw, William 3
"Sheep Among Wolves" 65
"The Sheep and the Lambs—A Dream" 86
"The Shepherd" 87
"Shewing how two men that are enemies to Joanna are like Bullocks that are yoked in and are unable to Hurt her" 89
Shiloh 3, 5, 55, 91, 100
S.H.T. 78
Shumway, Rosslyn E. 71
Sinnock, James 44, 45
"Sitting by" 66
SIXTH BOOK OF WONDERS! BEING A VERBATIM COPY OF THE SIX SEALED LETTERS DATED SEPTEMBER 1813, ANNOUNCING "THIS DAY THE REV. JOSEPH POMEROY MARRIED TO JOANNA SOUTHCOTT, THE GREAT PROPHETESS AND THE WONDER OF THE WORLD" 34
"The Sixth Hour to the Ninth" 86
Slater, Edwin 45
"The Small Still Voice" 40
Mr. Smith 29, 30
Smyth-Pigott, John Hugh 55
Socrates 5
Solomon, King 64, 88
SOUND AN ALARM IN MY HOLY MOUNTAIN 19

Sourby, Joseph 98
Southcott, Hanna 2
Southcott, Joseph 21, 88
Southcott, William 2, 91
"Southcottians and the Church" 55
"Southcottian Consolidation Roll of the United Churches Containing the Names of Such Persons who have Taking the Oath as Commanded by the Lord Thru Joanna Southcott: Approved by Conference Holden in London for Seven Days November 19th to the 26th 1844" 100
"Mr. Southcott's death" 91
Southey, Robert 4, 5
Spencer, John 44, 45, 48, 50
Spencer, Mary 98
"The Spirit of Truth" 90
"The Spirit's Answer to Foley's Sermon" 83
"The Spirit's Answer to Hann's Book" 84
"The Spirit's answer to Peoples Unbelief of the Harvests" 83
"The Spirit's answer to some events of 1811" 82, 83
"Spiritual Knowledge compared with Mechanism" 84
Spring, Mr. 87
Spurgeon, C. H. 65, 66
THE STANDARD 84
Stephens, Thomas 23, 58
Stocks, George 23, 58
"Stopping the Meetings till after the Birth" 85
THE STRANGE EFFECTS OF FAITH 3; PART I, 10, 11; PART II, 11; PART III, 11, 12; PART IV, 12; PART V, 12, 13; PART VI, 13, 14
"Strange Effects of Faith—Marriage Union" 36
". . . supposed the others could not be proper judges . . ." 11, 81
Swedenborg, Baron 39, 84, 89
"The Swerg. Communication" 89
Symonds, Mr. 69

"Table of Southcottian Sects" 55
"Table of the Kingdoms of Men and the Kingdom of God" 58
"The Tale of Agrippia, Adversity, and Prosperity" 88
"The Task" 52
Taylor, Mr. 97
Taylor, Charles 23, 58, 84
Taylor, Fanny 69, 78
Taylor, P. A. 45
Taylor, William 58
"The Temporal and Spiritual Sword" 87
"Temporal and Spiritual things Compared" 88
"A Testimony of Joanna Southcott, the Prophetess; sent by the Lord, to warn the people of his coming" 51
"The Testimony of the Southcottian Church in London, on the Late Visitation of Joanna Southcott, that the child was born on the 16th of December, 1814, proving it to be the man-child mentioned in her writings; also testified by scriptural authority; and to be no other than Christ re-born the 2nd time, and no second savior, as the world has reported" 48
"That I've rocked first in thee . . ." 79
"There to search concerning the fruit . . ." 81

"There is a limit to the feeling of horror" 88
"There is scarce faith to believe the Promises" 86
"Therefore I could not . . ." 81
THE THIRD BOOK OF WONDERS. ANNOUNCING THE COMING OF SHILOH; WITH
    A CALL TO THE HEBREWS 32
"This seed is of me, saith the Lord . . . to Elizabeth Reuben" 81
Thoms, John Nicholls. (See Toms)
"Thou didst awake this morning" 79
"Thou who fillest the Heavens with Thy Majesty" 94
"Thought on the Coming of the Lord" 87
"Threatenings to the Lukewarm" 95
"The Three Elect Children" 83
"Three Gardens, by G. Bennett" 86
"The Three Visions on one paper" 87
"Thus saith Christ" April 21, 1842 80
"Thus saith the Lord, Creations, God . . ." 80
Timbs, John 56
"Time, for worshipping in the spirit illucidated from the visitation of
    prophecy to Joanna Southcott during the years 1792-1814" 47
"To Messrs. Hagger, Copas, Pye, and Malby, with other London Be-
    lievers in Joanna Southcott's visitation" 47
Toms, John Nichols 55, 57
Torin, John 23, 58
"To the Believers of Joanna Southcott's visitation" 47
"To the Memory of Joanna Southcott" 101
Townley, Jane 20, 21, 50, 69, 70, 71, 74, 75, 76, 77, 79, 87, 91, 93, 107
Tozer, W. 86
T. P.'S WEEKLY 57
"Tragic Prophetess" 57
"The Transfiguration" 87
THE TRIAL, CASTING, AND CONDEMNATION OF THE PRINCE OF THIS WORLD,
    THE OLD SERPENT, DEVIL AND SATAN; AT THE COURT OF EQUITY, LITTLE
    JAMES STREET, GRAY'S INN LANE, LONDON, FROM THE 25TH TO THE 31ST
    OF DECEMBER 1846. TO WHICH IS ADDED A LETTER TO THE ARCHBISHOP
    OF CANTERBURY, SOLICITING HIM TO PRESENT TO THE HOUSE OF LORDS
    PETITION ON THE REAL CAUSE AND ONLY REMEDY FOR THE DISTRESS AND
    PERPLEXITIES IN ENGLAND AND ALL NATIONS 53
THE TRIAL OF JOANNA SOUTHCOTT 22, 60
"The Trial or Judgment of Satan" 87
"The Trinity" 75, 86, 89
"The Trinity and National Judgments" 89
TRUE EXPLANATIONS OF THE BIBLE REVEALED BY DIVINE COMMUNICATIONS
    TO JOANNA SOUTHCOTT. PART I, 23; PART II, 23, 24; PART III, 14; PART
    IV, 24; PART V, 24; PART VI, 25; PART VII, 30
A TRUE PICTURE OF THE WORLD AND A LOOKING-GLASS FOR ALL MEN 30
"The True Vine" 86
"Truth defended: or, Christ's Glorious and Peaceable Reign is at Hand"
    53
Turner, George 3, 23, 50, 58, 76, 78, 79, 85, 86, 89, 100
"Turner's dream of the three Sheep" 89
"Turner's Will and God's Will" 89
"The Two Witnesses" 49, 60

"Under his Wings shalt thou Trust" 106

Underwood, Ann 70, 74, 79
University Religion 5
"Uplifting of Hands" 53, 54
"Upon cutting the Communications" 86
"Upon Joanna going to her Father's house" 84
"Upon Joanna Southcott's History" 56
"Upon Marriage" 83
"Upon the Oath taken to the Lord" 88
"Upon the Secrets of the Lord to a Woman" 84
Usher, Archibishop 85

"Various Passages respecting the Messiah" 83
Vaughan, Henry 5
"Verses by G. Bennett upon Immortality" 89
Vincent, John 70
"Vindication for the Honour of God, in answer to J. Aked, Halifax" 50
"A vindication of Joanna Southcott's writings" 44
"The Vision seen at Medina" 83
"The Voice of the Spirit" 85

Wadman, Mr. 40
Waldron, Henry 98
Walford, Edward 56
Wardle, John Potter 95
"A Warning to the different Sects" 88
"A Warning to the nation from the prophecies of Joanna Southcott" 42
"A Warning to the World" 19
Watson, Ellen 93
Watson, W. 111
Watts, Isaac 95
"The Way to Happiness Described by Joanna" 86
Webster, Thomas 23, 51, 58, 62
"Weep not, weep not, nor longer mourn" 95
Wetherell, Jane 98
Wetherell, William R. 23, 51, 58, 79
"What Fellowship with the Panacea Society Entails" 59
"What is Abomination in the sight of God" 89
WHAT MANNER OF COMMUNICATIONS ARE THESE? 21, 26
"What the farm labourers can do and what they Cannot do" 66
"When I can Read my Title Clear" 95
W.H.H. 65
White, James 4, 5
White, Thomas Jesson 108
WHO ARE THE DELUDED? OR MYSTERY UNMASKED 43
"Who is Joanna Southcott? What is her Ark or Box?" 60
"Whosoever' Religion" 60
Wilkinson, Jemima 57
"Will unbelievers be cut off by the year 1807" 86
Wilmot, Mrs. 84
Wilson, Henry 56
Wilson, John 23, 58, 83, 85, 86, 87, 95
Wilson, Mrs. 85
Wilson, Samuel 98
"John Wilson's Reproofs and c." 83

"Wilson's Testimony of the Illness" 86
Winter, William Layton 23, 58
WISDOM EXCELLETH THE WEAPONS OF WAR, AND HEREIN IS SHEWN THAT
JUDGMENTS ARE THE STRANGE WORKS OF THE LORD, BUT MERCY HIS
DARLING ATTRIBUTE 32
"The Wise Virgins" 85
"Woolland stung by a Bee—Vinegar and Honey" 85
"The Woman in the Wilderness, or the wonderful woman, with her
wonderful seal, wonderful spirit, and wonderful child, who 'Is to rule
the nations with a rod of Iron'" 49
"The Wonderful Woman" 78
"Wonderful Prop." 93
Wood, Rev. Basil 85
Wood, Robert Esq. 64
Woolcott, Mr. G. 38
WORD TO THE WISE; OR A CALL TO THE NATION THAT THEY MAY KNOW THE
DAYS OF THEIR VISITATION FROM THE PROPHECIES THAT ARE GIVEN TO
JOANNA SOUTHCOTT, WITH THE REASONS ASSIGNED WHY THE SPIRIT OF
PROPHECY IS GIVEN TO A WOMAN; AND WHICH IS EXPLAINED FROM THE
SCRIPTURES IN THE FOLLOWING PAGES 18
Wordsworth, William 2, 5
Wright, Eugene P. 71
Wroe, John 3, 4

"A Year's Troubles" 87
Young, John 23, 58

Zebulin, Joseph 60, 61, 70
Zwi, Sabbathais 57

This catalogue has been printed in Caledonia type
Design & typography by
Kim Taylor
1968

Modernist Literature

To my students,
and to Amanda and Laura

Modernist Literature

Challenging Fictions

Vicki Mahaffey

Blackwell
Publishing

© 2007 by Vicki Mahaffey

BLACKWELL PUBLISHING
350 Main Street, Malden, MA 02148-5020, USA
9600 Garsington Road, Oxford OX4 2DQ, UK
550 Swanston Street, Carlton, Victoria 3053, Australia

The right of Vicki Mahaffey to be identified as the Author of this Work has been asserted in accordance with the UK Copyright, Designs, and Patents Act 1988.

First published 2007 by Blackwell Publishing Ltd

1   2007

Library of Congress Cataloging-in-Publication Data

Mahaffey, Vicki.
    Modernist literature : challenging fictions / Vicki Mahaffey.
        p.   cm.
    Includes bibliographical references and index.
    ISBN-13: 978-0-631-21306-2 (hardcover : alk. paper)
    ISBN-10: 0-631-21306-6 (hardcover : alk. paper)
    ISBN-13: 978-0-631-21307-9 (pbk. : alk. paper)
    ISBN-10: 0-631-21307-4 (pbk. : alk. paper)
    1. English fiction—20th century—History and criticism—Theory, etc.   2. American fiction—20th century—History and criticism—Theory, etc.   3. Modernism (Literature)—English-speaking countries.   4. Fiction—Appreciation—English-speaking countries.   5. Books and reading—English-speaking countries.   6. Authors and readers.   7. Reader-response criticism.   I. Title.

    PR888.M63M35 2007
    823'.91209113—dc22
                                                                          2006022479

A catalogue record for this title is available from the British Library.

Set in 12 on 13.5 pt Perpetua
by SNP Best-set Typesetter Ltd, Hong Kong
Printed and bound in Singapore
by Markono Print Media Pte Ltd

The publisher's policy is to use permanent paper from mills that operate a sustainable forestry policy, and which has been manufactured from pulp processed using acid-free and elementary chlorine-free practices. Furthermore, the publisher ensures that the text paper and cover board used have met acceptable environmental accreditation standards.

For further information on
Blackwell Publishing, visit our website:
www.blackwellpublishing.com

Contents

Preface   vi
Acknowledgments   xx

Part I: Introduction   **1**
1   Why Read Challenging Literature?   3

Part II: Readings   **71**
2   Partnering: Holmes and Watson, Author and Reader,
    Lover and Loved, Man and Wife   73
3   Window Painting: The Art of Blocking Understanding   124
4   Watchman, What of the Night?   169
Conclusion   200

Notes   203
Bibliography   226
Index   231

Preface

In James Joyce's *Ulysses*, Stephen Dedalus teaches a class on Roman history and Milton's "Lycidas" on the morning of June 16, 1904. His headmaster predicts that Stephen won't stay long at the school, remarking that he was not born to be a teacher. Stephen agrees, calling himself "a learner rather."[1] This book is addressed to learners, of all ages and backgrounds. Before you begin it, I would encourage you to examine your reaction to the question this book raises: is it important to challenge fictions and to be challenged by them in turn? Emerson once wrote, "The secret of Genius is to suffer no fiction to exist for us."[2] To have a more rewarding literary experience, we must first come to terms with common fictions that circulate about literature, all of which contain some truth, but that truth can be misleading because it is incomplete and contingent upon circumstance. Is fiction primarily entertainment? Does it reflect the world in which it was produced? Is it created by larger-than-life geniuses who differ in kind as well as degree from the rest of us? Or are authors just social misfits who wrote because they were ill suited for more materially productive pursuits? Was the difficulty of modern literature designed to make readers feel undereducated and inadequate?[3] Or does formidable textual terrain promise to renew a reader's curiosity and intellectual energy? As a reader, do you typically read to find confirmation of what you already know or to destabilize that knowledge by discovering its limits – or both?

If I ask you to scrutinize your own attitudes toward the subject, it seems only fair that I disclose my own. The investment of an author in her subject is sometimes obscured by the scholarly objectivity that academics strive to project; however, it should be clear that anyone who takes the trouble to learn very much about a topic must have an emotional as well as an intellectual investment in it. My commitment to modernist literature arose out of a passionate interest in innovation and learning, and a conviction that modernism embodies and fosters a process of constant self-reinvention that, while difficult at the outset, is immensely rewarding in the end. The question to be answered is one proposed in Angela Carter's "The Lady of the House of Love": "Can a bird sing only the song it knows or can it learn a new song?"[4] Modernist literature has defined learning in unconventional ways, ways that go beyond those of even the greatest educational institutions. Virginia Woolf, writing on the eve of World War II, asked her readers to concede that "education, the finest education in the world, does not teach people to hate force, but to use it"; rather than "teaching the educated generosity and magnanimity, [education] makes them on the contrary so anxious to keep their possessions . . . in their own hands, that they will use not force but much subtler methods than force when they are asked to share them." And she asks, "are not force and possessiveness very closely connected with war? Of what use then is a university education in influencing people to prevent war?" She proposes that what is needed is a new kind of education that is both experimental and adventurous, that teaches "the arts of human intercourse; the art of understanding other people's lives and minds."[5] Modernist literature emerged out of this drive for a freer, less socially conservative form of education.

Modernist literature, as I am defining it, consists of works written between 1890 and 1940 that trace or inspire what Wallace Stevens in *Notes Toward a Supreme Fiction* calls "freshness of transformation" in perception, thought, and feeling.[6] Such works stimulate engaged readers to interpret more independently, more sensually, more thoughtfully, more joyfully, less deferentially. In this sense, modernist literature is pedagogical, but without the pretentiousness or superiority associated with pedagogues; it is concrete, experiential, and sometimes disorienting because it operates according to different laws than the ones that most contemporary readers unconsciously expect to govern literary works.

Sometimes modernist literary "instruction" begins with the disappearance of a textual crutch, such as the omniscient and trustworthy narrator upon whom we rely for guidance through a textual inferno; when, unlike Dante, we lack a Virgil (or narrator) to guide us through what is unfamiliar, we have to pay more concentrated attention to style, sound, imagery, and form in order to flesh out and assemble those patterns we call "meaning." Some works offer a different kind of guide, such as Sherlock Holmes, who teaches us to solve puzzles through his example, while exhorting us to sharpen our powers of observation, challenge our initial assumptions, and delay the process of drawing conclusions. In still other instances, we are encouraged to identify with unexpected heroes: a Jew in Dublin; a young black woman in *Their Eyes Were Watching God*; a hermaphrodite – the Greek prophet Tiresias – who blindly observes the modern war-torn world in *The Waste Land*.

Modernist literature instructs readers in still another way: because it is attuned to the movements of the unconscious mind as well as to conscious thoughts and intentions, it helps readers learn to hear the undertones of language as well as its conventionally agreed-upon meanings. As *Finnegans Wake* warns, working from an analogy between reading and watching a film, "if you are looking for the bilder [a word that when pronounced evokes the English word "builder," but when spelled designates the German word for "pictures"] deep your ear on the movietone!"[7] The phrase suggests that if you want to get a visual image of what you read ("bilder"), or if you want to hear the voice of the author (the "builder"), you must pay attention not just to what words mean, but more importantly to the way they *sound* and to what those sounds suggest.

Of course, good literature has always engaged different levels of meaning, but the innovations produced by modernist writers work to change the reader's experience of the text by violating the implied contract between writer and reader. In a departure from the usual practice of the nineteenth-century novel, the modernist writer – by making the narrator untrustworthy, fallible, or absent altogether – simultaneously erased himself from the text and scattered himself throughout it.[8] The most important difference between modernist literature and what preceded it, though, is not a difference of form. Rather, it arises out of some writers' resistance to an important societal change. As cheaper methods of printing made it increasingly feasible to disseminate more texts to a larger reading public, that public demanded a different kind of fare. Readers developed an appetite for books that could be readily "consumed," and many serious writers refused to standardize their works to comply with the growing demand for writing that was familiar and easy to recognize. Instead, they continued to view literature as an art form that should be rich and strange and stimulate the reader's curiosity. If we try to *see and hear* that which is not immediately comprehensible instead of insisting upon understanding it from the outset, it becomes easier to perceive a subtext, with its traces of the buried emotions, memories, and associations that color and shape consciousness. By focusing too exclusively on the intentional meaning of a text, we blot out its poetry, its capacity to simulate the sensory power of lived experience.

In short, modernist literature demands that we approach it differently from the way we read other contemporary texts, such as the newspaper. Unless we do, we will miss half of its pleasure and most of its meaning. When we read books that are easy to understand and assimilate, we often forget that they are comfortable precisely because they share and confirm our preexisting assumptions, and sometimes even our prejudices (literally "pre-judgments"). Such reinforcement makes it easier for well-defined cultural communities to act on shared prejudices in ways that seem justified and fulfilling, even to the point of waging war against offenders. Naturally, better reading habits won't bring world peace, but they do provide a mechanism for individuals to examine and reevaluate their unconscious assumptions. Thoughtful reading develops the senses, sharpens perception, and affords unexpected pleasures that are often lost in the race for meaning and validation. Moreover, it has the capacity to strengthen the reader's sense of interpretive responsibility, which in time — if sufficiently widespread — could have useful repercussions for society as a whole.

Wallace Stevens alludes to the silent, delicate interdependence of the psychological and the social at the end of *Notes toward a Supreme Fiction,* when he compares the soldier's war with the "war between the mind/ And sky, between thought and day and night/ . . . The two are one. They are a plural, a right and left, a pair." He muses, "How simply the fictive hero becomes the real" (234). It is because of this ease with which fiction becomes real that we must labor to make our literary fictions more challenging, more textured and comprehensive. Fictions that countenance a reader's repression (of what she doesn't know or understand) make it easier for that same reader to overlook social policies of oppression (of *people* she doesn't understand). Moreover, when reading is less oriented toward consumption and more oriented toward adventure, readers become less interested in what they can retain and more attentive to what they may discover.

Reading is a highly personal, potentially ethical activity as well as an intellectual one.[9] If a reader feels implicated in what she or he is reading, the experience is almost completely different from one in which the reader feels detached and evaluative (inclined to judge what he reads). ("The partaker partakes of that which changes him," Stevens 219.) The same is true of writing: to understand how one is implicated in the problems one is analyzing promotes self-knowledge and replaces deference or defiance with responsibility. To treat a book as fundamentally alien to our own experience is no better than automatically assimilating it into what we already know and understand. A more rewarding alternative is to find a way in which we can use our own experience as a bridge to (but not an equivalent of) something that stands outside it.

One question that drives this book is how we recognize and learn to defeat our own unconscious suppositions of superiority (and fears of inferiority) that – when unquestioned – govern our lives. Both the desire for superiority and the fear of inferiority presuppose detachment from the other; dominance and submission are not postures that promote and sustain conversation or meaningful human intercourse. I claim that one's encounter with a book follows many of the same patterns as an encounter with other people, which is one reason why the Nazi burning of 25,000 books on May 10, 1933 in Berlin's Opernplatz (now Bebelplatz) was so deeply unsettling: it prefigured the incineration to come of millions of human beings who would be similarly rejected as "un-German," people with whom the Nazis denied having any connection (see Angelika Bammer's photograph on the front cover). As the poet Heinrich Heine once wrote, "Where you are burning books, / You will also burn people."[10] The book burnings serve as a vivid portent of the holocaust to come, signaling a crucial aspect of my argument: that our way of engaging with books is predictive. The book preserves the voice of its author, acting as her emissary, but with its "spine" and through its connection with an author's *corpus*, or body (of work), it is also a symbolic representation of an author's physical being. When specific books were selected for burning in Berlin, that act was a test, a forerunner of the selection and silencing of people that would shortly follow. The book burning was also preemptive; symbolically, the fire consumed a means of "reading" or interpreting the future, of understanding the full human meaning of what was about to happen.

I would like to recount two stories from my own childhood to demonstrate the two complementary pitfalls of defining one's relation to the unfamiliar (and unfamilial). The first challenges the urge to demonize groups of people (in this case the German people who had supported Hitler). The second is an example of the opposite problem: the tendency to identify too deeply with the experience of another (here a black American high school girl), to the point of forgetting one's own problematic position relative to hers. I have included these experiences in France and Texas for two reasons: as an important reminder of the humanity and fallibility of the person writing this book,[11] and as a way of supporting my larger claim that we tend to read people in much the same way that we read books.

The first story – heard rather than remembered – begins on August 1, 1955. Imagine a converted World War II propeller plane, the Flying Tiger, a shark's mouth painted on its nose, leaving from the airport then called Idlewild in New York (now JFK), bound for Paris. On board, as the result of a phone call to her Brooklyn hotel, is a woman, 24 years old, with her children, aged 1 and almost 3, who is to be reunited with her husband when they land in France. The trip takes eighteen hours. Upon arrival, the exhausted children promptly get sick as the reunited family drive from Paris to Luxembourg near the French Air Force base where the father is stationed. They spend the night at Mondorf-Les-Bains, close to the borders of both Germany and France, at an inn that has one featherbed for the four of them and a bathroom down the hall. The children are still sick, and the mother takes the older child in her arms and goes to the bar to ask for water. A dark-haired German man in his thirties or forties overhears her request, turns to her, and unexpectedly says – in heavily accented English – "Why should you and your daughter be allowed to live? Why are *you* alive when you Americans killed *my* wife and daughter?" The quest for water abandoned, the mother rushes back upstairs, distraught.

I was the older child, and this was my first uncomprehending experience of the complexities of war and its twisted aftermath. The German man's dead daughter had been my enemy and counterpart; she too was a child, and her father was understandably still enraged and grief-stricken at her loss. But any pity my mother might have had for this man would have felt uncomfortable, not only because Americans had killed his daughter, but because it was relatively easy to justify that action; after all, she was born into a nation that had both engaged in and justified crueler slaughters of innocent people on a much more massive scale.

Now, half a century later, it seems to me that for one uncanny moment in a chance encounter, the national antagonism between two people – an American and a German – was briefly balanced by a common bond: love for their families. This is a place where disidentification with an "enemy" becomes dishonest and dehumanizing. And this is where my interest in World War II begins: had it been easier for ordinary people to experience the kinship that subtends very real differences – difference of what the Nazis called "race," difference of language, difference of sex – then the horror of a mid-century journey to the heart of darkness might have been a little different as well.

The scars of conflict were still apparent in Europe when my family moved there in 1955. We lived in a war-torn landscape, not only devastated by the events of ten years earlier but also strangely alive with still-dangerous munitions from World War I. The French Air Force base where my father worked was in Étain, which is near Verdun. If you were to drive along the eastern border of France, you could see acres and acres of land sealed off from the public because of unexploded bombs, shells, and mortars that been there for almost forty years. At one poorly maintained ossuary, a brick building with windows that had been painted over, some of the paint had peeled away, revealing the entangled bones inside, the remains of a mass grave of soldiers who had died at the battle of Verdun in the spring of 1916.

The village of Étain was rural and agricultural; the ground floors of most of the houses were used to store manure, which any passerby could see and smell. We lived on the base, in a trailer surrounded by other trailers filled with the families of officers. In the winter, ice would form on the ceiling of the trailer, and I would wake up in my top bunk bed with water dripping on my nose. There were mice in the trailer, too, and we would jump on the furniture when we saw one scurry across the floor. I went to a French nursery school, where no one spoke English, for which my father paid twenty-five cents a month. My parents bought wine at a local store where you could bring empty bottles and fill them up at large vats for about a dollar per case. They would chat with the villagers, who asked them if it were true that the streets of America were paved with gold. Village life was frozen in time, but as you left the village you entered a world still bristling with the machinery of violence. When you crossed the border into Germany near Trier, you could see a multitude of pill boxes dotting the mountains on the German side, with the long barrels of their enclosed guns pointing at the traffic on the bridge that connects France and Germany. The uniformed German border guards still approached all cars with the distinctive goose-step that spoke of war. In Le Havre, you could still see huge submarine pens that had been hastily built by the Germans, and a railroad track that was used to reinforce concrete bunkers that were hit but not destroyed by bombs. St Sebaldus Church in Nuremberg, from which my mother's family (Sebald) derived its name, had been damaged in the bombing, and was slowly being rebuilt. In Inglestadt, Germany, NATO forces had taken over a German airfield, with serviceable runways and underground fuel bunkers that survived the war intact. My father's Air Force unit was on red alert because Hungary was in crisis, and America was anticipating the possibility of a new war with Russia. The Americans' strategy was to disperse their aircraft so that in the event of a war against Russia they could not be taken out by a few concentrated strikes.

Two wars over and yet still strangely, horrifyingly present; another war on the horizon – which mercifully never happened – with my father involved in the preparations for it. In this atmosphere of rural tranquility surrounded by threat and ruin, so near a country where Americans were blamed and sometimes hated for bringing the consequences of war home to civilian German families, I came to consciousness in several national languages, and learned to inhabit the landscape of a brutal history. Even our vacations were haunted; when we traveled to the Bavarian Alps, I was initially dazzled by the majestic heights and inspired by images of Heidi as we climbed to a tearoom on a mountaintop. That charming tearoom was Hitler's Eagle's Nest, where he met with Mussolini to design strategies of extermination and war. This vivid impression of an evil that runs contrary to appearance – an experience it took me years to put into words – became one of the stimuli that taught me to value careful analysis. As a practiced and even talented reader, and as someone who had witnessed firsthand the deceptive nature of superficial impressions, I grew increasingly convinced that none of us can read the signs of human desire and fear as well as we should, and must. This is partly because we usually read to discover deliberate intent and literal meaning, despite the fact that other meanings – sometimes dangerous ones – lurk not in the text, but in the subtext, which we are often helpless (by training) to interpret.

Evil masked by tranquil appearances was not something we left behind when my father's tour of European duty was over. I was to reencounter it dramatically when at the age of 5 I moved with my family from France to the American South. The beauty of live-oaks festooned with Spanish moss along bayous in New Orleans and Houston, the brilliant blue of a sky that seemed bigger above the flat land: these were vivid images, hiding all but occasional traces of racial hatred. Those signs were illegible at the time to a white child in a segregated world. Although in overheard conversations, even a child might detect traces of fear or contempt directed against black, Creole, or Mexican Americans, the issue of American racism came sharply to the forefront of national attention in September of 1957, seven months after our return from France. I can't be sure exactly when I registered the horror of what happened in Little Rock, Arkansas, when nine black students attempted to enter Central High in the wake of the Supreme Court's 1954 decision to desegregate the schools. It seems likely that I wouldn't have absorbed the impact of what happened until I myself was in high school.

During my junior year of high school in Houston, I chose to perform a dramatic monologue from Martin Duberman's play *In White America*, which focuses on the standoff at Central High. I have a vivid memory of drama tournaments in which I played the role of a brave, frightened black girl. The experience required me to imagine and try to express the complex feelings of the Little Rock Nine, to re-create a love of learning and a hopefulness inspired by legislative change that would soon be severely tried by vicious, prolonged resistance. I discovered, too, that my eagerness to identify myself with these brave students by playing the role of a black girl was startlingly naïve: black and white observers alike deplored my exploration of cross-racial identification, for reasons it took me years to understand. I had no idea that race raised issues of allegiance, and that someone who seems to have questioned her racial allegiance would be viewed as a traitor by all.

Although I cannot say for sure when the fascination took root, I, like countless other schoolchildren across the nation, was riveted by the story of how these nine students were reviled, spat upon, and physically attacked as they tried to enter a formerly all-white Southern school in the hope of receiving a better education. The fear and contempt that segregation had kept hushed and implicit were suddenly angrily articulated and acted out. On September 2, Governor Orval Faubus called out the Arkansas National Guard to prevent the students from entering Central High. Jeering segregationist crowds surrounded the school, some protesters waving Confederate flags; one of the besieged students, Elizabeth Eckford, related that her dress was wringing wet with spit. On September 20, a federal judge ordered the National Guard to withdraw, and three days later police escorted the nine students into a side entrance of the school, but the students had to leave before the day was even half over. The police were afraid that they couldn't control the mob outside, which was demanding that the police give them one student to lynch or hang as an example. That night, the editor of the *Arkansas Gazette* tersely summed up the situation by saying, "I'll give it to you in one sentence. The police have been routed, the mob is in the streets and we're close to a reign of terror." Finally, on September 25, after three weeks of conflict, paratroopers belatedly called out by Eisenhower took control of the National Guard and, armed with bayonets and rifles, escorted the students up the steps of the school. Once inside, the students were met with a chorus of children yelling "the niggers are in . . . get them out." A black effigy was burned across the street. The students, however, did not give in to intimidation; they stood their ground, despite abuse that continued all year. Then in 1958, Ernest Green – one of the nine – became the first black student to graduate from Central High.

These memories of national and racial hatreds demonstrate the ease with which one may demonize or identify too closely with the experience of someone else, dangers that also affect one's way of reading, imbalances to which modernist writers have themselves fallen subject in different ways. To name just the most dramatic example, Ezra Pound's anti-Semitism – his radio speeches against Jews and his identification with Mussolini's position during World War II – landed him in a cage near Pisa, charged as a traitor to the United States, and then in a lunatic asylum. Pound's protégé James Joyce, in dramatic counterpoint, cast a half-Jewish Irishman as the cuckolded hero of his twentieth-century version of the *Odyssey*, but many readers were outraged, not only by the sexual explicitness of Joyce's epic, for which it was banned, but also by the careful way Joyce qualified – and thereby humanized – the heroism of his everyman. By neither demonizing his protagonist nor worshiping him, and thereby respecting the balance between sameness and difference I have been prescribing, Joyce drew almost as much fire as Pound. Moreover, Joyce viewed his books as the envoys of his person, respecting with almost superstitious seriousness the bond between the book and the living individual. He was determined, for symbolic reasons, to publish *Ulysses* on his birthday, and when the Maunsel edition of *Dubliners* was destroyed by its printer, he identified it with his own body. The proofs of *Dubliners* had been burned or guillotined in Ireland, which is why Joyce decided never to return there, writing that Ireland had crucified him once by proxy, and the next time would do so in the flesh.

The connection between books and living people brings me back to the Nazi book burnings in Berlin's Opernplatz in 1933. Angelika Bammer (whose hauntingly beautiful image of the Israeli artist Micha Ullmann's memorial to the book burnings, *The Library of Burned Books*, is reproduced on the cover of this book) writes that one of the biggest problems in contemplating a violent event is "the distance between it and us, the very distance that is the ground of memory."

> We are either too removed, so that loss is registered as mere fact and the dead become just numbers. Or we are too close and falsely identify ourselves with those we purport to be remembering. This problem is critical in both social and personal terms. For while detachment and identification can be problematic in just these ways, resulting in indifference or sentimentality, they are, at the same time, indispensable elements in our relationship to troubling pasts, as detachment is necessary for critical thought and identification is necessary for empathy. The search for a proper balance between the two thus has ethical, psychological, and political urgency.
>
> Memorial art makes this search its mandate. It struggles for words that, as Franz Kafka famously wrote, will shatter the frozen sea within us that is our feelings. At the same time, it works to create forms that will channel the flood of feeling, once released, to ends that will be productive.[12]

Micha Ullmann's memorial to the book burnings captures that haunting, tremulous balance between the presence and absence of those "offensive" books that were destroyed by students celebrating the end of an "intellectualism" they called "exaggerated" and "Jewish":[13] books by Freud, Hemingway, Heine, Brecht, Helen Keller, Chagall, Dreiser, Klee, Jack London, Thomas Mann, Marx, Upton Sinclair, H.G. Wells, and many others. The installation is an underground library with empty shelves, and in Bammer's photograph, that buried, empty library, stripped of its contents, is luminous in the darkness. The photograph adjures the viewer to look beneath the surface for what is no longer there: this is also a way of reading, a method that those missing books – like modernism more generally – encourages and rewards.

Bammer's photograph of Ullmann's memorial serves as a poignant reminder that World War II was a war of one category of people (or books) against other categories, and that those categories were defined and perpetuated by reductive images of the self and others. The media – literature, art, music, as well as the popular press, television, and film – serve as the main conduits through which such perceptions are disseminated or refuted, which is why books – books of the sort the Nazis burned – are central to the discussion of my own book.

If we are to consider how people are classified or characterized – politically, legally, and in literature – it might be helpful to turn briefly to the implied "contract" between writer and reader as a more compact instance of other social contracts. Shortly after the turn of the twentieth century, experimental writers such as Virginia Woolf, James Joyce, and Gertrude Stein reformulated the implied contract with their readers in the hope that, by doing so, they could promote greater equality between writer and reader. Such presumptive equality is congruent with other ideals of equality, especially the equality of women and men, and of gentiles and Jews. In many different social arenas, contracts were increasingly seen as a way of formalizing the competing claims between employer and worker, man and wife. They were also a more liberal alternative to slavery and to outdated marriage laws. Any discussion of freedom in the modern period is likely to invoke at some point the ideal of a contract, which rested on "principles of self ownership, consent, and exchange."[14] If, as Charles Taylor has persuasively argued, "human identity is created . . . dialogically,"[15] developing partly through its unconscious response to the ways it is represented or reflected by others, then our identities are shaped by our "contractual" dialogues, including the tacit pact between author and reader. The most effective means of identity formation are not coercive, because coercion is easily identified and can therefore be resisted, mentally if not physically.

According to the implied reader–writer contract of the nineteenth-century novel, the reader's self-image is shaped – perhaps even distorted – through the use of flattering and shaming reflections that speak to the reader's fears and desires. Oscar Wilde alluded to the power of art to reflect the reader in the preface to *The Picture of Dorian Gray* (1891), when he wrote, "It is the spectator, and not life, that art really mirrors." Wilde indicts the propensity of readers to look for flattering rather than real-istic reflections of themselves (and not others) when, casting the reader as the brutish native enslaved by Prospero in Shakespeare's *The Tempest*, he asserts that "The nineteenth century dislike of Realism is the rage of Caliban seeing his own face in a glass," and "The nineteenth century dislike of Romanticism is the rage of Caliban not seeing his own face in a glass."[16] Wilde taunts the nineteenth-century reader by suggesting that, like Caliban, he or she is an unformed, not yet fully socialized being who looks to art for an acceptable (and partially recognizable) self image. This would change, beginning in the 1890s, as books and poems increas-ingly came to embody the multiplicity, changeability, unknowability, and potential treachery of a heterogeneous and imperfect self. Book in hand, author and reader are plunged into the midst of what might be called life/art together; privileged vantage points – in the form of omni-scient perspectives – are few and suspect, but authors and readers who accept the new "contract" experience a fresh exhilaration at the prospect of engaging less predictably in the flux of experience (both literary and actual). One of the most succinct examples of this new immanence of perspective is Ezra Pound's "In a Station of the Metro":

> The apparition of these faces in the crowd;
> Petals on a wet, black bough.[17]

Although the title of Pound's poem identifies the setting, no one describes it, introduces the speaker, or explains the connections between the two lines and the two impressions (urban and natural, respectively) that are implicitly equated via a semicolon. The reader is given a sensual and aural puzzle without a key; we can only "solve" the puzzle by being willing to experience it imaginatively, by using our own resources to connect the two images; the author refuses to do it for us.

I would like to look more closely at the assertion that the attitude of the reader toward a writer represents the more general stance of an individual toward authority, exploring the connection it assumes between how we read and how we behave in a larger social setting. Modernist literature provides valuable insight into how the implied contract between author and reader serves as a template for our unconscious contract with what James Joyce in *Finnegans Wake* called "awethorrority" (authority: the "awe" and "horror" with which subjects are conditioned to regard those in control; 516.19). Authority designates that system through which meaning is defined and legislated, usually by someone or something perceived as exempt from its own laws. When people read in an uncritical way, they are also – often without realizing it – deferring to the author's authority. This is vicarious reading – unconsciously accepting the author's or narrator's judgment of what is right and wrong. Many books relieve us of the responsibility of ethical choice, which is part of their value as entertainment. But what do we lose when we habitually abdicate our capacity to interpret? Our independence of mind. Our ability to engage on an equal footing with the author. Our responsiveness as ethical subjects. Moreover, when we don't practice our interpretive skills, they lose sharpness and flexibility.

As you read this book, I hope you will think about the implied contract between us. I would prefer that you explore these ideas *with* me, instead of thinking of them as something imposed on you *by* me. Although I am loosely referring to modernist literature in historical terms, as a set of movements that took place between 1890 and 1940, my intention is not to define modernist literature at all, but to create an atmosphere that enables you to interpret these works more freely, more honestly, and more meaningfully for yourselves. What most attracts me about modernist literature is the faith expressed by its most daring practitioners in the responsibility and capacity of the reader to interrogate and interpret an increasingly illegible world with insight, precision, humor, and flexibility. That is why I have chosen to focus on their most challenging fictions, together with the romanticized fictions of individual freedom that they challenged.

Acknowledgments

This book could not have been written without the help of independent, active, thoughtfully challenging readers of the kind that modernism tried to make more numerous.

Those who offered valuable suggestions in the research phase of the project include Eileen Radetich, Damien Keane, Justin Gundlach, Sam Kaplan, Alex Fleck, and Scott Browning. Several people read drafts of the chapters and helped to make them clearer and more shapely. These include Laura and Amanda Dennis, Joanne Ahearn, Veronica Schanoes, Josephine Walker, Sara Gordon, Jack Mahaffey, Sarah Boote, Connie Steltzenmuller, Jill Shashaty, and Justin Dyer. Colleagues willing to take issue with my arguments in productive ways include Ronald Bush and Andrew Gibson. The person who resisted every sentence with acute and constructive observations, though, was Constance Abrams. For whatever fluency the prose may now possess, I thank her. I am also grateful to Monica Park, whose gifted illustrations to *The Waste Land* I had hoped to include. More generally, I would like to express my appreciation for my graduate and undergraduate students at the University of Pennsylvania, especially those who took my course on Literary Authority and the Holocaust. My debt to them, and to two other important "learners" outside the classroom, is acknowledged in the dedication.

I have presented versions of the arguments at St John's College, Oxford, the Sorbonne, the University of York, the University of London at Royal Holloway, the University of Edinburgh, the University of Michigan, Tulane University, and Oklahoma State University. A grant from the University of Pennsylvania Research Foundation helped to cover some of the costs of researching this book.

I am grateful to Professor Angelika Bammer for permission to reproduce her beautiful photograph of Micha Ullmann's memorial on the cover of this book.

The author and publisher would also like gratefully to acknowledge the permission granted to reproduce the copyright material in this book:

Wallace Stevens, extract from "Asides on the Oboe," from *The Collected Poems of Wallace Stevens* by Wallace Stevens. Copyright © 1954 by Wallace Stevens and renewed 1982 by Holly Stevens. Used by permission of Alfred A. Knopf, a division of Random House, Inc.

Every effort has been made to trace copyright holders and to obtain their permission for the use of copyright material. The publisher apologizes for any errors or omissions in the above list and would be grateful if notified of any corrections that should be incorporated in future reprints or editions of this book.

Part I Introduction

Chapter 1 Why Read Challenging Literature?

And why do you not judge for yourselves what is right?
Luke 12:57

Modernist literature, a term that loosely designates the innovative literature produced in the first half of the twentieth century, often goes unread – dismissed because of its arcane allusions, experimental procedures, and perceived difficulty. In the popular view, modernist writing is characterized by willful obscurity and shot through with nostalgia for a rapidly waning elite culture – a nostalgia mired in the ugly politics of the time.[1] This view, while justified in a few precise instances, misses the most important point about "high" modernist literature in general: that it was deeply engaged with questions of how we categorize, define, identify, and interpret the multiplicity of the world around us, questions that were erupting more destructively in the emotional and political cross-currents of Stalinist Russia, partitioned Ireland, a divided Spain, Fascist Italy, and Nazi Germany.

Modernist literature gloried in experiments with form, but its experimentation was not detached from the social conditions that shaped it; on the contrary, it was part of a richly varied pattern of literary reactions to one of the least stable periods of human history. The years leading up to 1940 were marked by intense social pressure; to quote the caption that begins Charlie Chaplin's first full-length talking film, *The Great Dictator* (1940), "This is a story of a period between two world wars – An interim in which Insanity cut loose. Liberty took a nose dive and Humanity was kicked around somewhat." Social instability tended to push writers in one of two directions: toward fresher and more dynamic articulations of what they saw, or toward codification – the attempt to establish and enforce the "rules" of discourse. The distribution of social privilege was under attack on many levels, from the sexual, racial, and religious to the international, and class and economics were vitally at issue everywhere. Modernism celebrated and rejected the strange (and the stranger); it welcomed foreignness yet feared contaminating the family.

Interestingly, even today most prospective readers tend to balk at the prospect of reading modernist literature, complaining that its erudition makes readers feel inadequate (rather than curious). A few years ago, when a committee commissioned by Random House chose *Ulysses* as the most important book of the twentieth century, a renegade group on the internet protested by conducting its own poll: the winner was Ayn Rand's *The Fountainhead*. The question I hope to answer is this: what is at stake in the continuing popular preference for books with a conventional narrative structure and a strong moral message over those that force us laboriously to rethink our most comfortable assumptions and expectations? Clearly, we still expect books to be readily comprehensible on a first reading. What are the social implications of a communal desire to read and understand quickly and easily? Why should we make the effort to read challenging literature in an age of television, film, and other popular entertainments?

In the pages that follow, I have begun to address these questions by looking more closely at the implications of traditional narrative structure, especially its reliance upon a narrator whose perspective is greater than that of the characters or the reader. Henry James associates the conventionally reliable narrator with "the consciousness of the artist," identified as "the watcher" who looks out from "the house of fiction" through an elevated window – the literary form – at "the spreading field, the human scene."[2] The function of these watchers is typically to help us synthesize and interpret events, but such syntheses are necessarily reductive; they inevitably delimit and tame the flux of the real.

A traditional narrative structure is also limiting in another way: it privileges conscious, rational understanding over subconscious (and sensual) forms of awareness, as well as emphasizing the perspective of the individual over more communal and cooperative forms of knowing. Collective and unconscious perceptions are equally disruptive to the shape of most stories; they must be part of the subtext rather than of the text itself. We can better appreciate the limits of traditional fiction by construing James' description of fiction as a "house" from a different angle: like a house, fiction can be comprised of more than one story, but its structure is nonetheless a single one. As the modernist movement gained momentum, fiction became less like a house and more like an urban street. No longer was the "story" the main unit of division; instead, the stimuli were more various and dynamic, and the focus moved to collective experience. What used to be dismissed as insignificant details emerged – through synecdoche – as essential indices to the richness of a complex, dynamic, sensual whole, as art attempted to offer a more comprehensive experience rather than a mere narrative slice. In order to experience modernist art, we must either watch the action from several different windows in succession, or else leave the window altogether to enter the human mêlée on the street, observing what we find there on the same level as everyone else.

My argument moves from a critique of the structure of traditional stories to an interrogation of the possible social implications of interpretive (or readerly) passivity. I argue that when we learn to read too passively, deferentially, or vicariously, we become less willing to assert our values through action by calmly and reasonably defying other authority figures when they direct us to do something at variance with our conscience. When it becomes habitual, reading, as a movement of the mind and heart,[3] becomes predictable, inflexible, resistant to novelty. I use Stanley Milgram's famous obedience experiments to understand the psychology of deferring to authority, and I trace some of the historical consequences of such obedience through Christopher Browning's account of ordinary men who murdered large numbers of Jewish men, women, and children during World War II.

Next, I consider the extent to which the exercise of obedience may be regulated by the desires and fears that circulate around the issue of being evaluated or judged, which triggers a subconscious expectation of reward or punishment. If, as Michel Foucault recommends in *Discipline and Punish*,[4] we regard Jeremy Bentham's panopticon as a model of modern society, and if we agree that the operations of that society have been internalized by individuals, it becomes eerily apparent how individuals may be regulated – without brutality or coercion – through a sensation of being watched. Foucault argues that we have internalized this impression of being under constant surveillance, but I argue that we also unconsciously identify with the watcher, as we can see most clearly when we read. Such an analysis suggests that individuals are socially regulated by the illusion that they are watching and evaluating others while they are simultaneously being watched and evaluated themselves. Part of the pleasure of reading popular fiction comes from the sensation of having special access to the characters' private lives, enjoying a position of superiority that exempts us from the judgments we deliver.

I look at the German concentration camps of the 1940s as instances in which the usual psychological self-policing turned outward and was brutally redirected toward groups who were designated "Other." The argument here, which I make with the help of Primo Levi's *Survival in Auschwitz*,[5] is that the robotic arbitrariness of the concentration camp system of "correction" is not as aberrant as some would like to believe. (This idea, that the matrix of the camps is still very much that of society as a whole, has been more recently picked up by Giorgio Agamben and it is also apparent in J.M. Coetzee's *Elizabeth Costello*.[6]) Levi suggests that many of us thoughtlessly subject ourselves to the regulated, meaningless routines, arbitrary judgments and punishments that were forcibly imposed upon inmates of concentration camps. Levi also intimates that a more thoughtful and compassionate orientation toward ourselves and the community would call into being a desire to communicate through (not around) the barriers imposed by differences in language, nationality, and religion. He himself tries to communicate with a French inmate through Dante, forging a connection through their shared reference to a text that requires careful explanation and interpretation; this kind of intense recitation and exegesis is for Levi a replacement for what he calls the "unlistened-to story" (60).

Finally, I attempt to step back and present the historical context of modernist writing as an essential determinant of its innovative formal characteristics. Instead of defining modernism as the writing of a "lost generation" that came to maturity between two world wars (a definition that constructs modernist writing as a highly intellectualized "waste land" that linked two large-scale catastrophes), I argue that it was the product of the escalating tension between social freedom and social restriction. In particular, I trace the successive explosions of new social liberties that began in the 1890s with the "New Woman" movement and the debates over homosexuality that erupted during the Wilde trials, and continued through Home Rule agitation in Ireland, the Bolshevik revolution in Russia, the Harlem Renaissance in America, and the roaring twenties version of market capitalism. These expansive, revolutionary tendencies were dramatically countered by the widespread depression of the thirties and the coming to power of massively repressive regimes in Germany, Italy, Spain, and Russia. modernist literature is shaped by these tensions between innovation and retrenchment, expressive freedom and renewed efforts to enforce the old rules.

All this in pursuit of an answer to the question asked in the title: why read challenging literature? The answer is that such literature forces readers to face and make interpretive choices that narrators used to make for them, and it also helps readers come to terms with the meaning of those choices. Modernist literature erodes the sharp distinction between writer and reader, and in so doing presents readers with interpretive ethical dilemmas. If ethical action is only possible as the result of a deliberate, thoughtful choice between fully imagined alternatives, then a literature that confronts us with more difficult interpretive challenges offers a socially relevant discipline. But it is equally important to consider the pleasure that such reading affords, which I address in the conclusion of this chapter. This final section analyzes the intellectual and even sensual pleasure of extending the reach of thought and compassion by "practicing" – over and over – the difficult art of examining life by engaging in more adventurous ways of reading.

On Stories

> it's a low art, tale-telling . . .
> Margaret Atwood,
> *The Penelopiad*

On the door of my office, I have a cartoon strip from *Pearls before Swine* of a mouse in front of a microphone, being interviewed.[7] The interviewer, who calls the mouse "sir," is asking him where he stands on various political issues, such as whether he's pro-choice. The mouse replies, "Ohhhhh No No No No No No Nooooo . . . Not at all . . ." When he is asked why, he answers, "Because in high school, they made us read 'Ulysses' and it was the most incomprehensible crap I've ever read in my life." The interviewer says politely, "Sir, that's *Joyce* . . . I'm asking if you're pro-CHOICE," and the mouse responds, "Well, if I had a choice, I wouldn't read Joyce."

The reader's stake in modernist literature is captured in that rhyme of "Joyce" and "choice." As I argued above, texts that are too easy to follow weaken the discipline of choice. Modernist literature is designed not to be "read," as we usually understand the term, but to be performed, in the etymological sense of "perform" as "to finish making" something by making (or testing) interpretive choices. This so-called "difficult" literature demands that we "play" it as if it were a musical score, act it out as if it were a play. What is gone is the artificial coherence of a narrative, with its beginning, middle, and end; it has been displaced by apparent chaos, which, as we know from physics, is actually at a deeper level highly structured. The experience of reading has changed from one of identification with a protagonist, in a world in which the characters are all related to one another in some meaningful way, to imaginative travel through a maze of interpretive and sensual possibilities. Such a shift is highly adaptive to changes in the developed, international world. We now have more choices along with more opportunities: to play more than one part in a drama or more than one instrument in atonal, experimental compositions; we are called upon to apply more than one national or linguistic or generic context to the actions of more than one protagonist with whom we have no *a priori* connection. In the tragi-comedy of the twentieth and twenty-first centuries, we are in the position of being asked to empathize with an increasing number of differently – and at least arguably – "good" points of view, and to manage the interplay between them with sometimes euphonious, sometimes cacophonous, but always unpredictable results. No longer buoyed by a dominant narrative current in fiction, we are asked – as in life – to make choices at every turn.

Lyric poetry has always demanded that we respond to it performatively, by experimenting with different modes of engaging with it, but in the twentieth century fictional prose and long poems were radically transformed as well. So-called "modernist" techniques gradually began to change the appearance of literature, presenting an intellectually or sensually challenging surface that initially seems to hold the reader at a distance. On first reading, *The Waste Land* and *Ulysses* seem to be arcane, emotionless puzzles. Readers who get to know the texts more intimately, though, find that re-reading produces a more complicated and intense emotional and intellectual reaction. They discover that they are being drawn into a fuller, not a diminished, engagement with the text.

If we understand this alteration in the surfaces of texts by considering it in relation to the changing landscape of the real, as it became more densely populated, urban, and transient, it becomes apparent that the increasingly compressed topography of the social world was being mirrored in a denser prose literature that was more layered with meanings and references. No longer could the setting or context of a work be taken for granted or established descriptively with the expectation that it would remain stable. Literature itself came to resemble a bustling city: dynamic, initially overwhelming, and even incomprehensible, teeming with sounds and sights that it was impossible to encompass on a first encounter, or even a second or third. As Virginia Woolf wrote in her 1917 short story "The Mark on the Wall," modern urban life is a high-velocity affair, its keynotes change and variety:

> Why, if one wants to compare life to anything, one must liken it to being blown through the Tube at fifty miles an hour – landing at the other end without a single hairpin in one's hair! Shot out at the feet of God entirely naked! Tumbling head over heels in the asphodel meadows like brown paper parcels pitched down a shoot [sic] in the post office! With one's hair flying back like the tail of a racehorse. Yes, that seems to express the rapidity of life, the perpetual waste and repair; all so casual, all so haphazard. . . .[8]

Rapid velocity, haphazard intersections of thoughts, sensations, and people: these are characterizations of modern urban life. Is it possible to comprehend such a world? Who can comprehend Hong Kong, or Cairo, if to comprehend means to make come together in the mind, to embrace, to encompass? In the early twentieth century, the centers of life continued to move from the rural countryside to the "unreal cities" of Eliot's *The Waste Land*, the London of Woolf's *Mrs Dalloway*, the Dublin of Joyce's *Ulysses*. Another way to represent this city is through its apparent opposite, a barren desert or silent bog. The flip side of noise is nonsense: the fitfully comprehensible string of words coming from the Mouth in Beckett's *Not I*, or the competing toneless speeches from the urn-people in his *Play*.

Time in modernist texts developed folds and involutions; instead of being chronological or sequential, narratives began to break and flow like waves, with an alternating rhythm that was also reshaping the idea of the self from a static entity into something that was more generally unstable, although it also fluctuated regularly from the mind to the world and back again. The concept of the self as a pendulum moving between isolation and connection, thought and sensual experience, coherence and dissolution, was anticipated by Walter Pater in his famous conclusion to *The Renaissance*, when he wrote that what is real in this life "fines itself down" to what he called "this strange, perpetual weaving and unweaving of ourselves."[9] Such a movement is perceptible in Molly's diurnal weaving and unweaving of her thoughts at the end of *Ulysses*, and in the fluctuation between vision and blindness in James' *The Ambassadors*. To quote Joyce's *Finnegans Wake*, "It [the self, the world, day and night] is a sot of a swigswag, systomy dystomy, which everabody you ever anywhere at all doze. Why? Such me [search me; such is me]."[10]

To appreciate the motivations behind modernist storytelling, think of what old-fashioned stories are like, and how we typically read them. Stories used to unfold as more-or-less chronological narratives. Why, in the early twentieth century, did this structure begin to seem inadequate, or false? Vladimir in Beckett's *Waiting for Godot* begins to wonder whether stories that focus on a sequence of external events can only be told by those who are unaware, or "sleeping." He worries that such storytellers are somehow insensitive to other people's experience, and he suspects their stories are untrue to the nature of experience, asking:

> Was I sleeping, while the others suffered? Am I sleeping now? Tomorrow, when I wake, or think I do, what shall I say of today? That with Estragon my friend, at this place until fall of night, I waited for Godot? That Pozzo passed, with his carrier, and that he spoke to us? Probably. But in all that what truth will there be?[11]

Vladimir ruminates about the disturbing naïveté of the seemingly realistic, factual stories told by narrators such as himself, stories that record the actions — or the inability to act — of characters who may well be oblivious to the feelings of those around them. Such "sleeping" tellers fail to intimate the full truth of experience because their definition of an event is so impoverished; their senses are veiled, their cognition and compassion disabled. Unlike Beckett himself, they fail to register life's uneven pathos, its fun and its tedium, its servility leavened by brief hopes of heroic or compassionate action.

In Woolf's *The Waves*, after two hundred pages of impressionistic prose from the "immediate" (rather than retrospective) perspectives of six characters as they mature over time, Woolf lets Bernard try to tell the story of his life in a more traditional way to an imagined dinner guest. Bernard begins by expressing his frustration with the project of trying to explain to someone he doesn't know (or has only met once, on board a ship to Africa) the meaning of his life. He explains to his phantom listener, who is also the reader, that he has an illusion

> that something adheres for a moment, has roundness, weight, depth, is completed. This, for the moment, seems to be my life. If it were possible, I would hand it to you entire. . . . But unfortunately, what I see (this globe, full of figures) you do not see. You see me, sitting at a table opposite you, a rather heavy, elderly man, gray at the temples.[12]

Too much is lost when the author tries to present his or her life as a story; the fullness of experience is compressed into the image of the aging teller. Bernard, while imaginatively enacting the traditional conception of writing as an imaginary, one-way conversation, suggests that it would be virtually impossible for him to sum up the meaning of his life for his silent partner. Not only do the two of them lack sufficient shared experience, but Bernard's story will to some extent become inseparable from his person: his present age, his sex, his appearance.

Bernard tries to explain his frustration with the usual stories he might be expected to tell by criticizing their singularity, the way they simplify (and artificially beautify) the complex mutations of place and time. Such stories, he says, distort the internally contradictory, roiling experience of identity, connection, and sensual apprehension:

> In order to make you understand, to give you my life, I must tell you a story – and there are so many, and so many – stories of childhood, stories of school, love, marriage, death and so on; and none of them are true. Yet like children we tell each other stories, and to decorate them we make up these ridiculous, flamboyant, beautiful phrases. How tired I am of stories, how tired I am of phrases that come down beautifully with

all their feet on the ground! Also, how I distrust neat designs of life that are drawn upon half-sheets of note-paper. I begin to long for some little language such as lovers use, broken words, inarticulate words, like the shuffling of feet on the pavement. (238)

Bernard wants to capture, not a neat design retrospectively and artificially superimposed upon experiential chaos, but the flux of a more comprehensive and dynamic present. He wants to forgo his aesthetic distance by paying more attention to minor details and close-ups, what he calls "the divine specific" (249): Percival scratching his thigh, a middle-aged woman in a restaurant taking off her cloak. He asks, "what is the use of painfully elaborating these consecutive sentences when what one needs is nothing consecutive but a bark, a groan?" (251). When he contemplates the ordered ways we try to shape and contain our lives, through rituals and stories, he exclaims,

> But it is a mistake, this extreme precision, this orderly and military progress; a convenience, a lie. There is always deep below it, even when we arrive punctually at the appointed time with our white waistcoats and polite formalities, a rushing stream of broken dreams, nursery rhymes, street cries, half-finished sentences and sights – elm trees, willow trees, gardeners sweeping, women writing – that rise and sink even as we hand a lady down to dinner. (255)

As Bernard argues, conventional stories don't do justice to our periperal experience of the larger life, nor do they allow us to express the memories and linguistic nonsense that serve as the subliminal score to "ordinary" (etymologically, "ordered") ritual dramas of the present. Like consciousness itself, such stories screen out "noise" and what Freud referred to as the "day residue" that reappears in our dreams. Because our stories are – like our consciousness – selective, everything seems designed, and it is harder to hear chance harmonies amid discordances, when "Life's nonsense pierces us with strange relation."[13]

The piecemeal sights and sounds that Bernard invokes as representations of quotidian experience can also be understood philosophically, in a way that is almost mystical, to help the perceiver come to terms with the bleakness of reality. This is how T.S. Eliot explains the felt imperative to penetrate more deeply into experience in "East Coker":

> We must be still and still moving
> Into another intensity
> For a further union, a deeper communion
> Through the dark cold and the empty desolation,
> The wave cry, the wind cry, the vast waters
> Of the petrel and the porpoise.[14]

Eliot's call for a "deeper communion" through "the dark cold and the empty desolation" echoes Bernard's search for a "fin" that breaks the waste of waters in *The Waves*. In different ways, both are trying to move beyond a well-shaped narrative's efforts to find human meaning in desolation, and are instead looking to establish communion with waste and death (*fin*, or end). The old stories had come to seem narrow and self-important. In *A Room of One's Own*, Woolf describes her boredom upon reading "a new novel by Mr A" as a product of the writer's myopic preoccupation with the self:

> . . . after reading a chapter or two a shadow seemed to lie across the page. It was a straight dark bar, a shadow shaped something like the letter "I." . . . One began to be tired of "I." Not but what this "I" was a most respectable "I"; honest and logical; as hard as a nut, and polished for centuries by good teaching and good feeding. I respect and admire that "I" from the bottom of my heart. But – here I turned a page or two, looking for something or other – the worst of it is that in the shadow of the letter "I" all is as shapeless as mist. . . . There seemed to be some obstacle, some impediment of Mr A's mind which blocked the fountain of creative energy and shored it within narrow limits.[15]

Although Woolf goes on to associate the shadow of "I" falling across the page with a self-regard that makes Mr A's story repetitive and predictable, she is implicitly advocating greater humility on the part of the storyteller, suggesting that such humility may produce greater textual richness.

Eliot, too, recommends a direction that involves forsaking the ordered successes of the past and plunging back into the chaos of the unknown and unpossessed, for

> In order to arrive at what you do not know
> You must go by a way which is the way of ignorance.

In order to possess what you do not possess
You must go by the way of dispossession.
In order to arrive at what you are not
You must go through the way in which you are not.
("East Coker," III)

Eliot's advice grows out of the awareness that "the pattern is new in every moment, /And every moment is a new and shocking/Valuation of all we have been" ("East Coker," II). One of the main challenges of modernist writing in the twentieth century was to re-awaken in its audience a willingness to relinquish the self-satisfaction of easy accomplishment in favor of immersion in the flux, the seeming desolation, of what is left to know.

The most immediate – if not the most popular – way of disrupting the illusion of knowing is by darkening or obscuring the textual surface. Stylistically, such obfuscation may serve to express the elusiveness and even the horror of reality; one could argue that it symbolically forces its readers to bear witness to the unspeakable incoherences and violent nonsense of the real. Giorgio Agamben emphasizes the expressive potential of a "dark, maimed" language, associating it with a child they called Hurbinek in Auschwitz, paralyzed and speechless, who took to repeating a word that no one could understand, something like *mass-klo* or *matisklo* (37–8). Agamben positions such a sound at the very beginning of language, connecting it with the effort to bear witness to something for the first time, in a way that is indecipherable to everyone else, insisting that "language, in order to bear witness, must give way to a non-language in order to show the impossibility of bearing witness" (39; we might compare the sounds made by Wagner's Rhinemaidens at the beginning of *The Ring of the Nibelung*, sounds that are also meant to signify the origins of language). When we experience something new, we cannot yet name or convey it. In recent years this idea has been used to explain why it is difficult for disenfranchised groups to articulate their experience, but in "Burnt Norton," the first of Eliot's *Four Quartets*, the idea is expressed not from the perspective of the handicapped child or the colonized subject, but as a function of the speaker's inability to convey novelty: "Words, after speech, reach/Into the silence" (V). Words alone will not carry meaning into the place of understanding, where opposite truths can (and must) coexist. So in "East Coker," the speaker relates,

> So here I am, in the middle way, having had twenty years –
> Twenty years largely wasted, the years of *l'entre deux guerres* –
> Trying to use words, and every attempt
> Is a wholly new start, and a different kind of failure
> Because one has only learnt to get the better of words
> For the thing one no longer has to say, or the way in which
> One is no longer disposed to say it. (V)

Agamben would seem to agree, when he suggests that the complete witness is not the author or the reader, but "he who by definition cannot bear witness":

> To bear witness, it is therefore not enough to bring language to its own non-sense, to the pure undecidability of letters *(m-a-s-s-k-l-o, m-a-t-i-s-k-l-o)*. It is necessary that this senseless sound be, in turn, the voice of something or someone that, for entirely other reasons, cannot bear witness. (39)

Such humanly constructed, purposeful, if indecipherable, non-sense is not only to be found in the utterings of characters in Beckett's trilogy (*Molloy, Malone Dies, The Unnamable*), it is also in the smoky sky-writing of Woolf's *Mrs Dalloway*: "Glaxo"; "Kreemo"; "toffee,"[16] the verbal play of Gertrude Stein in *Tender Buttons* ("Eel us eel us with no no pea no pea cool, no pea cool cooler, no pea cooler with a land a land cost in, with a land cost in stretches"),[17] and it is the "language" in which Joyce's *Finnegans Wake* is composed. It represents a strenuous effort to dig beneath the language of the known that has become false and formulaic, to render that originary fire of the dumb and incapable, personified in Hurbinek, "child of death," whose eyes Levi in *Survival in Auschwitz* describes as flashing "terribly alive, full of demand, assertion, of the will to break loose, to shatter the tomb of his dumbness" (cited by Agamben 37).

Thus "meaning" may be little more than an impoverished, self-reflecting extract from a much fuller repository of possibilities. In a story Woolf drafted in 1917–18, "An Evening Party," one of the conversationalists cries, "how sad a thing is sense! How vast a renuncia-tion it represents!" (*HH* 93). In Woolf's view, sense and rationality are created by excluding sensual and imaginative apprehensions. Woolf depicts the pursuit of rational truth as academic and joyless: a pursuit of soulless perfection. An alternative to funneling a fuller experience through reason and convention is to engage instead with refuse and rubbish, thereby taking up residence in what Yeats famously referred to as "the foul rag and bone shop of the heart" ("The Circus Animals' Desertion").[18] This is what the aspiring politician Charles learns to do in Woolf's "Solid Objects": he begins to hunt and gather the "gems" that other people have discarded, even to the point of abandoning his ambi-tion and his career. When his hand touches something unexpected buried in the sand, Woolf describes him as regaining the lost simplicity of childhood: "his eyes lost their intensity, or rather the background of thought and experience which gives an inscrutable depth to the eyes of grown people disappeared, leaving only the clear transparent surface, expressing nothing but wonder, which the eyes of young children display" (*HH* 96–7). What Charles discovers by forgetting his political career in his quest to gather accidentally beautiful broken objects is the mystery and wholeness people once apprehended as children. Woolf has one of her unidentified voices explain this in "An Evening Party":

> Don't you remember in early childhood when, in play or talk, as one stepped across the puddle or reached the window on the landing, some imperceptible shock froze the universe to a solid ball of crystal which one held for a moment – I have some mystical belief that all time past and future too, the tears and powdered ashes of generations clotted to a ball; then we were absolute and entire; nothing then was excluded; that was certainty – happiness. (*HH* 92–3)

The temporary apprehension of a precious, unattainable wholeness is what much modernist literature aims to recapture, through Joyce's epiphanies – those moments of textual revelation in which the trivial and the significant exist in perfect equipoise,[19] Woolf's moments of being,[20] or the "image" of Imagist poetry: the presentation of an "intel-lectual and emotional complex in an instant of time."[21] It is what Eliot refers to in "The Dry Salvages" (the third of the *Four Quartets*) as the moment of "sudden illumination" (II). He reminds us that given the ongoing current of time, meaning is something we experience only after the fact: "We had the experience but missed the meaning, /And approach to the meaning restores the experience/In a different form, beyond any meaning/We can assign to happiness" (II). A literary approximation of comprehensiveness – experience charged with its ultimate meanings – looks and sounds like nonsense or babble to a world that shaped its perceptions through a process of exclusion, and this is indeed how most readers react to their first experience of Joyce's *Ulysses* or *Finnegans Wake* or Pound's *Cantos*. But through a shift of expectation, such works become models of a great city in space and time, or Blake's universe contained in a grain of sand, or an object contemplated by a wondering child.

Bernard in *The Waves* tries to explain how rational, narrative language falsifies experience: when we select words or sentences from the flux of language and experience, or when we privilege the separateness of a person by isolating that person from the people who shaped his or her individual development, the result is a trick, a distortion, a lie: "Whatever sentence I extract whole and entire from this cauldron is only a string of six little fish that let themselves be caught while a million others leap and sizzle, making the cauldron bubble like boiling silver, and slip through my fingers" (220). Just as the sentences he might "catch" to convey the story of his life are rendered inadequate, even false, by those he did not choose, so is his own identity wrapped up in that of his five friends, and cannot be dissociated from theirs.

> [Faces] press their beauty to the walls of my bubble – Neville, Susan, Louis, Jinny, Rhoda and a thousand others. How impossible it is to order them rightly; to detach one separately, or to give the effect of the whole – again like music. What a symphony with its concord and its discord, and its tunes on top and its complicated bass beneath, then grew up! Each played his own tune, fiddle, flute, trumpet, drum or whatever the instrument might be. (220)

In *The Waves*, Bernard concedes that one can understand the impulse to write in "the biographic style," as we can see when he provisionally constructs such an account: "About this time Bernard married and bought a house. . . . His friends observed in him a growing tendency to domesticity. . . . The birth of children made it highly desirable that he should augment his income" (222). His complaint, however, is that this style turns him into "a certain kind of man," when in truth there are "many Bernards" (223). What is lost is not only his identification with so many other people, but – more importantly – his ignobility, his human fallibility. He says, "it is not one life that I look back upon; I am not one person; I am many people; I do not altogether know who I am – Jinny, Susan, Neville, Rhoda or Louis; or how to distinguish my life from theirs" (237). He reveals himself to contain a squatting, rude primitive as well as a writer with a normal domestic life. He insists, "There is the old brute, too, the savage, the hairy man who dabbles his fingers in ropes of entrails; and gobbles and belches; whose speech is guttural, visceral – well, he is here. He squats in me" (249).

In short, traditional narrative turns its protagonists into *heroes*, softening their flaws. And not only are flaws important for representing reality, they are also, as Freud argued, far more revealing than the orderliness they disrupt. This insistence on the fact that heroism is a lie as well as a truth – the heroic action merely a fortuitous selection from a more heterogeneous soup of human qualities – also affects Joyce's way of recasting Homer's Odysseus as a compassionate, perceptive, thoughtful, forgetful man who is both an outsider in Dublin (by virtue of his half-Jewishness) and a half-willing cuckold, a man who has disappointed his father (who committed suicide) and emotionally abandoned his wife. Literature that presents its protagonists as perfectible encourages in its readers an intolerance for heterogeneous inconsistency in the self and others; in its affirmation of the attainability of the ideal, it creates an allergy to the real, denying what Eliot beautifully refers to as "The life of significant soil" ("The Dry Salvages," II).

The idea that life is a sequence may be an illusion of youth; at least, this is Eliot's proposal in "The Dry Salvages":

It seems, as one becomes older,
That the past has another pattern, and ceases to be a mere sequence –
Or even development: the latter a partial fallacy
Encouraged by superficial notions of evolution,
Which becomes, in the popular mind, a means of disowning the past.
    (II)

Eliot's suggestion that a perception of life as sequential allows us to disown the past helps to explain why it is important to question literary and poetic form, to pass beyond chronological order to something both less and more patterned, something that is as spatial as it is temporal. If we see time as a pattern as well as a sequence, the past becomes something that must be meaningfully *integrated* with present and future. This explains Eliot's insistence on the paradoxical assertion that "all time is eternally present" ("Burnt Norton," I). The past cannot be disowned without loss of self, loss of world; it is woven into the pattern of time future. If we see time as a pattern, we appreciate life's inscrutability instead of viewing it as fully determined; it draws our attention to the vital possibilities that are always – quietly or fiercely – in the present.

In Woolf's *The Waves*, after recounting the death of Percival, Bernard proposes that stories distort experience in yet another way: because they end. In a reality viewed as dynamic and whole, endings are provisional and inconclusive. Individual lives expire, but the flow of life is ongoing, everchanging. Bernard asks, as he "sits – imperfect . . . weak . . . [and] lonely,"

> Should this be the end of the story? A kind of sigh? A last ripple of the wave? A trickle of water in some gutter where, burbling, it dies away? Let me touch the table – so – and so regain my sense of the moment. A sideboard covered with cruets; a basket full of rolls; a plate of bananas – these are comfortable sights. But if there are no stories, what end can there be, or what beginning? (229)

Eliot tried to convey a similar idea through the paradoxical assertion in *Four Quartets* that "The end is where we start from" ("Little Gidding," V). Joyce, too, acted to resist the artificiality of conclusion when he referred to the growing corpus of *Finnegans Wake* as only a "work in progress," and when he constructed the book as quite literally circular (without an end). The book opens in the middle of a sentence; we don't reach the beginning of that sentence until the book's pages have run out: "A way a lone a last a loved a long the" (628.15–16). *Finnegans Wake*, then, is structured to resemble an *uroboros*, the legendary snake with its tail in its mouth, its "stories" demoted to the status of repeated motifs in the complex and dense fabric of a linguistic world, a world that presents itself as nonsense but is actually saturated with meanings.

Samuel Beckett's *Endgame* (*Fin de Partie*) dramatizes the tedium and predictability of our collective fascination with endings. Even the beginning of the play is infected by the sense of an ending; as Clov intones, "Finished, it's finished, nearly finished, it must be nearly finished. [*Pause.*] Grain upon grain, one by one, and one day, suddenly, there's a heap, a little heap, the impossible heap."[22] In the mechanical chess game of life, every day, every life, is an endgame, hailed by Hamm as that "Old endgame lost of old, play and lose and have done with losing" (82). Even in *Endgame*, though, the end contains small beginnings: the flea – which Hamm and Clov are desperate to exterminate – from which life might begin again, and the small boy whom Clov sees through the telescope. What we call ending is simply a pause in an ongoing cycle of repetitions: of days, seasons, years, behaviors, lives. As Wallace Stevens suggests by a paradox in "Sunday Morning," even the briefest occurrences don't end as long as the cycles continue: "Nothing endures/As April's green endures."[23] The brevity and cyclical regularity of human and vegetable life is what Eliot, in "Little Gidding," calls "the recurrent end of the unending" (II). In a similar spirit, Eliot's *The Waste Land* ends, not with a conclusive climax, but in a moment of delicate equipoise between the sadness of ending and the possibility of new life that individual readers resolve unconsciously, depending on their needs and temperaments. *Ulysses*, too, concludes with "the incipient intimations of proximate dawn,"[24] suspended between night and day, Molly's laughter and her tears.

At the end of the passage about the falseness of endings, Bernard in *The Waves* suggests several reasons *why* we tell stories in artificially coherent ways: for money, to excuse ourselves for erring, to place ourselves in a more favorable light, to represent the dominant culture as whole. He comments, "Life is not susceptible perhaps to the treatment we give it when we try to tell it" (267). Why else would we try to explain our experiences to a stranger who does not answer, if not to rationalize our actions, or to increase the perception of our value? (We might hope to establish a connection and to pass on our experience, but in a one-way conversation we can never know whether the effort was successful.) Bernard concedes, though, that telling our story to someone else has at least one salutary effect: it allows us to see ourselves more clearly, more objectively: under the pressure of someone else's gaze, someone who sees only what is physically before him in the present moment, a narrator begins to see things differently, regaining his "sense of the complexity and the reality and the struggle" of his or her life (294).[25] Even this one gift from a purely passive, imaginary reader or listener inspires Bernard to dismiss his shadowy audience with gratitude.

By struggling to order his or her experience, an author may, as Bernard suggests, be left with a fresher appreciation of its fullness, but what effect do such stories have on the *reader*? The danger of reading orderly narratives is that they interfere with an appreciation of what Bernard calls "the mystery of things" (252), which no one – neither author nor reader – fully understands. This mystery offers not only the wonder of ignorance, it is also the source of comedy, of the "missed understandings" celebrated as verbal misrule in such works as *Ulysses* and *Finnegans Wake* ("*Hirp! Hirp! for their Missed Understandings!*" *FW* 175.27). What Bernard seems to want the reader to experience is a sober *and* joyful affirmation of the mystery and comedy of human, urban, and global existence, a freshened awareness of the kaleidoscopic, polyphonic, and cacophonous interplay of all things. Many modernist writers concluded that traditional storytelling, in granting dignity to the narrator and coherence to his or her experience, promotes complacency, competitiveness, and pugnacity. Yeats wrote in "Meditations in Time of Civil War," "We had fed the heart on fantasies, / The heart's grown brutal from the fare; More substance in our enmities / Than in our love."

Say, then, that writing in the "narrative method" operates like a one-way conversation with a relative stranger. We have observed the narrator's frustrations with traditional stories told in the "biographical style," recounting Bernard's view that the effect of telling stories to a stranger is to cut the narrator down to size, to deflate his or her pretensions, turning him or her into an ass who can be justly laughed at by any passer-by (250). Bernard reconstructs the scenario of being "watched" by his listener:

> I catch your eye. I, who had been thinking myself so vast, a temple, a church, a whole universe, unconfined and capable of being everywhere on the verge of things and here too, am now nothing but what you see – an elderly man, rather heavy, grey above the ears. . . . That is the blow you have dealt me. I have walked bang into the pillar box. (251–2)

James Joyce's Stephen Dedalus makes a similar point in the "Scylla and Charybdis" section of *Ulysses*, when he asks, "Who helps to believe?

Egomen. Who to unbelieve? Other chap" (9.1079–80). If storytelling is salutary for the teller, helping him to believe in himself and in others, while exposing him to reactions that may puncture that belief, how do his stories affect the reader? Bernard doesn't tell us in *The Waves*; the dinner guest departs silently. Unless that silence is itself an answer: does storytelling of a more or less traditional kind *silence* the reader? Make him or her less vocal, less angry, less resistant? In the words of Yeats, again in "Meditations in Time of Civil War," when we look at a beautiful, finished, ordered work of art, whether house or poem, does such contemplation "take our greatness with our bitterness"? Are we not only soothed but also possibly placated by neatness of form or narrative, rendered more passive, less prone to construct something ourselves? Still, readers are sometimes galvanized by what they read. What kind of literature, then – as opposed to propaganda – inspires or authorizes its readers instead of sedating or cowing them, and how?

In "Mr Bennett and Mrs Brown," Woolf suggests that the old contract between author and reader emphatically needs to change, that the reader should forgo the familiar deference in favour of a new, analytically acute partnership. She chides,

> In your modesty you seem to consider that writers are different blood and bone from yourselves; . . . Never was there a more fatal mistake. It is this division between reader and writer, this humility on your part, these professional airs and graces on ours, that corrupt and emasculate the books which should be the healthy offspring of a close and equal alliance between us.[26]

The relation between writer and reader, Woolf recognizes, is a symptomatic one: the attitude of a reader toward a writer represents the more general stance of an individual toward authority, whereas the attitude of a writer toward a reader is potentially self-aggrandizing. Woolf saw that the hierarchical relation between writer and reader must evolve into a more equal partnership since, as she remarks, in this same essay, at the beginning of the twentieth century, "All human relations have shifted – those between masters and servants, husbands and wives, parents and children. And when human relations change there is at the same time a change in religion, conduct, politics, and literature" (96–7). She implies that a change in the relation between writer and reader corresponds to a greater parity between groups that have been artificially opposed and differently valued: men and women, darker and lighter races, younger and older individuals, people of varying creeds. Writing has evolved from a one-way explanation and plea into a dialogue; the conversation is virtual rather than actual, but it is nonetheless quite real.

Near the end of the modernist period, the ability of many ordinary people to "judge for [themselves] what is right" was tested and found sadly wanting, first through the capitalist excesses that led to the Great Depression of 1929, and then, even more disturbingly, when the majority of Germans failed to defy Nazi orders even when some of those orders were hideously inhumane. The idea that the Holocaust was facilitated by a widespread abdication of interpretative power was set in motion by Hannah Arendt, who argued that a concept of the *banality of evil* may come closer to pinpointing the psychological reality of what happened during the Third Reich than the more popular theory that the perpetrators were inhuman monsters.[27] Stanley Milgram supported Arendt's position with his findings in psychology and Christopher Browning followed suit with a landmark sociological study. The question of how the relationship between author and reader microcosmically illustrates larger social and political configurations is illuminated by the application of such discoveries to the reading process, which is where our habits of interpretation begin.

The Passive Reader: Milgram's Obedience Experiments

Stories told in a traditional way, from the point of view of someone with greater knowledge than the characters or the reader, implicitly subordinate both the characters and the reader to the relative omniscience of the author/narrator. Some of the pleasure of reading and listening derives from the reader's position of not-knowing, or not-yet-knowing, when it is hedged by the reassurance that someone – the storyteller – *does* know, and over time will unfold that knowledge. One troubling question, however, is whether listening to stories (or watching films or television) can also encourage passivity precisely by relieving the audience of interpretive responsibility. One role of literary criticism has always been to redress that potential imbalance, which it does not only by helping readers to be receptive to the perspectives of authors and narrators, but also by developing active responses, such as curiosity and even skeptical resistance.

Stanley Milgram's well-known and controversial obedience experiments were designed to test social conditioning – the extent to which we do what we're told by a respected authority in a reputable context regardless of our own concerns about the possible results of those actions. Milgram's results may also be illuminatingly applied to the relations between author, reader, and text. Both are concerned with the power of an authority (experimenter, teacher, author, storyteller) to neutralize an individual's personal response. The optimal relation between an individual and an "authority" maintains a delicate balance between the individual's receptivity and his or her resistance, but the highly controversial results of Milgram's experiments suggest that in practice, and contrary to expectation, most individuals will not support their own judgments through action; their acts will typically be obedient, even if this causes great discomfort and internal conflict. Something similar happens to readers: we learn that our genuine responses to what we read are somehow "wrong," and we learn to "overcode" those responses with the "correct" response, which is the one that is expected and that will be rewarded.[28] As a result, reading – especially reading literary classics – often comes to seem like a pointless and rather boring exercise that requires us not to challenge and rethink our perspectives, but to disqualify our actual responses in favor of more "reputable" ones.

Let us look more closely at Milgram's obedience experiments in order to explore how, psychologically, this might happen without our realizing it. In Milgram's laboratory, the experimenter is loosely in the role of the author or narrator, and the "subject" of the experiment – the person whose responses are actually being tested – generally corresponds to the reader. The "text," in both cases, consists of whatever the subject/reader is trying to interpret and respond to: in the case of Milgram's experiments, it is a paid actor in the next room who is supposed to be receiving shocks after every wrong answer. In the laboratory as in many classrooms, the subject is told that she is evaluating the learner, whereas in reality the "text" is being used to interpret her.

Milgram set out to investigate obedience as "the psychological mechanism that links individual action to political purpose."[29] He wanted to isolate the point at which obedience to authority turns into principled disobedience, and to do this he set up a series of experiments around the idea of correcting another's error: subjects thought they were administering a series of shocks to someone trying to learn to memorize word pairs.[30] The subjects were told that the experiment measured the effects of punishment on learning, and they believed that the "learner" was a volunteer like themselves who just happened to draw that role in a lottery, whereas the learner was actually a professional actor and the "lottery" was rigged. The subject "managers" were told to administer shocks of increasing intensity whenever the learner made a wrong answer. What Milgram discovered, much to his surprise, was that "almost two-thirds of the participants fell into the category of 'obedient' subjects," an unexpectedly large percentage (5). Despite the fact that the subjects were drawn from a broad spectrum of working, managerial, and professional classes, "a substantial proportion continue[d] to the last shock on the generator," despite stress, protests, screams, even sudden silence (5).

One of the most disturbing aspects of Milgram's analysis is his account of how his subjects interpreted their actions, an interpretation that he believes is socially conditioned (unconsciously learned by living in a particular society). Most subjects were less concerned about the effects of their actions on the other person than on the assessment of their own performance, whether it was "good" or "bad." Milgram describes the typical subject as someone who does not "respond with a moral sentiment to the actions he performs. Rather, his moral concern now shifts to a consideration of how well he is living up to the expectations that the authority has of him" (8). In other words, in a situation structured by a believable, external authority, ordinary people, without realizing it, gave up their capacity for moral judgment and even their personal responsibility for their actions, evaluating their own performance only in terms of how well they obeyed. They allowed the meaning of their act to be determined by its context, while neglecting its human consequences (9). Although many subjects experienced conflict while obeying orders, they failed to realize "that subjective feelings are largely irrelevant to the moral issue at hand so long as they are not transformed into action. Political control is effected through action" (10). The level of obedience to authority was not significantly different for men and women, either; although women felt more conflict, their actions were as obedient as those of the men (63). Milgram was able to conclude, therefore, that "the problem of obedience . . . is not wholly psychological. The form and shape of society and the way it is developing have much to do with it" (11).

This is also true of reading: learning to read, or interpret, is not only an important means of intellectual and emotional development, it is also a social process. How we are taught to reflect on what we read or understand therefore has significant social implications.[31] To understand the role of obedience in reading, remember the useful social function it serves: societies inculcate obedience in order to ensure the efficiency and coherence of a system. Efficiency in a social system depends upon the suppression of local control, as is apparent if we think about a situation in which it is not desirable to encourage too much autonomy in the participants, such as a committee meeting. When individuals in the meeting are encouraged to express divergent opinions, it becomes much more difficult to obtain a result. The connection between obedience and efficiency is apparent even in the English language, for example in the connection between the two meanings of the verb "order," a word that means to command, but also to create order; by implication, the two are equivalent. As Milgram explains, "Hierarchical structures can function only if they possess the quality of coherence, and coherence can be attained only by the suppression of control at the local level" (121; we will return to the issue of what it means to suppress local control in the discussion of Joyce's *Dubliners* in Chapter 2).

Reading, too, serves an important function in society: popular books – along with their offspring, film and television – serve as a powerful means of socializing individuals early in their development. Arguably, one of the most important functions of books is to suppress local control by altering the reader's attitude. Books may do what authorities do, by taking an individual who is in an autonomous state (such as a child, a notoriously autonomous being) and inducting him or her into what Milgram clumsily calls an agentic state, in which "the person sees himself as an agent for carrying out another person's wishes" (in this case, the author's; 133). Books thus subtly support the need of parents and schools to limit a child's autonomy and promote social growth by teaching him or her to listen; this is an important function at the time, because obedience is a crucial safeguard for a child, whose judgment is severely limited by inexperience. However, Milgram's investigation probed the extent to which obedience may have become a frighteningly indiscriminate social habit in adults as well, and it raised provocative questions about how well people distinguish between different kinds of authority and how attentive they are to the effects of their actions.[32]

It is helpful to remember that both in the family and in school, an individual learns through rewards and punishments that "deference is the only appropriate and comfortable response to authority" (137). When the individual complies with authority, he or she is moved up a notch in the social hierarchy, "thus both motivating the person and perpetuating the structure simultaneously. This form of reward, 'the promotion,' carries with it profound emotional gratification for the individual but its special feature is the fact that it ensures the continuity of the hierarchical form" (138). This is what Oscar Wilde is talking about in his deliberately outrageous critiques of authority in essays such as "The Soul of Man Under Socialism"; he argues that it is immoral for individuals to be kind to the poor, for example, because it placates them and makes them less resistant to an unjust system. Wilde asserts that the poor are "ungrateful, discontented, disobedient, and rebellious. They are quite right to be so. . . . Disobedience, in the eyes of any one who has read history, is man's original virtue."[33] He continues, "The proper aim [is not to behave altruistically, but] to try and reconstruct society on such a basis that poverty will be impossible" (1079). Every time we are rewarded we become less capable of doing that, more complicit with the system that strokes us.

Rewards, as Milgram argues, result in

the *internalization of the social order* – that is, internalizing the set of axioms by which social life is conducted. And the chief axiom is: do what the man in charge says. Just as we internalize grammatical rules, and can thus both understand and produce new sentences, so we internalize axiomatic rules of social life which enable us to fulfill social requirements in novel situations. (138)

Finally, Milgram stresses that "It is the appearance of authority and not actual authority to which the subject responds" (140). What this means for literature is that most well-socialized readers will respond to the status of the author more strongly than to the content of the book, which is why Wilde begs his readers not to degrade books to the authoritative category of classics, since readers will then defer to them instead of engaging personally and honestly with the issues they raise (1092).

Social systems are most effective when they give citizens "a sense of voluntary entry into its various institutions," because if the illusion of voluntary participation has not been created, obedience will stop when there is no external authority to enforce it. (When the teacher leaves the room, the spitballs start flying.) "In the case of *voluntary* obedience to a legitimate authority, the principal sanctions for disobedience come from *within* the person. They are not dependent upon coercion, but stem from the individual's sense of commitment to his role. In this sense, *there is an internalized basis for his obedience, not merely an external one*" (141; Milgram here anticipates Foucault's argument in *Discipline and Punish*, discussed later in this chapter). Inculcating an internalized basis for obedience – the illusion of voluntary participation in what is perceived as a legitimate social power structure – is one important function of education. Voting in democratic societies could be seen as promoting the same illusion, turning people into agents, while giving them the impression that their individual opinion makes a difference. This is why, as Wilde says, "To live is the rarest thing in the world" (1084). We are taught simply to exist, and this is primarily accomplished by teaching individuals *not to take responsibility for their own interpretations or actions*, but to rely instead upon the interpretations of an authority in expectation of some reward.

Such an analysis has vital connections with existentialist philosophy, especially Jean-Paul Sartre's insistence upon the importance of individual choice, although the version presented here does not echo the existentialist's sense that the unknowability of the universe results in bleakness. Individual action, in Milgram's view, takes place not in an existential vacuum, but as part of an elaborate social machinery that virtually perpetuates itself. As Milgram comments,

> Control the manner in which a man interprets his world, and you have gone a long way toward controlling his behavior. . . . *There is a propensity for people to accept definitions of action provided by legitimate authority.* That

is, although the subject performs the action, he allows authority to define its meaning. (145)

We learn to abdicate responsibility *by not generating our own interpretations or attempting to understand their long-range consequences.* When we act in a disobedient or thoughtfully resistant way, we may experience a subconscious sense of having been faithless, as if we deserted a cause to which we voluntarily pledged support (164). Beckett dramatizes the absurd sense of fulfillment generated by mindless obedience in *Waiting for Godot*, when the tramps explain with satisfaction that although they are "bored to death," they have at least kept their side of the bargain: they waited, which also means they faithfully served something or someone. Didi proclaims, "We are not saints, but we have kept our appointment. How many people can boast as much?" and Gogo replies, "Billions" (51).

Interestingly, when we abdicate responsibility, we also lose the capacity to respond (we can hear this connection in the word "responsibility" if we think of it as "response ability"). That is why individuals who assume the role of agent become more obedient, but also more joyless, less vital. Because Wilde was fighting the loss of social responsibility along with the capacity to respond, he juggled two seemingly different roles that actually reinforced one another: he was a social critic but also an aesthete, advocating political reform while celebrating pleasure and the importance of being responsive to beauty. Being responsive is crucially connected to being responsible, although most people tend to assume that the reverse is true (that people who love art are somehow disconnected from social or political realities). Furthermore, the link between abdicating responsibility and losing one's response-ability explains why obedient readers gradually stop feeling the pleasure of discovery; learning becomes a mechanical task to be done well or poorly. When learning is regarded as a task, readers often feel compelled to resist anything new, regarding novelty or originality as an unwelcome distraction or even frustration because it interferes with the efficiency of that task.

If, as Wilde says in "The Soul of Man Under Socialism," the option of disobeying is the "original virtue," Milgram helps to explain why.[34] He gave several of his subjects a test after the experiment, asking them how much each of them felt "responsible for the fact that this person was given electric shocks against his will," and he found that the answers were significantly different for obedient and disobedient subjects. The subjects who found the strength to disobey believed themselves to be *more* responsible than the experimenter for the suffering of the learner and they saw the victim himself as *less* responsible (they didn't think of him as deserving punishment). Obedient subjects, in contrast, blamed the experimenter and the learner more or less equally, and they themselves took less responsibility for the consequences of their acts (204).[35]

In Milgram's view, our successful and seemingly voluntary induction into the social system may result in an abandonment of our shared humanity as we merge our individual personality into larger institutional structures; one of the dangers of this is that, for the most part, we do not realize that we are doing it (188). What we think we are doing is being loyal, disciplined, and self-sacrificing; according to Milgram, these desirable and valuable traits are also "the very properties that create destructive organizational engines of war and bind men to malevolent systems of authority" (188). He argues that

> the kind of character produced in American democratic society . . . cannot be counted on to insulate its citizens from brutality and inhuman treatment at the direction of malevolent authority. A substantial proportion of people do what they are told to do, irrespective of the content of the act and without limitations of conscience, so long as they perceive that the command comes from a legitimate authority. (189)

He cites Harold J. Laski's article on "The Dangers of Obedience," in which Laski pleads,

> Our business, if we desire to live a life not utterly devoid of meaning and significance, is to accept nothing which contradicts our basic experience merely because it comes to us from tradition or convention or authority. It may well be that we shall be wrong; but our self-expression is thwarted at the root unless the certainties we are asked to accept coincide with the certainties we experience. (cited by Milgram 189)

Wilde was essentially making the same plea when he advocated the exercise of Individualism in "The Soul of Man Under Socialism," writing that "Individualism[36] is a disturbing and disintegrating force. Therein lies its immense value. For what it seeks to disturb is monotony of type, slavery of custom, tyranny of habit, and the reduction of man to the level of a machine" (1091). Wilde sees society as working in tandem with more popular forms of art to enslave the individual by relieving him or her of interpretive and aesthetic autonomy, and his aim is to free art so that it may counter these mechanical social forces.

What, then, do we want from an ethical subject, or from a thoughtful, receptive yet potentially resistant reader? A model could be adapted from the response of one of the individual subjects Milgram described, whom he called Gretchen Brandt, who began compliantly but became defiant when she believed the shocks had become dangerous:

> The woman is firm and resolute throughout. She indicates in the interview that she was in no way tense or nervous, and this corresponds to her controlled appearance throughout. She feels that the last shock she administered to the learner was extremely painful and reiterates that "she did not want to be responsible for any harm to him . . ." The woman's straightforward, courteous behavior in the experiment, lack of tension, and total control of her own action seems to make disobedience a simple and rational deed. . . . Ironically, Gretchen Brandt grew to adolescence in Hitler's Germany and was for the great part of her youth exposed to Nazi propaganda. When asked about the possible influence of her background, she remarks slowly, "Perhaps we have seen too much pain." (85)

Milgram's description of his ideal subject in several respects applies to the ideal reader, the ideal teacher, or the ideal student. For someone in any of these roles, the challenge is to preserve the ability to respond, which in turn inculcates, signifies, or constitutes a "responsibility" to one's interlocutor that over time extends to other social relationships. What I am suggesting is that we are subtly taught to relinquish responsibility when as readers we learn to privilege an author's (or a teacher's or critic's) view over our own, instead of holding the two views in suspension and forging meaningful connections between them.

Ordinary Men

The link between responsibility and the ability to respond is chillingly illustrated in Christopher Browning's account of how a group of "ordinary men" from a German police battalion were taught to override their own values in order to massacre Jewish families in Poland between 1941 and 1943. In *Ordinary Men: Reserve Police Battalion 101 and the Final Solution in Poland,* Browning argues that the records of this police battalion's activities powerfully support Milgram's findings, as well as complicating those findings in illuminating ways.[37] Browning, too, is interested in the question of how men understood the issue of individual choice when they complied with commands to shoot an estimated total of 38,000 defenseless Jewish men, women, children, and even infants, sometimes at close range. He paints a vivid picture of their 53-year-old commander, Major Wilhelm Trapp, weeping when he gave the order for his battalion to massacre 1,500 Jews at Józefów in July of 1942, and offering any men who did not feel able to participate the option of reassignment (interestingly, Major Trapp was one of only two members of the battalion to be executed after the war, in 1948; 57, 144). The shootings at Józefów were particularly demanding for the perpetrators, who, unhabituated to murder, faced their unarmed victims, marched with them, shot them in the neck as they lay on their faces in the forest, and were sometimes spattered with their remains (64). The men returned "depressed, angered, embittered, and shaken" to consume the generous quantities of alcohol that had been provided for them to help them cope (69).[38]

What is most remarkable about the response of these older German policemen at Józefów is that despite the fact that they had been explicitly offered a choice by their commander about whether they wished to proceed, most of those who were later interrogated denied having had any choice about whether to participate, and they defended themselves for not having challenged the assignment: "Faced with the testimony of others, many did not contest that Trapp had made the offer but claimed that they had not heard that part of the speech or could not remember it" (72). Browning lists some of the rationalizations they offered, which ranged from fatalism (that the Jews would be killed whatever they themselves decided) to one man's astonishing testimony that he was "saving" children by shooting them, since their mothers (who were necessary to their survival) were also being shot. The men who quit shooting cited their main reason for desisting as "sheer physical revulsion"; they "did not express any ethical or political principles behind this revulsion" (72–4).

The issue of whether the policemen exercised free will when carrying out (inhumane) orders from their superiors received a slightly different twist one month after the Józefów massacre, when the officers were informed that the "entire Jewish population [of Łomazy, numbering 1,700] was to be shot" (79–80) by drunken Hiwis (*Hilfswillige*, or Ukrainian, Latvian, and Lithuanian anti-Communist and anti-Semitic "volunteers" recruited from POW camps; 52). Under the leadership of the sadistic and increasingly drunken Lieutenant Gnade, the police were ordered to round up and guard the Jews, but they themselves didn't actually have to shoot until later, when the Hiwis became too drunk to continue. The policemen involved felt less responsible, for many reasons: they weren't the actual executioners, at least for most of the massacre; the killing process was more depersonalized (they weren't paired with their victims and the rotations were more rapid); and the men were more habituated to the horror of what they were doing (85). Browning argues that the men also

> did not bear the "burden of choice" that Trapp had offered them so starkly on the occasion of the first massacre. No chance to step out was given to those who did not feel up to shooting; no one systematically excused those who were visibly too shaken to continue. Everyone assigned to the firing squads took his turn as ordered. Therefore, those who shot did not have to live with the clear awareness that what they had done had been avoidable. (86)

What Browning underscores here is what happens when someone – here Trapp – makes explicit what is usually implicit: that action is governed by choice. By openly giving the men the choice that they always had, and diminishing the consequences for exercising it, Trapp interfered with the automatic deference to authority that helps individuals rationalize obedient and conformist behavior. Lieutenant Gnade, in contrast to Trapp, did not respond to the horror and pathos of the situation (however ineffectually and sentimentally Trapp reacted, his response was nonetheless visible). Unexpectedly, Gnade's zest for cruelty seems to have allowed the men to disavow responsibility more easily.

As Browning emphasizes, then, the men's denial that they had a choice about whether or not to kill at Łomazy does not mean they actually lacked one. What it did mean was that they had to make an effort if they chose to avoid killing, and "following orders reinforced the natural tendency to conform to the behavior of one's comrades" (87), which in turn made the choice of obeying easier to bear. At Józefów the men had been aware of making a personal decision and of paying a "cost" for not shooting, which was to separate themselves from the group and to have themselves viewed as "weak" (87). Later, in December 1942, when men from the battalion were ordered to "hunt" down Jews after the ghettos had been "cleared," once again the killing took place face to face. This search, or *Judenjagd*, was far from passive, in that the "hunters" tracked down and killed their quarries like animals; therefore it was inescapably evident that "each individual policeman once again had a considerable degree of choice" (127) about whether or not to participate. However, Browning reports that "Only a minority of nonconformists managed to preserve a beleaguered sphere of moral autonomy that emboldened them to employ patterns of behavior and stratagems of evasion that kept them from becoming killers at all" (127).

In his final chapter on "Ordinary Men," Browning presents the extraordinary implications of his research on Police Battalion 101, which he relates not only to the results of Milgram's obedience experiments, but also to Philip Zimbardo's Stanford prison experiments (cited 167–8), Theodor Adorno's theories of the authoritarian personality (cited 165–6), and the tension always present in Holocaust studies between a demonization of the perpetrators as monstrous versus an insistence on seeing both perpetrators and resisters as occupying what Primo Levi called "the grey zone" of moral ambiguity, inner conflict, and compromise (cited 186–9).

Browning's application of his own findings to those of Milgram complicates Milgram's analysis in ways that help us understand what is at stake in other non-coercive processes governed by an authority or author, such as reading literature. Browning asks,

> Was the massacre at Józefów a kind of radical Milgram experiment that took place in a Polish forest with real killers and victims rather than in a social psychology laboratory with naïve subjects and actor/victims? Are the actions of Reserve Police Battalion 101 explained by Milgram's observations and conclusions? (173–4)

His answer, although qualified, affirms that "many of Milgram's insights find graphic confirmation in the behavior and testimony of the men of

Reserve Police Battalion 101" (174). The authority system at Józefów was more complex and internally inconsistent than in most of Milgram's experiments, since Trapp was a weeping commander sending a double message: that the men could choose whether or not to kill. Because of Trapp's conflict, the men's actions may be more a result of conformity than a response to authority, although one should remember that authority and conformity are mutually reinforcing (175). The events at Józefów also support Milgram's conclusion that direct proximity to the results of one's actions (here the dead bodies) reduces compliance by making it more difficult for perpetrators to deny responsibility (176). The Nazis learned that, and it was one of the reasons why extermination camps were devised to replace mass shootings. Indoctrination was also used to distance perpetrators from their victims: "constant," "pervasive," and "relentless" "denigration of Jews and . . . proclamation of Germanic racial superiority" (182). Browning concludes that these men were not monstrous but typical, in a way that aligns him with such thinkers as Hannah Arendt and Zygmunt Bauman, and, more subtly, with Simon Wiesenthal, but against Theodor Adorno and Daniel Goldhagen.[39] He warns that we are all susceptible to the kinds of pressures that the German men in Police Battalion 101 faced from 1941 to 1943: "Within virtually every social collective, the peer group exerts tremendous pressures on behavior and sets moral norms. If the men of Reserve Police Battalion 101 could become killers under such circumstances, what group of men cannot?" (189).

It is vital to come to grips with the question of whether the rank-and-file perpetrators of Nazi war crimes were monstrous or typical, because if they are typical, the danger of a repetition (of the sort evidenced by the more recent massacres in Cambodia, Bosnia and Herzegovina, and Rwanda) remains an ongoing problem. The problem becomes *ours*, as we contemplate a collective responsibility for larger social formations we (habitually) participate in and support. The major irony of treating Nazi perpetrators as inhuman "monsters" is that it repeats the attitude of the Nazis toward the Jews, on a different scale. When, in *The Sunflower*, the dying Nazi confesses his part in the Jewish genocide to the young inmate Simon Wiesenthal, he says that his platoon leader justified himself by insisting on the difference of the Jews: "And when you shoot one of them it is not the same thing as shooting one of us – it doesn't matter whether it is a man, woman, or child" (49).[40] Wiesenthal confesses that his fellow inmates in the camp tended to think the same way about the Nazis, viewing them as "all alike" (80).[41] But in one of the responses to Wiesenthal's narrative, Robert Coles writes that he would not "(foolishly, outrageously) . . . compare any of us ordinary 'sinners' to the Nazi monsters, the leaders or their minions" (127). What if such comparisons are not outrageous, but a crucial safeguard for the health of the individual conscience? If we regard Nazis or their minions as "monsters," are we denying *their* humanity, and if so, what are the larger implications of such a move?

Quite obviously, reading passively is quite different from actively committing murder, in part because the results of the two activities are dramatically different (no harm is directly inflicted on another human being through the act of reading a work of literature in an obedient or vicarious way).[42] However, if we agree with Browning that the actions of the men in Police Battalion 101 were the extraordinary and extreme results of ordinary or normal social behaviors, then it may well be important to look more closely at the way these social behaviors are inculcated and reinforced through education, and, more specifically, through the *way* we learn to decode and interpret meaning, and how we respond to the activity of narrators. The formal characteristics of the books we read are also significant: to the extent that a book "defines" and "gives meaning and coherence" to the social situation it describes, it may be said that its very form conditions its readers to defer to its authority (see Browning 176, Milgram 142). The more a narrator inclines to omniscience and indulges in editorializing on the action, the more passive a reader is inclined to become. This is why fragmented experimental modernist texts, even when their authors profess conservative values, often have a paradoxically liberating effect on their most conscientious readers: works like *The Waste Land*, *Ulysses*, *The Waves*, the *Cantos*, Beckett's trilogy, and *The Sound and the Fury* seem to refuse any dominant meaning or coherence, choosing instead to multiply the frames of reference available. (In a contrast that is more apparent than real, Beckett's plays achieve a comparable effect by starkly limiting the frame of reference.)

To the extent that reading promotes emotional identification with people of different backgrounds, it may interrupt the distancing mechanisms that are necessary in order to obey authority. Moreover, such partial imaginative identification with several different groups disrupts or complicates tribal identification with a single group, thereby lessening its destructive potential. The power of identification was apparent at Józefów when men pleaded to be excused from shooting women and children because they themselves were fathers (although the identification wasn't strong enough to inspire the men to rebel against or subvert the massacre). Literature can make people who have no children identify with parents, encouraging people who are not Jewish or Muslim or Christian to see through the eyes of someone who is.

One of the most vital lessons to be learned from the National Socialism movement is how strong the power of imaginative identification can be. Identification (with an Aryan and specifically Germanic lineage) worked very effectively in Nazi Germany to create a mass movement out of a party that never won a majority of votes. The problem was that the identification was, in a sense, tribal, which made it all the more ironic that it sought to exterminate other groups that had not fully assimilated for various complex reasons, including the Jews and the Gypsies. Looked at another way, the vicious prejudice against Jews was utterly consistent with the tendency to categorize by "groups." This is why Browning's emphasis on the importance of conformity is so important; he suggests that for the men in Police Battalion 101, their solidarity with one another in a fraught situation far outweighed their identification with their victims. The greatest moral challenge for a heterogeneous global society, then, would be to promote a perfect equipoise between identification and difference. The "best" books, in the sense of the books that best meet such a need, would be those that most finely balance accessibility and challenge, familiarity and strangeness.

Systems of "Correction"

As both Milgram and Browning have argued, the problem of choice – choosing an ethical course of action based not on what we are told but on our own responses to a situation or "text," responses for which we are responsible – is complicated by the fact that we make choices within the context of a social system that works to maximize efficiency by disguising the option of individual choice. (As Estragon asks in Beckett's *Waiting for Godot*, "We've lost our rights?" Vladimir answers shortly, "We got rid of them," 13.) Drawing attention to the fact that we have choices sometimes only intensifies the conflict that individuals feel between obeying authority and conforming to the group, on the one hand, and analyzing the situation independently and acting in accordance with their own values, on the other. Moreover, the subordination of the individual to the social system is ensured in another way: by subjecting him or her to systematic evaluation, which is enforced by rewards and punishments. The potential waywardness of individual choice is further discouraged by the fear of negative evaluation and a punitive or shaming "correction," which codes individual actions as "right" (reinforcing the system and supporting its efficiency) or "wrong" (undermining the system or disrupting its efficiency). The evaluative, punitive aspect of the social system is enacted most clearly in prisons, or "houses of correction."

In the prison experiments he performed at Stanford (a deliberate extension of Milgram's work), Philip Zimbardo clarified the aspect of Milgram's project that some critics dismissed as "theatrical": its concern with role-playing.[43] Zimbardo's experiments analyze the truth that inheres in the social roles we agree to play: a truth that is social rather than individual, since social functioning depends upon the distribution of roles. As Zygmunt Bauman insightfully suggests, Zimbardo eliminated what is perhaps the most contrived aspect of Milgram's experimental structure: the monolithic, external authority that seemed to sanction whatever might happen in the laboratory: the "universally revered institution (science), embodied in the person of the experimenter." In contrast, "All authority which ultimately operated in Zimbardo's experimental context was generated by the subjects themselves."[44] Zimbardo simply assigned roles to the subjects, dividing them into two polarized groups (prisoners and guards). Like Milgram, he gave one group the power to "correct" the other in the context of a simulated "house of correction," which is how Zimbardo's findings can be applied to less physical, more verbal symbolic prerogatives of "correcting" others.

Zimbardo's experiment reinforces the view that societal options are pre-scripted, that a culture works like an ongoing theater, offering a (limited) range of roles that most subjects unconsciously understand and are able to play on short notice. Moreover, a particularly powerful theme for the role-playing is "correction" and the punishment that accompanies it. Such a view would explain Bauman's concern over "the easiness with which most people slip into the role requiring cruelty or at least moral blindness – if only the role has been duly fortified and legitimized by superior authority" (168); people who play such roles do so in a familiar social context where there is always a right side and a wrong side (see Joyce's sharp-witted emendation of this in *Finnegans Wake* when he says, "There are two signs to turn to, . . . the wright side and the wronged side," 597.10–11). The readiness with which people will assume the tyrant's role is matched only by their willingness to accept the part of helpless victim; this, too, is a familiar role that subjects will play with distressing avidity if it is assigned to them. Zimbardo's experiment is startling because the participants came to *believe* in the reality of the theatrical situation so quickly and so completely. As the experimenters concluded, "the depressed affect of the prisoners, the guards' willing-ness to work overtime for no additional pay, the spontaneous use of prison titles and I.D. numbers in non-role-related situations all point to a level of reality as real as any other in the lives of all those who shared this experiment."[45]

Zimbardo and his colleagues created a "mock" prison, a functional, limited approximation of a prison that prohibited severe physical punish-ment, sexual abuse, and racist practices. They chose twenty-one male college subjects who were "normal" or "average," "without a history of crime, emotional disability, physical handicap, or intellectual or social disadvantage" (54), and they randomly assigned them to two groups, prisoners and guards, issued uniforms to both (khaki shirts and trousers, reflecting sunglasses, whistle and nightstick for the guards, and for the inmates muslin smocks with an ID number on the front and back, a cap, rubber sandals, and a light chain and lock for one ankle; 58). In three barred cells constructed in a basement at Stanford, three subjects were imprisoned around the clock (the "guard" subjects, in contrast, worked on three-man, eight-hour shifts and were allowed to go home when off-duty; 56). Prisoners were referred to only by their number, and were "counted" three times a day at roll-calls. They were also initially granted privileges: three meals a day, three supervised toilet visits, two hours a day for reading or letter-writing, a few visiting and exercise periods, and movie rights (59). The experiment had to be prematurely terminated after six days, since five prisoners "had to be released because of extreme emotional depression, crying, rage, and acute anxiety" (60). Both guards and prisoners became increasingly negative as the study progressed, and the encounters between guards and prisoners were characteristically "negative, affrontive and dehumanizing" (60). Both groups became more deprecating of themselves and others as they internalized the deprivation of their environment, and the aggression of the guards escalated daily, even after "prisoner deterioration became marked and visible and emotional breakdowns began to occur in the presence of the guards" (62). Eerily, the artificial situation became vividly real in a very short time. The guards later explained their extreme behavior by saying they were simply "playing a role," thereby abdicating responsibility, when according to Zimbardo the roles had become "as real as any other" (63). The prisoners also changed in accordance with their roles: after experiencing stages of disbelief, rebellion, and attempts to work within the system, they became passive, dependent, lacking in affect, disloyal to the other prisoners, physically ill, or excessively obedient. Believing in one's role, even in make-believe, was enough to make it "real."[46]

Foucault's Prison

Milgram, Browning, and Zimbardo all illustrate the power of role-playing to create a social reality for which the "actor" feels little responsibility because the "play" itself is so familiar: it is a social morality play in which right is clearly divided from wrong, good from bad, and error must be punished. According to this plot, humanity readily splits into two opposed sides, and the losing side will be contained, suppressed, or eliminated. In *Discipline and Punish: The Birth of the Prison*, Michel Foucault offers the historical hypothesis that during the eighteenth century, this social "theater" grew in sophistication and eventually became internalized. He vividly illustrates an important modern change in disciplinary practices by contrasting a public spectacle in 1757, in which the criminal is gruesomely drawn and quartered, to Jeremy Bentham's model of the panopticon, in which prisoners are simply enclosed in a defined space and are subject to constant surveillance.[47] Foucault uses the difference between these two modes of reprisal to argue that social concern has shifted from punishing an *action* (for which the body is tortured) to punishing a perpetrator's entire being (through unremitting vigilance and a judgment of his soul, his inherent worth). He asserts that we have created a "micro-physics of power" that reinstates the old hierarchies of right and wrong, mighty and weak, more insidiously within the consciousness of individuals (26). The modern prison, he suggests, is nothing less than the noumenal human soul, which relentlessly objectifies, categorizes, subjugates, or even disqualifies what it knows (30, 223).

If, as Foucault suggests, the older political hierarchies have become microcosmic and internal, moving inside each individual in the form of a constant critical surveillance of the body by the mind, this internalization and this naturalization of the mechanisms of dominance and exploitation explain the contradiction between our *perception* that a given society is democratic and free and our *experience* of it as arbitrary and unjust. Such a "capillary functioning of power" extends regulation "into even the smallest details of everyday life" (198). As specialists who seek to "know" and thereby control as much as possible, we are deeply complicit in the oppressions and injustices of our social order: "it is not that the beautiful totality of the individual is amputated, repressed, altered by our social order, it is rather that the individual is carefully fabricated in it" (217). We are indeed cogs in a social machine (202), but the machine's function is not to promote the growth and change of individuals, but to ensure the perpetuation and extension of the existing system; by practicing our respective disciplines, we are ourselves effectively disciplined.

Foucault's vivid metaphor for what has happened to the social system and to the experience of individuals within it is Bentham's panopticon, a prison structure with a surveillance tower in the middle surrounded by a circular building of cells. The tower allows one surveyor to observe many people without being seen in turn (200). Instead of a multitude of people watching a single punishment, as in the old public spectacle used to deter people from committing crimes, we now have a single unseen presence keeping an eye on the multitude. As Foucault puts it, "Our society is not one of spectacle, but of surveillance" (217). He stresses the importance of the fact that the external power "tends to the non-corporeal"; it is imagined as that which cannot be objectified: the godlike power of surveillance itself. This force is conceived as "a faceless gaze that transform[s] the whole social body into a field of perception" (214). It is relatively easy, then, to see how this invisible, all-seeing social and psychological power might be related to the elevated invisible privilege exercised by the writer, and vicariously assumed by the reader in the most internalized and private "discipline" of all, the discipline of reading.

What the model of the panopticon doesn't show, however, is how the social system allows each of us to imagine ourselves in the tower, while actually being in a cell. To put it another way, all citizens have a subliminal sense of being watched that is masked by our identification with the superior and invisible presence in the tower: the creator, whether author, leader, or god. The brilliance of the system is to allow each member to feel powerful through the mastery of some discipline, even while unobtrusively disciplining every participant and subjecting him or her to the surveillance of the system. This would explain why individuals are so sensitive to evaluation; everyone in the system has a subconscious awareness of being watched and evaluated, which inculcates a desire to be rewarded and a fear of being punished.

The process of reading and writing also serves as a micro-example of our participation in a larger social system. When we read, we vicariously experience the writer's panoptic superiority to a host of characters, subjecting all to our evaluations and analyses. This is the superiority Joyce objects to when he refuses to use quotation marks to frame a character's reported speech, when he calls inverted commas "perverted commas." When we assume such an elevated position, it blinds us to the complementary reality that we are ourselves constantly subject to the gaze and evaluations of others; it allows us to experience the illusion that we are exercising godlike autonomy and interpretive power, when in fact we are constantly being monitored and regulated. When audiences walked out in protest against early productions of Samuel Beckett's *Waiting for Godot* (1952), their disgust was arguably a reaction to having been denied some "higher" or more comprehensive perspective on the play's minimalism; an audience member knows no more than the characters, and therefore the illusion of superior understanding or power has been punctured. Unsurprisingly, then, when the play was performed for 1,400 convicts at San Quentin prison in November 1957, their reaction was totally different from that of presumably more sophisticated and "free" audiences: they reported not only comprehension but also enthusiastic appreciation of Beckett's portrayal of how the expectation of being visited by a "higher meaning" that promises redemption is repeatedly and indefinitely prolonged.[48]

Modernist writers sought to forgo the position of the godlike writer in the tower, asking the reader to do the same. Stephen Dedalus literally leaves the tower where he has been staying at the beginning of *Ulysses*, Eliot pictures the "Falling towers" of Jerusalem, Athens, Alexandria, Vienna and London (*The Waste Land*), and Yeats invites the honey-bees to build in the "loosening masonry" of the wall of *his* tower, which he uses as a symbol of his own crumbling power ("Meditations in Time of Civil War," VI). In Woolf's *To the Lighthouse*, the tower's purpose is not to survey the populace, but to warn ships away from the rocks that could destroy them. The eye of the lighthouse does not see; instead, it is designed to be seen, and to be heeded. In one sense, it "sees" mechanically, with a beautiful but unseeing eye that opens in darkness to shine light through it: "The Lighthouse was then a silvery, misty-looking tower with a yellow eye that opened suddenly and softly in the evening." It was a "stark and straight" tower, "barred with black and white," implacable as death or imprisonment, but "nothing was simply one thing. . . . The other was the Lighthouse too."[49]

On the one hand, many modernist writers were discarding the fiction of an omniscient narrator (the surveyor in the tower), letting characters and even objects "speak" more and more puzzlingly for themselves. On the other hand, during the Third Reich, the system of social "correction" reasserted itself with a vengeance, becoming a real, chillingly bureaucratic and efficient system of classification and extermination in which large numbers of people were punished, tortured, and killed not for what they'd done but for who they were. In one of these camps, a survivor – Primo Levi – records his struggle to communicate more immediately and urgently to a fellow inmate through literature, attempting to find an alternative to his nightmare of the "unlistened-to story." Although Levi's memoir takes the form of a conventional story, that story records an agonized awareness of the limitations of storytelling together with an understanding that listening, too, follows a formula: stories are designed to contain horror, not to make readers confront and fight it; stories are designed to distance readers from the realities they describe, to mediate between the spectator and the spectacle. Levi asserts that the camps were structured in a way that harmonizes more closely with the implicit imperatives of modern life than most people realize, and he asks his readers to learn to "read" or interpret differently if they want to avoid unconsciously assuming the routine, obedient, apathetic habits that that were brutally forced on the inmates of the camps.

Primo Levi and the *Arbeitslager*

In one of the most beautifully written and moving of the many Holocaust memoirs, translated as *Survival in Auschwitz* and more literally *If This Be a Man* (*Se questo è un uomo*), Primo Levi describes another, more lethal version of the house of correction-through-surveillance represented by the panopticon: the *Arbeitslager*, or work-camp. Instead of a house of correction, this is a "house of the dead" (31). Here no correction is possible, because the "crime" is defined not through deliberate action but through an accident of birth, compounded by continuing ties of affiliation. The punishment for such a hapless "crime," when it is not immediate execution, is meaningless work, according to a mechanical rhythm of minimal life: "Every day, according to the established rhythm, *Austrücken* and *Einrücken*, go out and come in; work, sleep and eat; fall ill, get better or die" (36). What makes existence so deadly is not the fact of being watched and judged, because the judgment is so arbitrary, so clearly undeserved, and because there are few SS men actually overseeing the *Häftlinge*, or prisoners. Behind its two rows of barbed wire, this camp trains inmates in mechanical obedience, thoughtlessness, a refusal to question, and apathy: "We have learnt . . . to reply *'Jawohl'*, never to ask questions, always to pretend to understand" (33). On the walls of the *Tagesraum* are "proverbs and rhymes in praise of order, discipline and hygiene" (32). The men come to resemble "puppets" (26, 30), and any curiosity is brutally rebuffed.[50] When he first came to the camp, Levi broke off and tried to suck an icicle to quench his thirst, only to have a guard snatch it from him. When he asked why (*warum*), the guard pushed him away with the words, "*Hier ist kein warum*" (there is no why here, 29). This Dantean "hell," to which they were brought by a "Charon" (22, 21), had as its infamous inscription above the door, "*Arbeit Macht Frei*" (work gives freedom), when in fact work signified the loss of freedom, and the real if invisible legend was the one above the gate to Dante's hell: Abandon all hope, ye who enter here. For Levi, modern hell is a living death, a prolonged boredom haunted by the expectation of horror.

> Today, in our times, hell must be like this. A huge, empty room: we are tired, standing on our feet, with a tap which drips while we cannot drink the water, and we wait for something which will certainly be terrible, and nothing happens and nothing continues to happen. What can one think about? One cannot think any more, it is like being already dead. (22)

The hell in which Levi found himself in the *Arbeitslager* is important not only as an eyewitness account of the physical torture of life there, but also because of a pain he characterizes as "literary": specifically, a linguistic or narrative isolation. First, he is plunged into a world in which people are speaking many unknown languages: "one is surrounded by a perpetual Babel, in which everyone shouts orders and threats in languages never heard before, and woe betide whoever fails to grasp the meaning" (38).[51] With acrid irony, Levi recounts how the prisoners of many nationalities were forced to build a Babel-like tower, the Carbide Tower of Buna (the synthetic rubber factory the prisoners were constructing), which was cursed for being "based on the confusion of languages and erected in defiance of heaven like a stone oath" (73). He reported with satisfaction that its erection was appropriately futile: the factory would never produce even a pound of rubber. Levi relates that its bricks "were called *Ziegel, briques, tegula, cegli, kamenny, mattoni, téglak,* and they were cemented by hate; hate and discord, like the Tower of Babel, and it is this that we call it: — *Babelturm, Bobelturm*; and in it we hate the insane dream of grandeur of our masters, their contempt for God and men, for us men" (73).

Levi's linguistic isolation (as an Italian speaker in a German camp in Poland filled with people of many nationalities) was not, however, as severe as what might be called a narrative isolation. From the moment of being put in the transport train, the prisoners were no longer heard or answered. Levi relates, "We suffered from thirst and cold; at every stop we clamoured for water, or even a handful of snow, but we were rarely heard" (18). Since they were not listened to, the travelers stopped trying to communicate with the outside world (18). When they arrive at the camp and try to ask the SS man questions, he merely "smokes and looks [the questioner] through and through as if he were transparent, as if no one had spoken" (23). When Levi recounts how they had everything taken from them, all their possessions, even their hair, he concludes that the worst loss of all was the loss of their collective and individual voices: "if we speak, they will not listen to us, and if they listen, they will not understand" (27). Not being heard takes away the desire to speak; when a strange prisoner arrives among them, Levi explains, "he does not speak willingly; no one here speaks willingly" (29). Survival, though, is something that Levi associates closely with "telling the story, bearing witness," refusing to consent to one's inhuman treatment; to want to tell the story is the only way "to remain alive, not to begin to die" (41).

The hope that leaks through degradation throughout *Survival in Auschwitz* is the hope of telling stories that are listened to, and listening to the stories of others in turn, especially in one's own language. Stories here are the spiritual equivalent of food. Levi's daydream while working is that "a woman would pass, and she would ask me 'Who are you?' in Italian, and I would tell her my story in Italian, and she would understand, and she would give me food and shelter. And she would not believe the things I tell her, and I would show her the number on my arm, and then she would believe" (43–4). Worse, though, than the daydream of telling one's story to a receptive audience – which is only awful because "the moment . . . of awakening is the acutest of sufferings" (44) – is the nightmare that balances it. Two collective dreams get reported: the dream of eating, "a pitiless dream which the creator of the Tantalus myth must have known," which is accompanied by the sound of dreamers licking their lips and moving their jaws (61), and a second nightmare that Levi identifies as "the ever-repeated scene of the unlistened-to story" (60). Sleeping head-to-foot in a two-foot wide bunk with a much heftier bunk-mate, Levi dreams that he is with his sister, a friend and several other people, and

> They are all listening to me and it is this very story that I am telling [the story of the camp] . . . It is an intense pleasure, physical, inexpressible, to be at home, among friendly people and to have so many things to recount: but I cannot help noticing that my listeners do not follow me. In fact, they are completely indifferent: they speak confusedly of other things among themselves, as if I was not there. (60)

Levi reacts to their indifference, their disinterest, with "a desolating grief": "It is pain in its pure state, not tempered by a sense of reality and by the intrusion of extraneous circumstances, a pain like that which makes children cry." He wakes himself up, only to remember that he has dreamed this same dream over and over since his arrival; moreover, he has recounted it to his friend Alberto, who tells him "that it is also his dream and the dream of many others, perhaps of everyone" (60).

The pain of the "unlistened-to story" is, in inverted form, the inspiration for Levi's own book. The fear of losing the energy to speak, intertwined with the nightmare of not being heard, produce in him an extraordinary passion to communicate. In its own way, Levi's dilemma is a nightmare reprise of the problem of modernist storytelling – he knows that stories are important, but how might we tell stories in a way that makes people *really* listen, and not simply half-attend out of habit? When he fears that the nightmare of "the unlistened-to story" is everyone's nightmare, he is registering an important insight: that listening has a structure, too, an order or architecture that is based on experience and expectation. Because what we hear is so closely linked to what we already know and anticipate, listening is not really as open as it seems; on the contrary, it coexists with deafness to what is unknown and therefore unexpected. To the extent that they are unconsciously assimilated to the known, all stories are "unlistened to"; the deepest power of a story, then, may be found in the moment when it is interrupted (either by a disjunction within the narrative or by the voice or thoughts of the listener). A rupture within the narrative implicitly pleads with the reader to stop the process of unconscious assimilation and to begin again: to realize with something like awe that the language of this story is foreign as well as familiar. This is what happens in the eleventh chapter of Levi's memoir, when he undertakes to teach Italian to his campmate Jean by reciting whatever he can recall of the twenty-sixth canto of Danto's *Inferno* (the Ulysses canto).

The desire to learn – and teach – one's own language, which is unknown to the listener, works to acknowledge yet reverse the "tower of Babel" syndrome in the camp, and the act of teaching the language through literature allows Levi to tell his and Jean's own story more intensively, more poetically, with a richer layering of meanings than he could otherwise do in such a short period of time. When Levi and Jean go to pick up the ration of soup for their group, they begin to talk about ordinary things: "We spoke of our houses, of Strasbourg and Turin, of the books we had read, of what we had studied, of our mothers" (111). Once the communication has begun, they decide not to waste the hour, and Levi begins to quote the passage from the *Inferno* in which a "wavering flame" comes to resemble "a speaking tongue vibrant to frame/ Language" (112).

By implication, Levi and Jean become Ulysses and Diomedes, trapped together in a single flame in hell. Dante looks into a valley and sees flames dotted over it like fireflies, and he asks Virgil what they are. Virgil replies that every flame is a trapped soul, whereupon Dante becomes interested in the double flame that contains Ulysses and Diomedes, a flame that Virgil asks to speak. Dante describes the flames as tongues, an image that recalls the way in which the tongues of fire at Pentecost – in which all languages can be understood – serve to reverse the division of tongues that ensued from the tower of Babel. The outer tongue of flame becomes the inner tongue of speech, and the voice of Ulysses is heard – through Dante's tale and then through Levi's. The narrative world of Dante and Levi is very different from one structured around Nazi towers of Babel, in which it is the *listener* who is punished for not comprehending the incomprehensible. Here, it is the teller not the listener who suffers, and his articulate suffering constitutes an urgent challenge to the listener to try to understand the previously inconceivable.

After the lines describing how a flame throws out a voice to tell its story, Levi remembers a phrase about setting forth to travel with a strong and audacious courage, and he feels a more hurried pressure to remember, to understand, and to make his companion understand Dante's words, in the original Italian, which Jean does not know. He thinks,

> Here, listen Pikolo, open your ears and your mind, you have to understand, for my sake:
>
> > 'Think of your breed; for brutish ignorance
> > Your mettle was not made; you were made men,
> > To follow after knowledge and excellence.'
>
> As if I also was hearing it for the first time: like the blast of a trumpet, like the voice of God. For a moment I forget who I am and where I am. (113)

Dante's carefully crafted language has the power to help Levi and Jean recall a fullness of being that the camp would deny them. The Italian title of the book, *Se questo è un uomo*, "if this be a man," abuts against the insistence of Dante through the voice of Ulysses recited by Levi that "you were made men." Levi hopes that Jean "has received the message, he has felt that it has to do with him, that it has to do with all men who toil, and with us in particular; and that it has to do with us two, who dare to reason of these things with the poles for the soup on our shoulders" (114). Here is the power of literature: it is a fire, a voice, that can sound through hell and address itself even to the damned; it is about the reader or listener, and about that listener's obligation to "follow after knowledge and excellence" rather than reel back into bestial self-surrender. This is why Levi detains Jean: "it is vitally necessary and urgent that he listen, that he understand . . . before it is too late" (115). Levi feels that he has intuited "something gigantic," a reason for their being there, before they are "drowned" in the cabbages and turnips, *"choux et navets," "Kraut und Rüben,"* of today's soup. This is his answer to the pain of the "unlistened-to" story – a moment of shared understanding between himself and Jean about Dante, and about themselves – their suffering and their capacity to connect and to generate lived meanings, however briefly; it is a thought-charged moment with a flickering power to restore their ability to think and feel in a meaningless, highly regulated social environment.

Primo Levi offers an image of banal thoughtlessness as the supreme evil: "if I could enclose all the evil of our time in one image, I would choose this image which is familiar to me: an emaciated man, with head dropped and shoulders curved, on whose face and in whose eyes not a trace of a thought is to be seen" (90). The loss of will, the refusal to think or to desire are characteristic of people whose "souls are dead," who are driven by an "interminable rhythm" as "the wind drives dead leaves" (51). Levi identifies the most urgent meaning of the camp as a warning to people outside to assume a fuller freedom in their own lives: "If from inside the Lager, a message could have seeped out to free men, it would have been this: take care not to suffer in your own homes what is inflicted on us here" (55). His gentle suggestion is that ordinary citizens in daily "free" life cede the joys of expression, protest, humor, and autonomy to the forces that control their lives, and do so out of habit and apathy, without coercion. In Levi's view, a concentration camp is not only a gruesome historical fact, but a metaphorical, exaggerated representation of the world of alienated labor in the so-called "free" world. He reports to have learned that "our personality is fragile, that it is much more in danger than our life" (55). What supports the life of the personality, of the spirit, is the word, the formation of small communities through (forbidden) communication.

If, as Levi suggests, the *Arbeitslager* is indeed a microcosm of life in the "free" world (its rules enforced through coercion instead of being internalized, as is the case outside the camp), then it is important to look closely at the value of storytelling in such a context. Stories are so sharply missed, so deeply desired, because they are one of the primary means of establishing community, and community is almost impossible when competition for resources is so fierce. Under such conditions, in which vigilant self-interest seems essential to survival, the dream of exchanging one's stories is immensely appealing, but the inmates fear that their stories will not be believed, that they will not matter. Although Levi's own book constitutes such a story – one that is clear, eloquent, and persuasive – the encounter with Jean calls the adequacy of such stories into question. When Levi wants to communicate intensely with Jean, he does so by quoting and interpreting poetry in a language that Jean does not know about a literary hell that never existed. By implication, our social conditions have changed so markedly that meaningful communication – of the kind that forges community – is no longer generated through an exchange of simple narratives. Communication in a multi-national world, in which individuals are constantly evaluating themselves under pressure, has to disrupt the illusion of understanding in an effort to create common ground. In a routinized environment, formulaic stories can no longer be heard or deeply felt. Ironically, despite multiple differences in language and personal history, all stories have started to sound the same. Levi knew that he could only hope to communicate with Jean by challenging them both with a canto that he himself could not easily remember and that Jean could not readily understand.

Beyond Correction

The deep parts of my life pour onward,
as if the river shores were opening out.

It seems that things are more like me now,
that I can see farther into paintings.
I feel closer to what language cannot reach.
       Rainer Maria Rilke, "Moving Forward"

When T.S. Eliot reminds us that "garlic and sapphires" are *both* in the mud ("Burnt Norton," II); when Yeats locates the abstract in the concrete, and the desired in the discarded, by having Crazy Jane cry that "Love has pitched his mansion in/ The place of excrement" ("Crazy Jane Talks with the Bishop"); when Joyce's Stephen forsakes his (shorter, fatter) tower and Yeats insists that his, like the "bloody arrogant power" it mocks, is "Half dead at the top" ("Blood and the Moon"), all – like Levi – are seeking a common ground for communication in times of extremity. Instead of striving to elevate themselves above their readers, they would "lie down where all the ladders start,/ In the foul rag-and-bone shop of the heart" (Yeats, "The Circus Animals' Desertion"). Not only are they denied the superior vantage point of a tower, the characters in Samuel Beckett's works are often buried alive, rendered immobile in sand, or trash bins, or urns. In *A Room of One's Own*, Virginia Woolf explains the frustrating and humbling effects of a reading a work in which the author has forsaken the high ground of claiming greater perspective than her reader:

> The effect was somehow baffling; one could not see a wave heaping itself, a crisis coming round the next corner. Therefore I could not plume myself either upon the depths of my feelings and my profound knowledge of the human heart. For whenever I was about to feel the usual things in the usual places, about love, about death, the annoying creature twitched me away, as if the important point were just a little further on. . . . She made me feel, on the contrary, that instead of being serious and profound and humane, one might be – and the thought was far less seductive – merely lazy-minded and conventional into the bargain. (91–2)

That fulcrum of realization, in which one realizes that the reality of one's situation has corroded one's fantasy of superiority, is also what gives Joyce's "The Dead" in *Dubliners* its eerie, ephemeral beauty. Gabriel teeters between a complacency that allows him to condescend to his aunts and a vision of its complement, his glimpse of himself as their "pennyboy," a fatuous fellow. The reader, too, finds him- or herself on a similar see-saw, unsure of who is more alive or dead: the people inside or outside the story. Where is the fiction? Is fiction an entertainment that can be begun and abandoned, or is it the perception that we – as readers – have a broader, more vital perspective than the characters in books?

Modernist fiction is obsessed less with power, or right and wrong, or punishment, than with a shocking communion with a contradictory and everchanging reality. As the narrator of Rebecca West's *The Return of the Soldier* reflects,

> there is a draught that we must drink if we are to be fully human. I knew that one must know the truth. I knew quite well that when one is adult one must raise to one's lips the wine of the truth, heedless that it is not sweet like milk but draws the mouth with its strength, and celebrate communion with reality, or else walk for ever queer and small like a dwarf.[52]

As West's metaphor implies, knowledge of the truth is a form of voluntary communion or communication with something other than one's desires or fears. The typical limitation of formulaic fiction – which also gives it entertainment value – is precisely that it is designed to placate our desires and fears, and not to communicate some implacable "truth" that can help a person attain a fuller and more contradictory comprehension of reality. In Woolf's *To the Lighthouse*, Lily complains about her "formidable ancient enemy," "this truth, this reality, which suddenly laid hands on her, emerged stark at the back of appearances and commanded her attention." Feeling "half unwilling, half reluctant," she is exquisitely aware that this "was an exacting form of intercourse" (151). In sharp contrast, formulaic fiction does not invite or reward a prolonged dialogue; it is self-contained, as is our response to it. Like the observer in Bentham's panopticon, we attend most popular performances secure that we ourselves are invisible; while we may watch, the art will not look back.

The audience's assurance of safety from scrutiny is challenged by much modernist literature, sometimes comically, as when Joyce taunts the reader (in wicked "blackvoice") for feeling lost in *Finnegans Wake*: "You is feeling like you was lost in the bush, boy? You says: It is a puling sample jungle of woods [pure and simple jumble of words]" (1.5, 112–

13). The audience's exemption from scrutiny is also challenged more chillingly in Beckett's short play *Catastrophe*, which he dedicated to Václav Havel. In it, the protagonist is exhibited on a pedestal on stage, posed like a mannequin by a self-important director and his assistant, stripped down to his ash-colored pyjamas, his face lowered so that it can't be seen, his balding head and crippled hands accented by whitening. The director, finally satisfied, says, "There's our catastrophe" – our disaster, our theatrical denouement, and, as the etymology of "catastrophe" suggests, our over-turning. The overturning takes place when the director barks, "Now . . . let 'em have it." The general light fades, then the light on the body fades, and finally light rests on the protagonist's head alone. The director pronounces "Terrific!" and we hear a "distant storm of applause," which falters and is stilled when the protagonist raises his head and fixes the audience with his eyes. There is a long pause, and the light goes out.[53] Our voyeuristic interest in a victim of catastrophe has been observed, checked, and returned to us when the protagonist raises his head and looks back. The audience has been uncannily mirrored, our exemption from observation challenged. We feel the shock of a brief communion with the reality of what we ourselves have been doing by entertaining ourselves with the spectacle of someone else's suffering.

When modernist literature tries to get beyond language, it does so not only by attempting to be more abstruse and cerebral than the common reader, but also by doing the opposite: it represents an attempt to be more embodied, more in touch with feeling in both senses: physical touch and emotion. Such literature attempts to escape from the modern social panopticon by not allowing the author, narrator, or reader an imagined place in the secret tower that grants an illusion of power and superiority. On the contrary, the reader-author-narrator is often as fettered as Beckett's Murphy when he ties himself with seven scarves, buck naked, to his rocking chair of undressed teak, in the hope of coming "alive in his mind."[54] Like Murphy, a modern everyman, we may easily end up upside down and immobile, blood gushing from the nose. As the narrator wryly comments, "Only the most local movements were possible" (28). In a similar vein, modernist literature is traversed by tramps who are forced to come to terms with the body because of the poverty of their surroundings, whether that poverty is purely economic or social and metaphysical. The homeless men in Orwell's *Down and Out in Paris and London* are bored, hungry, and tired; the tramps in Beckett's *Waiting for Godot* are also bored, but they perk up at the prospect of death by hanging and a possible posthumous (resurr-)erection. The writers' efforts to exhume the underlying physical and emotional life we must partially repress produce prose that is sometimes sexual, sometimes scatological, sometimes vulgar; it ranges from the thinly veiled paean to the phallus in D.H. Lawrence's poem "The Snake" to detailed descriptions of Bloom and Molly's bodily processes and orifices in *Ulysses*, to Beckett's determination to dramatize and film the movements of an apparently autonomous mouth (*Not I*), to Barnes' Doctor O'Connor in *Nightwood*, who "did not seem to see or hear anything but his own heart," unable to excuse himself for his animal nature, "the Squatting beast, coming out at night" (162).[55] The barks, the groans, that Bernard yearns for in Woolf's *The Waves* would be an acknowledgment not only of the inarticulateness of feeling as it occurs in the moment, but also of this animal power, a power that seethes beneath the veneer of modern "civilization." Such power is dangerous when it is unacknowledged, unheard, underestimated. As Barnes puts it (through the mouth of the doctor) in *Nightwood*, "A man is whole only when he takes into account his shadow as well as himself" (119).

To disavow the animal within the human is to accept woodenness. As Doctor O'Connor reminds Nora in *Nightwood*, "Even the contemplative life is only an effort, Nora my dear, to hide the body so the feet won't stick out" (134). Wallace Stevens makes a similar point in "The Emperor of Ice Cream" when he contrasts the cold immobility of a corpse with the melting delights of ice cream: "If her horny feet protrude, they come / To show how cold she is, and dumb. / Let the lamp affix its beam. / The only emperor is the Emperor of ice cream." Life gains its value from the very mortality – the uncomfortable law of change – that people seek to disavow in the effort to gain stability. Stevens, like a circus barker, invites readers to celebrate carnival confections that change – epitomized by ice cream – to counterbalance the permanence and immobility of death.

Barnes' Doctor Matthew O'Connor disdains the old morality play of right and wrong; he avers that a "good woman" is only a "bitch on a high plane" (146; conversely, a "bitch" could be viewed as a goddess on a low plane). O'Connor argues that good and evil must encounter one another if we are to attain any genuine comprehension:

Don't I know that the only way to know evil is through truth? The evil and the good know themselves only by giving up their secret face to face. The true good who meets the true evil (Holy Mother of Mercy! Are there any such?) learns for the first time how to accept neither; the face of the one tells the face of the other the half of the story that both forgot. (138)

Joyce concurs; the imperative to choose between opposites is a way to end up with half a world. In *Finnegans Wake*, the narrator argues with Kierkegaard's implicit call to choose between opposed alternatives in *Either/Or*, and proposes instead that we accept or reject both extremes together:

That's how our oxyggent [occident; oxygen] has gotten ahold of half their world. Moving about in the free of the air and mixing with the ruck. Enten eller, either or.
And!
Nay, rather! (281.24–9)

In other (poorer) words: reality is full of oppositions, alternatives, that seem to be asking us to choose between them, but if we choose one extreme at the expense of its opposite, we should realize that in so doing we have chosen to settle for half a reality. This is how the occident has gotten hold of half of the world (the other half, the orient, is presumably more careful to embrace both the yin and its opposite, yang). Similarly, when Nietzsche proposed that "What is done out of love always occurs beyond good and evil,"[56] he is endorsing a love of the real, which is *both* good and evil and *neither* good nor evil. In Beckett's *Murphy*, Murphy's mind is described as a virtual space that could not be accommodated to ideas of good and evil: the mental experience "did not function and could not be disposed according to a principle of worth. It was made up of light fading into dark, of above and beneath, but not of good and bad. It contained forms with parallel in another mode and forms without, but not right forms and wrong forms" (108). By implication, for all these writers the desire to engage more fully with a dynamic reality (whether that reality is external or, in the case of Murphy, internal) moves us beyond the world of correction, the primary aim of which is to *separate* bad from good in order to disavow or eliminate half of it: the "evil" half.

The argument that evaluation has been internalized in modern western societies illuminates what we do when we read by alerting us to the following possibility: thoughtless reading is often unconsciously driven by a need to separate the bad from the good. We begin reading with the expectation that we will be able to evaluate the characters without being evaluated ourselves. Similarly, we are constantly evaluating not only the characters but also the books they inhabit: are they good or bad? The point of reading, given such expectations, is to reassure ourselves of our essential virtue by identifying vicariously with "good" characters in "good" books. "Good" is such a capacious category that it can encompass many different definitions: for some people, "good" means smart, for others, it means physically powerful, or virtuous, or beautiful, or even ruthlessly successful. The important point about modernist literature, at least the books and poems I am discussing here, is that it does not reward such expectations; the works I have chosen to analyze are addressed to a different set of desires. These texts are designed not to help readers identify with some ideal of virtue, but to restore an awareness of the interconnectedness of all things. Instead of gratifying our desires and allaying our fears, they work to expose the interdependence of desire and fear, good and evil, and a host of other oppositions. These works reward those who are looking for a comprehensive and dynamic view of reality, a reality from which neither the reader nor the author is exempted by privilege or excellence. Nietzsche, the most contradictory and internally inconsistent of philosophers, thus insists that the increasingly rigid social, religious, economic, and national categories of the nineteenth century were creating the need for a more comprehensive philosophical outlook:

> Confronted with a world of "modern ideas," which would banish everybody into a corner and a "specialty," a philosopher – if there could be any philosophers today – would be forced to define the greatness of man, the concept of "greatness," in terms precisely of man's comprehensiveness and multiplicity, his wholeness and manifoldness. (section 212, p. 445)

As the twentieth century progressed, it became increasingly imperative not only to see or "read" the world more comprehensively, but also to appreciate the way that every individual is inescapably implicated in the fortunes of the whole. Instead of a newer, higher race of more comprehensive individuals of the sort Nietzsche envisioned, what was needed was a more comprehensive picture of the powerful, sublime, ordinary, and ugly impulses of the human race: its collective unconscious. A literature was evolving to address that need.

How Modernism Ended: A Historical Perspective

We are now in a position to map the changing models of relation between reader and text – specifically, the movement from categorical and evaluative reading to comprehensive reading – onto a larger historical grid. As the omniscient narrator's role diminished, we were left with narrative surfaces that were increasingly disorienting, obscure, or even chaotic and incomprehensible. Many experimental writers, while intrigued by new modes of expression, were also reluctant to relinquish the writer's traditionally privileged perspective *vis-à-vis* the reader. The widespread European uprisings of 1848 and the emergence of communist Russia evidenced a similar desire to change the relationship between those who had dictated political thought and those who unthinkingly responded. In the wake of these events, influenced by the teachings of Marx and Freud, the once-obedient working and middle classes were beginning to feel restive, capable of fuller and more autonomous self-expression. Then, across the world stage, dictators in several countries – Hitler, Stalin, and Franco – stepped back into the central towers of their respective panopticons to put the people once again under surveillance, strictly reclassifying them and punishing offending groups. This sudden expansion and equally sudden contraction of personal and expressive freedom was then abruptly punctuated by massive genocide.

The social and formal daring of modernist literature during the fifty years from 1890 to 1940 contrasts sharply with the nationalistic nostalgia and intolerance for innovation and difference) that climaxed in Hitler's "Final Solution." How modernism ended, what silenced the euphoric, creative experimentation of the modernist movement, was the Holocaust, what Jews refer to as the Shoah, what Gypsies called the *porraimos* or "the devouring"[57] – a systematic dehumanization,

degradation, and extermination of eleven million people – and the concentration camps that facilitated it. As Konnilyn Feig relates, these
camps evolved into "a vast, unprecedented network for the suppression,
containment, exploitation, and extermination of millions of people of
various nationalities designated as enemies of the state or as members
of subhuman, inferior, or irritating groups."[58] Six million Jews were
systematically murdered, but so were five million non-Jews, a number
that includes over a million young children.

What does the torture and murder of eleven million people in the
middle of the twentieth century have to do with modernism? The
answer is bound up with changing attitudes toward human differences:
differences of age, race, creed, nationality, gender, and sexual orientation. Modernist literature forces the reader to re-collect fragments,
fragments that represent not only the past, but also the range of human
and artistic differences that the Third Reich later aimed to scatter and
destroy. For the Nazis were out to exterminate difference: they started
with the Jews, and they went on to "re-educate" and sometimes to cas-
trate male homosexuals (lesbians were spared because they could still
produce children), to destroy Gypsies because they historically resisted
assimilation and spoke a different language (Fonseca 16), to punish disobedient clergy, to kill and experiment upon the physically disabled,
especially hunchbacks and dwarfs. They targeted the deaf, dumb, blind,
mentally and physically ill, and the aged; they imprisoned Jehovah's
Witnesses, Russian POWs, communists and socialists, and those they
considered "subhuman": Poles, Slovaks, Slavs, Ukrainians, and Russians.
They murdered large numbers of pregnant women and mothers of young
children and experimented on or sterilized many others (Feig 163–4,
173–4). They drowned or axed babies in huge groups, and at Birkenau
they burned thousands of children alive (Feig 174). The similarities
among the victims are greater than their differences. Part of what the
Nazis were trying to contain, through extermination, incarceration, or
commodification, was the bristly heterogeneity of individual and foreign
identity, a fact that was illustrated most vividly by the way they hunted
for tattoos among the prisoners. Tattoos were fetishized as signs of literal
and indelible self-expression; Nazis made these physical signatures
"fashion items," avidly seeking them for book covers, luggage, gloves,
and lampshades, creating a profitable sideline of the traffic in
human skin.[59]

The cluster of punitive and entrepreneurial activities surrounding the Holocaust constitutes, in its most inclusive formulation, a horrifying shutdown of individuality and a large-scale muting of protest. Intellectuals, artists, those engaged in sexual or artistic experimentation, "anti-social" groups or groups with international (as opposed to patriotic) affiliations, were silenced, gassed, or slaughtered. The unprecedented extent and fierceness of this reprisal against what we might call "international individuality" that promoted ties across national boundaries suggest that it was a powerfully nostalgic, frighteningly idealizing reaction to deeply threatening changes in the social fabric. The kinds of victims who were targeted give us clues about how to identify those changes that the Nazis so feared and despised, which are remarkably similar to the social changes that the Taliban outlawed in Afghanistan years later, to name just one example: feminism and women's suffrage; western capitalism; the sexual freedom of the 1890s and the 1920s, especially in Harlem and Berlin; and intellectual and artistic experimentation.

Modernism, as an earlier experimental celebration of precisely those differences, became a symbolic (and actual) target of Nazi hatred. Modernism had expressed the euphoria of exploring human potential through experimental innovation (in literature, art, science, and music), and it ran headlong into the politics of xenophobia, the fear of proliferating differences in a rapidly changing and increasingly global world. Nazi ideology tended to conflate any divergence from an idealized national and racial norm with "foreignness" and "degeneracy," which made originality a defect. The Nazis could not tolerate uniqueness in art just as they could not tolerate individual differences. They extradited and destroyed it.

The connection between Nazi policies toward art and human beings was shockingly apparent in Paul Schultze-Naumberg's influential book *Kunst und Rasse* (Art and Race, 1928), in which, influenced by Max Nordau's *Entartung* (Degeneration) of 1892, he juxtaposed works of modern art and photographs of people who were diseased or deformed. He was particularly critical of the elongated faces of Amedeo Modigliani along with other "degenerate" works by Karl Schmidt-Rotluff and Otto Dix.[60] In the visual arts, the campaign against avant-garde art reached a climax in the immensely popular *Entarte Kunst* (Degenerate Art) exhibit in Munich on July 19, 1937, in which over 650 artworks, taken from German museum collections, were displayed to the public as examples of "un-German" art. The National Socialists politicized aesthetic issues and aestheticized political ones. They burned books and confiscated thousands of examples of "degenerate" modern art. Only nineteenth-century realistic genre painting was "true Aryan art." Works outside this tradition were considered products of Jews, foreigners, Communists-Bolshevists, or the insane (see Barron, 9, 11). Modernism in art had been essentially outlawed since 1934, as Hitler "saw an attack on modernism as an opportunity to use the average German's distrust of avant-garde art to further his political objectives against Jews, Communists, and non-Aryans" (Barron 15). Since 1933, confiscated works of art had been put into *Schreckenskammern der Kunst* (chambers of horror for art), where they could be condemned by a general public that found it patriotic to be suspicious of novelty.

Nazi policy was designed to isolate and punish deviation, accidental or deliberate, natural or willful, from an arbitrarily defined "norm." Transgression was not only the target of Nazi hatred, but also its *modus operandi*. The value of transgression was not in question, merely the privilege of defining and enforcing the methods to be authorized: which would be legitimate, and which criminal? What kinds of society would be produced from different definitions of legitimate versus culpable transgressions? The problem is a version of the old cops-and-robbers struggle: cops and robbers are versions of one another, both transgressive, but in the service of different visions of society.

Let us posit, then, that both on the streets and between the covers of books people were struggling to define and enforce different conceptual models of virtue. On the one hand, there was the vision of virtue as purity, defined in opposition to heterogeneity, which was evil. This is the logic of racism, and it has the psychological advantage of allowing its practitioners to "prove" their own goodness – or cleanliness – merely by highlighting the contrast between themselves and others. One can be "good" without any internal effort to assimilate conflicting points of view; in fact, one can be good by *refusing* to assimilate new or alien perspectives. This is an easy goodness that conveniently justifies evil treatment of "impurity." The mode of reading that corresponds to this kind of thinking is one based on identification with a heroic protagonist who fights impurity and is ultimately vindicated.

An alternative way of defining what is "good" is to embrace a value that is comprehensive rather than "pure": to comprehend is to understand but also to encompass. In this sense, it recalls the etymological root of "salvation," the Latin *salvo*, which is health or wholeness. Those who value comprehensiveness may easily become targets of those who value purity, because comprehensiveness is necessarily impure or promiscuous, adulterated. When we read in a way that values wholeness, we are less concerned with the protagonist's superiority and more invested in finding hidden modes of relation that undergird the text and reach out to the world of experience. In other words, we attend more actively to the subtext, to the web of associations that unifies what may seem to be a chaotic carnival of words, images, and allusions.

Consider "goodness" in Richard Wagner's *Parsifal*. The opera is precariously poised on the divide between older and newer models of self-understanding. On the one hand, *Parsifal* celebrates purity through its protagonist, the "holy fool" who is able, through ignorance and simplicity, to cure the wounded king, Amfortas, and save the knights of the grail.[61] Wagner's story insists that Parsifal's goodness be read not only in terms of innocence, but also as a function of his capacity for imagination and compassion. Compassion is the means whereby he experiences the suffering of others, becoming, in a sense, as multiple and comprehensive as he was "pure." This compassion is underscored by the orchestra, which makes connections among the different characters and themes through the use of *leitmotifs*, mimicking the transgressive unconscious moving through conscious apprehensions of experience, and unifying the whole in a tribute to the complex and comprehensive totality of experience.

Literary modernism was similarly informed by a nonviolent dynamic of transgressive experimentation and was riven by eerie reflections and contradictions as artists struggled to design more or less exclusive or inclusive imaginative worlds. Its transgressiveness is apparent in the crossing of boundaries separating nations, genders, races, and genres. Its groundwork was laid in the 1890s, with the emergence of the "New Woman" novel, Ibsen's controversial social dramas, the political prominence of the "Irish question," the trials of Oscar Wilde, French symbolism, and the aesthetic movement in literature, a movement associated with "decadent" *fin-de-siècle* freedoms.

New forms of literature were shaped by the increasing social tension between innovative change and cautious retrenchment. Revolutionary perceptions transformed literature, but also bore witness to the birth of psychoanalysis; the transformation of Newtonian physics by the theory of relativity; the expanding influence of Marxism; the innovations in music associated with artists as different as Stravinksy, Schoenberg, and Billie Holiday; cubism in art (Picasso and Braque); German Expressionism; the beginnings of cinema; and of course the technological revolution.

It was a period of immense excitement and threatening change. In the wake of World War I, the boundaries of European countries were redrawn, the Austro-Hungarian and German empires were dismantled, and Ireland was partitioned. Paradoxically, other nations – Germany and Italy – were forging strong national units. Russia staged a revolution against the Tsar, but replaced him with violently repressive regimes (Lenin and Stalin). Spain was torn by civil war, women won the right to vote, and the era closed with the detonation of the first atomic bomb. The birth of the twentieth century, then, ushered in a period of new license laced with threat, of beauty haunted by intimations of terror. Heady freedoms were bound up with xenophobic agitation; terrors erupted, and then civil wars. In America, the suffrage movement and the Harlem Renaissance promised social change, but that promise was undermined by the near-collapse of capitalism in the Great Depression.

Events in Ireland, Europe, and America in the first half of the twentieth century may seem very different from one another now, but some writers of the period saw meaningful parallels linking the Irish, black Americans, and the Jews. Perhaps the most famous example is Joyce's *Ulysses*, which subtly seeks to intertwine the Irish and the Hebrew peoples, concentrating the triumphs and humiliations of both into modern characters who move through a Dublin illuminated and haunted by the epic grandeur of ancient Greece. Earlier, Oscar Wilde saw the defeated American South as a double of Ireland under British rule, arguing that "We in Ireland are fighting for the principle of autonomy against empire, for independence against centralization, for the principles for which the South fought."[62] Of course, Wilde idealized and oversimplified the position of the South by overlooking the issue of slavery; his was not the view of the periodical *Punch*, for example, which explicitly and repeatedly portrayed the Irish not as the Southern aristocracy, but as counterparts to the American Negro.[63] In America, most whites were resistant to the view that black Americans might be in a situation even remotely comparable to that of the Jews in Germany, as

Harper Lee most memorably demonstrated in her well-known (but not, strictly speaking, modernist) novel *To Kill a Mockingbird*. Lee dramatizes the hypocrisy of a society that condemns racism in Europe while celebrating bigotry in its own backyard. The 8-year-old protagonist, Scout, recounts with some puzzlement an incident that happened in her third-grade class after the conclusion of a black man's trial for allegedly raping a white woman in her Southern town. A school-fellow, Cecil Jacobs, is giving a current events presentation about Hitler, and begins, "Old Adolf Hitler has been prosecutin' the – ." The teacher, Miss Gates, interrupts him: "Persecuting, Cecil . . ."

> "Nome, Miss Gates, it says here – well anyway, old Adolf Hitler has been after the Jews and he's puttin' 'em in prisons and he's taking away all their property and he won't let any of 'em out of the country and he's washin' all the feeble-minded and – "
> "Washing the feeble-minded?"
> "Yes ma'am, Miss Gates, I reckon they don't have sense enough to wash themselves, I don't reckon an idiot could keep hisself clean. Well anyway, Hitler's started a program to round up all the half-Jews too and he wants to register 'em in case they might wanta cause him any trouble and I think this is a bad thing and that's my current event."[64]

Although Cecil doesn't fully understand what he has read, we know that what he interprets as Hitler's campaign to wash idiots refers to his early plan to "cleanse" the state by using euthanasia to terminate those he had judged "unworthy of life" because of mental or hereditary illness,[65] and when he alludes to Hitler's "program to round up all the half-Jews too" he's referring to the First Regulation to the Reich Citizenship Law of November 14, 1935 defining different categories of non-Aryans (one category is *Mischlinge* of the first degree or half-Jews).[66] Cecil's understanding of what Hitler is doing may be imperfect, but his opinion that "this is a bad thing" is accurate, if understated.

Miss Gates responds with patronizing complacency, by emphasizing the dramatic difference between Germany and America: she explains that America is a "DEMOCRACY" and

> "Germany is a dictatorship. Dictator-ship . . . Over here we don't believe in persecuting anybody. Persecution comes from people who are prejudiced. Pre-ju-dice," she enunciated carefully. "There are no better

people in the world than the Jews, and why Hitler doesn't think so is a mystery to me." (282)

Although Miss Gates thinks America and Germany are different, Lee is clearly dramatizing their underlying kinship, emphasizing the correspondence by underscoring the similarity between blacks and Jews. Cecil argues that even if the Jews are supposed to change money or something, "that ain't no cause to persecute 'em. They're white, aren't they?" (282).

Later that night, Scout is finally able to articulate what's bothering her about Miss Gates' hatred of Hitler: its hypocrisy. She tells her brother Jem that after the end of the trial she heard Miss Gates say about black men, "it's time somebody taught 'em a lesson, they were gettin' way above themselves, an' the next thing they think they can do is marry us." Scout's question is, "Jem, how can you hate Hitler so bad and then turn around and be ugly about folks right at home — ?" (284). Through Cecil Jacobs' overly literal interpretation of Hitler's campaign, Lee lampoons the tendency of ordinary citizens to interpret atrocity too narrowly, and through Scout's disturbance over Miss Gates' racism, she underscores the ease with which individuals can revile others for attitudes they regard as utterly normal in themselves. Lee treats Nazi racism and American racism as closely comparable, yet few citizens of the Southern town of Maycomb understand the parallel between what public opinion did to Tom Robinson and what Hitler was doing to the millions of Europeans he branded "unclean." This parallel was obvious to a contemporary cartoonist, Art Spiegelman, whose first idea for his graphic novel *Maus* involved depicting blacks as mice and the Ku Klux Klan as cats in a piece about racism in America. He recalls that the idea lasted about ten minutes, until he realized that he knew very little about racism in America. He then turned to the Nazis.

It is worth discussing Spiegelman's post-modernist graphic novel here because of the way it depicts the racial animus as an animalistic behavior. By associating all ethnic groups with different species of animals, Spiegelman globalizes racism as something that necessarily extends far beyond Germany and America (think of the horrifying treatment of the Chinese by the Japanese during the Rape of Nanking in 1937–8, and the way Americans dehumanized the Japanese in the Pacific a little later). At the same time, he is able to capture the irony of animals trying to strip other animals of human pretensions, reminding us of the close tie between mice and men. Spiegelman's work preserves the spirit of modernism in its concern with the mechanisms of dehumanization, and with its exploration of group identification and group hatreds, both of which may be facilitated or disrupted by art.

In *Maus: A Survivor's Tale*, Spiegelman adopts and exaggerates the same deceptive innocence that masked Nazi decrees aimed at "protecting" German Blood and Honor, an innocence that initially shields onlookers like Cecil from a full understanding of what is actually going on under the guise of state "benevolence." In the first three-page version of *Maus*, Art is called Mickey (after Mickey Mouse) and his father is telling him a sweet bedtime story that turns out to be a nightmare tale of the Holocaust.[67] The second volume of *Maus* (called *And Here My Troubles Began*) begins with an epigraph about Mickey Mouse from a German newspaper in the mid-1930s:

> Mickey Mouse is the most miserable ideal ever revealed. . . . Healthy emotions tell every independent young man and every honorable youth that the dirty and filth-covered vermin, the greatest bacteria carrier in the animal kingdom, cannot be the ideal type of animal. . . . Away with the Jewish brutalization of the people! Down with Mickey Mouse! Wear the Swastika Cross![68]

The Nazis declared war on Mickey Mouse by claiming a superior innocence, a racial and national "purity" that was not an agent of contamination. The worst atrocities ever committed on such a large scale were committed in the name of innocence, for the protection of German youth, against a people their captors identified with Mickey Mouse.

Why was Mickey Mouse such a useful image? The Irish poet Ciaran Carson suggests in "Queen's Gambit" that Mickey epitomizes the attempt of a rodent to be human, civilized, and friendly. Carson, while contemplating the grotesque Disney theme that emerged in an episode of Belfast street violence, explains: "It's why Mickey Mouse wears those little white gloves —/ Claws are too much like a mouse. And if the animals are trying to be people, / *Vice versa* is the case as well."[69] Carson approaches violence as a breakdown of the distinction between human and animal, and he depicts this breakdown as grotesquely mediated by Disney characters that recall innocence being violated.[70]

Violence, progressive social change, and literary modernism are all characterized by the breakdown of boundaries. Sometimes the breakdowns are liberating, and at others they are degrading and horrifying. E.M. Forster once wrote of modernist prose that "It is the product of people who have war on their mind."[71] Of course Forster was referring primarily to World War I, but there was another war going on as well, a war of definition, of representation, of dictation; a war to define what is human in an age of mechanical reproduction, of burgeoning population, and imperial expansion. The Nazis' effort to prove that Jews were not human ironically exposed their own ghastly inhumanity, but programs to dehumanize one group or another through degrading *or* idealizing representations are generally characteristic of the twentieth century as a whole.

The definition of Jewishness was a thorny problem for the Nazi party, given the difficulty of paternity issues, the paucity of complete records, and the differences in degrees of religious observances and affiliation, so that ultimately the Nazis had to ask whether people classified *themselves* as Jewish in order to categorize them. In *To Kill a Mockingbird*, Scout struggles to apply a definition of democracy as "equal rights for all, special privileges for none" to the racist practices of the Southern town where she lives. Modernist literature is the laboratory in which such definitions were variously hammered out or defied. Some modernist works are highly dictatorial and intolerant in tone; others refuse to provide readers with clear interpretive cues, prompting their audience to remain responsible for the interpretations they construct.

Stanley Milgram's investigation is relevant to the question of what is at stake in reading modernist literature because it showed how the social field engineers a short-circuit in the interpretive process by turning relationships that ought to be equal into hierarchies. The researcher dominates the subject, the writer controls the thoughts and reactions of the reader, and institutional authority trumps individual conscience. The formal innovations of high modernist writing constituted attempts to counter such short-circuits by forcing its audience to realize that the "Longest way round is the shortest way home" (*Ulysses* 13.1110–11), by enjoining readers to form a more equal partnership with authors in the production of meaning. It is sometimes said that art is impossible after Auschwitz. But after Auschwitz, active, alive, critical interpretation of authors – and through them, authority – is more crucial than ever before.

Having called this section "How Modernism Ended," I feel some pressure to address the subsumed question of *whether* modernism ended. As it is to most things, the answer is "yes and no." If we define modernism as a historical period that hosted a burst of innovative experiments and discoveries over many different fields, then yes, modernism ended in the forties with two holocausts: the genocide perpetrated by the Nazis and the nuclear holocaust that destroyed Hiroshima. If, however, we understand modernism to designate an attempt to grapple more immediately with an increasingly dynamic and contradictory reality, then modernism is still very much alive.

Reading Pleasure

The other major revolution of the time that was as important in its way as violence was sex. Brought into the scientific spotlight by Freud, sexual behavior and its "morality" split people into two camps during the modernist period. The relation between what was private and what could be made public was eroded: in Bloomsbury, a man dared to say the word "semen" in mixed company and an artistic movement was born.[72] In this case, a transgressive comment opened up a world of thought and expression that had previously been off-limits; conventionality was rejected as an artificial construct that dampened vitality and discouraged creative innovation. Ordinary, private life was not only something that could be publicly exposed with disastrous effects (as in the case of Charles Stewart Parnell, and, somewhat differently, of Oscar Wilde[73]), it could also be explored and celebrated. Both Woolf and Joyce penetrated the inner thoughts of their characters, recording them against a backdrop of quotidian urban details. Along with many others, including Samuel Butler, Marcel Proust, Henry James, Gertrude Stein, D.H. Lawrence, Ford Madox Ford, Djuna Barnes, William Faulkner, Ernest Hemingway, and Elizabeth Bowen, they mapped the forces of unconscious fear and desire, creating what E.M. Forster called the "psychological movement" in the literature between the wars, a movement that emphasized "the presence in all of us of the subconscious, the occasional existence of the split personality, the persistence of the irrational especially in people who pride themselves on their reasonableness, the importance of dreams and the prevalence of day-dreaming" (274–5). In addition to being psychologically acute, Joyce in particular explored a range of human sexual responses with such scandalous verisimilitude that *Ulysses* would be banned from the English-speaking world for over a decade. Somewhat earlier, Henry James tracked the stormy power of intercultural encounters, capturing the surge of vitality and the loss of innocence in Americans abroad.

The conflicts that raged in literature for these fifty years were reactions to the split between self and other, which became a political question, an erotic challenge, a concern with literary partnership, and even a grammatical issue, as Joyce underscored in *Finnegans Wake* by focusing on the pronouns "I" and "you," which he renders as "goy" and "Jew," and as Arthur Rimbaud indicated earlier through his famous assertion, "*Je est an autre* [sic; I is someone else; I is another]."[74] A greater premium was placed on the plasticity of language, its capacity to humanize or dehumanize individuals and groups, to inflate or deflate its characters. The capacity of names to *substitute* for the human gives language its dehumanizing potential. Shem asks in *Finnegans Wake* as the first riddle of the universe, "When is a man not a man?" The answer is when he is a name ("man" spelled backwards), a sham, or a Shem (the speaker's own name, which also means "name" in Hebrew). Although it can sham (and shame), language also has the capacity to convey a newly specific appreciation of the complex workings of self and other, to tell us, in the words of Wallace Stevens, "of ourselves and of our origins, / In ghostlier demarcations, keener sounds" ("The Idea of Order at Key West"). Where twentieth-century literature and history meet most squarely is over problems of definition: is definition important primarily for its capacity to confirm the limits of the thing defined, or for its powers to articulate and thereby extend its connection with other phenomena? Stevens suggests that in the process of melodious articulation we sometimes succeed in remaking our subject in the grammatical space between "I" and "you." In such cases, the subject is defined or contained while taking on a vivid particularity that opens up new possibilities for connection, which Stevens calls "fragrant portals." These are Stephen Dedalus' "portals of discovery" (*Ulysses* 9.229).

Such explorations are intensely pleasurable, and by calling this chapter "Why Read Challenging Literature?" I have made them sound dismayingly like an assignment or punishment. While reading difficult literature requires both discipline and persistence, it is not a punishment. As Pound asserted, "Gloom and solemnity are entirely out of place in even the most rigorous study of an art originally intended to make glad the heart of man." He quotes Laurence Sterne's definition of gravity as "a mysterious carriage of the body to conceal the defects of the mind."[75] The pleasure of reading difficult texts is neither narcissistic nor vicarious, nor does it offer an elevated prospect from which readers can look out over the turmoil of events. It is a participatory pleasure akin to traveling to a new place where the people speak a language one doesn't know. The pleasure is stimulating rather than reassuring: it is the pleasure of intercourse, or exchange. Reading an easily accessible book – like walking down the street where you live – doesn't prompt you to ask anyone for help. But traveling in a new place or reading a book that eludes comprehension compels you to ask others for guidance. In extreme cases, such as reading Joyce's *Finnegans Wake*, one cannot read it meaningfully in isolation; instead, meaning is optimally constructed in communion with others, as you "Wipe your glosses [glasses, exegetical glosses] with what you know" (204.fn 3). The goal of reading more challenging literature is not to assent to the conclusions of the author or narrator, but to discipline ourselves to accept the uncertainty of not knowing: to embrace lacunae, to understand conclusions as necessarily provisional and often ambivalent. High modernist literature serves as a field that helps to develop and reward such practices.

I have enlisted the considerable power of twentieth-century atrocities to suggest that readers have a responsibility to read – to question authority – more carefully, critically, respectfully, and even resistantly. But people don't typically change their comfortable habits in response to a threat. As Algy implies in *The Importance of Being Earnest*, in everyday affairs we are more likely to be moved by pleasure than by fear. (Ernest: "What brings you up to town?" Algy: "Oh, pleasure, pleasure! What else should bring one anywhere?" *Complete Works* 322). In an article in the *New Yorker*, Jonathan Franzen objects that the main problem with difficult literature is that it isn't pleasurable enough:

> My small hope for literary criticism would be to hear . . . more about the erotic and the culinary arts. Think of the novel as lover: Let's stay

home tonight and have a great time. Just because you're touched where you want to be touched, it doesn't mean you're cheap; before a book can change you, you have to love it.[76]

Let's think about what Franzen has assumed: that an erotic encounter is defined first and foremost by the immediacy of the pleasure it affords. Immediate pleasure is easy: think of eating, bathing, drinking, talking, even exercising: everyday life is filled with immediate – and fleeting – moments of sensual enjoyment. What is rarer is an experience of that richer, more lasting pleasure that comes from prolonged acquaintance. Franzen's metaphor for the kind of book/lover he prefers is inescapably promiscuous: he goes to bed with a book he's just met, that has not wooed him with its erotic elusiveness, its teasing promises of new and rich discoveries that can't be realized in a single encounter. What kinds of lovers *do* we prefer, anyway? Why have we forgotten that a book we can come to again and again, our pleasure growing with familiarity, is the best lover of all? Deferral of pleasure is deeply erotic, as we see in the *Odyssey*, where Odysseus returns to a *living* bed where he makes sweet love to Penelope again after twenty years of separation *because* he has had the cunning to defer the immediate siren pleasures of retribution and recognition.

What, then, is the role of the reader in modernist literature? It is to play all the different parts in the story or poem in order to gain an understanding or feeling of how or why they come together. It is to embrace the daunting, the foreign, and the multifaceted, without anxiety and without deference. We cannot approach a new lover by unthinkingly applying what we have learned elsewhere; instead, we watch and learn in a spirit of exploration.

To accept partnership with the unknown author is not only erotic, it is spiritual in the deepest sense of the term, traveling without a known destination. The willingness to engage playfully, provisionally, and also respectfully with what we don't yet know or care about is deeply ethical. When Hitler burned the experimental books and paintings of the modernist years, he was declaring war on autonomous thought and action itself, in favor of a more automatic, thoughtless, and easier response: obedience to authority and its mirror-image, the knee-jerk rejection of authority. In the process, he destroyed pleasure as well.

Part II Readings

Chapter 2 **Partnering**
Holmes and Watson, Author and Reader, Lover and Loved, Man and Wife

The material to follow includes readings of several works written during the modernist period, as well as discussions of selected plays by Samuel Beckett that were composed after World War II. These works are "challenging" in two different ways. Some of them challenge the reader implicitly: it is often difficult for readers to understand the point of these texts because they proceed from a different set of assumptions than the ones most readers bring to them. Others are not difficult to understand on a first reading, but they are nonetheless challenging, in that they take issue with dominant social fictions, such as the fiction that a democratic society ensures equal rights for all.

I am offering the analyses of James Joyce's *Dubliners* and Samuel Beckett's *Waiting for Godot* and *Endgame* to illustrate how and why these writers make the effort to trap readers into incomprehension, and how texts that may otherwise seem bewildering or pointless yield a wealth of surprising and disturbing meanings if we come to them with different questions, or if we train ourselves to notice different things. It is not enough to *tell* a reader that he or she has been indoctrinated in a way that has limited his or her ability to understand; in order to convey this point convincingly and draw attention to its disturbing implications, an author must make the reader experience the frustration of encountering his or her own blind spots. Most readers don't at first believe that the problem is with their vision and that they are responding predictably; instead, they feel certain that the problem lies in the text. I would like to demonstrate exactly how these works reward an alternative method of gathering and interpreting evidence, in the hope that readers of this book will learn from these examples how to look and listen differently. What we are currently trained to do is to evaluate a book or a play by the effect that it immediately produces on us, but that method is too passively responsive, too impatient, and too conditioned to generate insights that might change the way we approach problems. If, on the other hand, we imagine ourselves as having authored one of these texts that seem pointless or meaningless, and having done so for a good reason, aspects of the text that were cleverly buried become more apparent, and we are able to appreciate the very social conditioning that blinded us to them in the first place. This awareness can in turn change the way we read almost anything.

Take, for example, George du Maurier's *Trilby* (1894), which is not only easy to follow but was the first wildly successful "blockbuster" in the modern sense. The book seems to be a melodramatic chronicle of how a young girl goes from being a delightfully idiosyncratic model for bohemian painters in Paris to a famous singer who has lost all her agency; she is reduced to a mere mouthpiece for the arch-villain Svengali, who hypnotizes her in order to use her as his instrument. The lurid tale of how a free-spirited young woman is robbed of the rights over her own body by a determined and talented man who longs to possess her was avidly followed by readers as if it were a gothic horror story, a highly unlikely and unusual set of events, when in fact it is a tricked-up version of a sordidly common tale of the legal fate of women in the late nineteenth century.

Trilby is not a difficult novel to read, but it is nonetheless quite difficult to see the fate of the title character as potentially that of everywoman under laws that defined marriage as a form of legal servitude. What obscured the "ordinariness" of Trilby's experience, beneath its exaggerations – a hidden ordinariness that helps to explain the book's wide appeal – is a social fiction: the romantic mystification of marriage in the culture as a whole. A little over fifty years later, Gertrude Stein could playfully state the question: "What is marriage, is marriage protection or religion, is marriage renunciation or abundance, is marriage a stepping-stone or an end. What is marriage."[1] However, for a generation of women indoctrinated to believe that marriage was an honor won in a contest against many other worthy women, *Trilby* could express the counter-truth of that view only covertly, so as not to threaten its ideological supremacy.

Trilby's dilemma – the dilemma of lower-class women more generally – is portrayed first through the relationship between Trilby and the painter Little Billee and then through the connection between Trilby and Svengali. Trilby was literally too free (and too revealing) to be a suitable partner to Little Billee, and she was too much in Svengali's thrall to have any autonomy whatsoever. With Little Billee she was the model, not the artist. With Svengali, "her" art was really his, through the device of ventriloquism.

What is so memorable about Trilby is what Du Maurier calls her "irrepressible Trilbyness";[2] although she seems lively and autonomous at the outset, she is ultimately both exalted *and* destroyed by the art and then the music of the men who love her. Both the "angelic" painter Little Billee and the demonic Svengali abuse this freeloving young woman with the "virginal heart" (37) in opposite ways: Little Billee idealizes her "from the base upward" (35; Trilby's "base or pedestal," her foot, was "the handsomest foot in all Paris,"15), and Svengali utterly dominates her as "wife, slave, and pupil" (245), creating in her "the obedience and devotion of a dog" (246). While in the bohemian art studios of Paris and in the concert halls of the world, Trilby becomes "the greatest pleasure-giver of our time" (287), she was taught "shame" by Little Billee and dehumanized (reduced to an instrument) by Svengali.

> He [Svengali] had but to say "*Dors!*" and she suddenly became an unconscious Trilby of marble, who could produce wonderful sounds – just the sounds he wanted, and nothing else – and think his thoughts and wish his wishes – and love him at his bidding with a strange, unreal, factitious love . . . just his own love for himself turned inside out – *à l'envers* – and reflected back on him, as from a mirror. . . .
>
> . . . That Trilby was just a singing-machine – an organ to play upon – an instrument of music – a Stradivarius . . .
>
> . . . when Svengali's Trilby was singing – or seemed to *you* as if she were singing – *our* Trilby was fast asleep . . . in fact, *our* Trilby was *dead.* (299)

The men who claimed to love Trilby, who seemed to be uniting with her to create art, were actually enslaving her to their needs. Written by Du Maurier, himself a caricaturist (for the popular periodical *Punch*), the sensational best-selling novel was also a kind of caricature, and what it caricatured was marriage – the unequal partnerships that were considered normal, even desirable. *Trilby* is Shaw's *Pygmalion* in reverse: here, a vibrant, loving, idiosyncratic human being of questionable class is transformed through the art of a man who horribly refers to his mastery of her as "love."

Trilby exposes the abusive potential of unequal partnership, not only in marriage or between lovers, but also as something that concerns a commanding speaker and an obedient listener. When the speaker has too much power in that partnership, the ghosts of Svengali and the helplessly obedient Trilby are likely to be present. The Latin root of the word "obey" is akin to *audire*, to hear, which gives rise to the expression "To hear is to obey." When the ghost of Hamlet's father commands him to "List, List, O List!" the imprecation is not only for Hamlet to open his ears, but also to do what he is told. This etymological link suggests that in any speech act, the speaker claims authority, and the auditor is expected to obey. As the illustration from *Hamlet* implies, the relation between authority and auditor is far from equal: it is represented in a father's relation to his son, as well as a dead person's power over the living. In other contexts, this inequality marks a husband's authority over a (dependent) wife, and a master's control over a slave. Beginning in the late nineteenth century, the hierarchical relation of such couples began to shift, as we can see by the abolitionist and woman's suffrage movements. Slaves and wives alike, with considerable support, increased their agitation for equality, and their efforts eventually produced changes in the legal status of both groups.

Not surprisingly, such assaults on the necessity of obedience also affected the way audiences were to hear, or read, or interpret. Interpretation became less obedient, more autonomous and creative, as authors increasingly encouraged readers to accept a fuller and more equal partnership in the production of meaning. Consider, for example, the immense popularity of Arthur Conan Doyle's stories about a "new" kind of reader, Sherlock Holmes, and his attentive and even eloquent partner, Doctor Watson. Holmes and Watson together represent the newly composite, autonomous, ingenious interpreter that was being called into being by the social changes of the late nineteenth century, as well as by the new physics of the invisibles, which focused on such small things as radiation, molecules, atoms, and elementary particles. James Joyce's *Dubliners* was perhaps the first book that instead of being *about* a team of problem-solvers, was written for a reader willing to solve problems on his or her own. This kicked off the era in which modernist authors began to write for – and thereby call into being – a more independent and formidable brand of reader, one who was not exactly disobedient or resistant to hearing and obeying, but who refused to allow his or her interpretations to be limited to those of the narrator or protagonist.

The change in the author–reader relation was influenced not only by the ingenious interpreters to be found in detective fiction, but also by changes in the structure of marriage. Married women had to challenge not only the habit of obeying their husbands, but also the law that they must do so. Unmarried women had to construct socially acceptable ways to support themselves and make satisfying contributions to society. Women could not easily reinvent themselves along the lines of Sherlock Holmes because their freedom and education had been so severely restricted; instead, they designed a "new" woman who they hoped would someday enter into equal partnership with a "new" man to create a more productive and fulfilling dialogue.

Men and women had been interpolated into society differently, and had to "unlearn" their socialization in different ways. The literature of the 1890s suggests that middle-class men needed to become more cautious and responsible when making judgments, whereas women needed to become less hesitant and better informed. The Holmes and Watson team demonstrates the value of taking greater care to avoid mistakes, of analyzing problems more slowly and deliberately before offering solutions. The articles and stories on the new woman, on the other hand, urge women to take more risks, to offer new and different solutions – even if they are mistaken – in an effort to learn from experience (including that found in books) instead of merely from precept. In short, men – patterning themselves on Holmes and Watson – were being abjured to be more careful (in the two senses of that term that Holmes and Watson respectively demonstrate, taking greater care and being more caring), whereas women were challenged to become more assertive and daring – in the tradition of such literary heroines as Jane Austen's Emma and Charlotte Brontë's Jane Eyre – if they hoped to gain a greater degree of deliberative choice over the socially inculcated habit of obedience.

The following chapter falls into three sections, all demonstrating the rewards of equal partnership. The first section focuses primarily on the importance of exercising greater care in solving problems (or making interpretive choices). It takes as its iconic examples the Sherlock Holmes stories and Joyce's *Dubliners*. The Holmes stories offer two male partners as models of taking care (being sharply observant, like Holmes, and being emotionally empathic and caring, like Watson). Joyce's enigmatic stories focus on characters who are not models to be emulated, nor do they form successful partnerships with other characters. Instead, the reader is enjoined to partner with the author in an effort to understand how these characters – all of whom represent possible projections of ourselves – went wrong. The stories unfold their potentially rich implications only to readers who "take care" – in both senses of the word – in reading them.

The second section considers a different but related kind of partnership: marriage. In a marriage economy, young (and inexperienced) women have considerable power over men for a few short years, until they marry, when that power is transferred to the husband, as the legal and moral head of the household. In the 1890s, a great debate over marriage took place in the popular press as part of the "New Woman" movement. The literature proclaimed that if women would make the effort to distance themselves more critically, and even defiantly, from social mores, they could remake themselves as equal partners of men; in short, they were being directed to be more careful in their own thinking while caring less about what other people thought in order to free themselves from the habit of subservience. Modernist literature was in part a complicated – and sometimes contradictory – response to both of these early, strong revolts against the tyranny of habit. Several modernist works were inspired by the hope of moving from a master–slave model of relation to a model of equal partnership, and the promise of more lively and productive dialogue that went with it, although many were also tinged with nostalgia for the simpler and more stable categories of the elitist system that was being challenged.

Elementary, My Dear Reader: Sherlock Holmes and the Narrator of *Dubliners*

Although a pairing of Arthur Conan Doyle's riveting Sherlock Holmes tales with the exquisitely crafted but apparently pointless stories of

Joyce's *Dubliners* (1914) may seem odd at first, both kinds of stories were designed to encourage readers to exercise greater interpretive authority. In the Holmes stories, readers learned to admire (and be surprised by) Sherlock Holmes' powers of deduction; the entertainment derives from the fact that readers come to see what they missed in the unfolding of the mystery. As Holmes tells Watson in *The Hound of the Baskervilles* (1902), "The world is full of obvious things which nobody by any chance ever observes."[3] The stakes of paying closer attention are high, since solving the mystery is essential if justice is to be served for a crime that most often involves murder.

What readers learn is that they too readily make assumptions that interfere with their capacity to solve problems, and they overlook small details – deeming them insignificant – that ultimately constitute crucial pieces of the puzzle.[4] What the Holmes stories remind the reader, through the examples of Holmes, Watson, the murderer, and an occasional third-person narrator, is that human motivations are complex and often twisted, that we jump to seemingly obvious conclusions too quickly, and that our haste has the potential to compound the injustice by leading us to blame the wrong person (which is what the detectives of Scotland Yard typically do). Judgment (and sentencing) should be the *final* stage of the interpretive process, but more typically it is the way readers approach a dilemma.

In contrast, the characters in *Dubliners* do not themselves model a successful or rewarding interpretive approach. Instead, each story, narrated by a child or a "cinematic" narrator who offers no commentary on what is described, presents a puzzling sequence of scenes concerning deadness that has resulted from learned habits. In *Dubliners*, the reader has to learn to read in more than one way – like Holmes, like Watson, like an investigative reporter, like both a victim *and* a perpetrator of crime – in order to understand the larger implications of the stories and their relation to ourselves.

Usually, a reader's engagement with a book relies too heavily on identification with the protagonist and often the narrator as well; it is typically vicarious. To read vicariously is to read like a vicar, one serving as a substitute or agent for the author or narrator or even for God. When we become the "agents" of the narrator or author, we cede interpretive power to him or her. Like "the person entering an authority system," we view ourselves no longer as "acting out of [our] own purposes," but instead as "an agent for executing the wishes of another person."[5] In the case of the Sherlock Holmes stories, we readers admire Holmes, but find our mode of thinking reflected more accurately by Doctor Watson, who describes himself more than once as Holmes' "agent" (see, for example, *The Hound of the Baskervilles* 95, 106, 152). However, Watson is more than just Holmes' agent; he is also Holmes' partner in the sense that his emotional responsiveness counters and softens Holmes' obsessive detachment, his "cold and unemotional manner," his addiction to "brainwork," and his view of the world as "dreary, dismal, unprofitable."[6]

Unlike Watson, Holmes is not a vicar or agent for anyone else; on the contrary, he is careful to resist identification with any one position because it narrows the field of observation: this is the reason his methods are so surprising and successful. Holmes observes first and waits to draw conclusions until he has gathered a mass of apparently ill-assorted evidence and it has crystallized into an improbable but irrefutable pattern. Holmes is an attentive and acute reader of signs, an unconventional interpreter who is bound to no authority other than the accumulated knowledge on the subject; he is responsible ultimately to himself: his methods, his values, and his determination to get accurate results. Holmes proceeds not by calculating probabilities, but by eliminating the impossible and thereby discovering a truth – even if it is an improbable one. As he chides Watson over and over, "You will not apply my precept. . . . How often have I said to you that when you have eliminated the impossible, whatever remains, *however improbable*, must be the truth?" (*The Sign of Four* 42). Like a particularly insightful literary critic, he navigates his way to a solution not by what is familiar and easily comprehensible, but by focusing on what doesn't make sense. He tells Watson at the end of *The Hound of the Baskervilles*, "The more *outré* and grotesque an incident is the more carefully it deserves to be examined, and the very point which appears to complicate a text is, when duly examined and scientifically handled, the one which is most likely to elucidate it" (169).

The Sherlock Holmes stories insist that the reader think more like a narrator, using careful observation, analyzing "backwards" from what is observed, relating any problems to the larger archive of "literature" on the subject, and then chronicling what was learned. Under the pen of Conan Doyle various models of "reading-narrating" are offered not only by the main narrator, Watson, the physician and healer, but also by a second "narrator" – the investigative Holmes – a third narrator who provides background information, and finally by the murderer himself.

Conan Doyle's innovative narrative splintering forestalls vicarious – or thoughtless – identification with a single point of view. In *A Study in Scarlet* – the first of the series, published in *Beeton's Christmas Annual* in 1887 – it is difficult to differentiate between narrators and readers. Narrators *are* interpreters, a kinship that by extension lessens the difference between authors and readers. The main narrator (or writer) is of course Doctor John H. Watson, from whose "reminiscences" most of the text is ostensibly taken. Watson's charm comes from his enthusiasm and his emotional and imaginative involvement in the story that is unraveling, but his power as a narrator is both limited and enhanced by the fact that he is no quicker than the reader at understanding what is going on. As Kyle Freeman writes, Watson "can frame the story more dramatically than the detective could because [he] is in the dark about the outcome";[7] nevertheless Watson often offers data and reports to Holmes, who dispassionately refuses to offer a narrative until he has formed a conclusion. Watson's role is simply to help the detective accumulate data from which he can construct a solution. As Watson explains in *The Hound of the Baskervilles*: "Much of what I tell you is no doubt quite irrelevant, but still I feel that it is best that I should let you have all the facts and leave you to select for yourself those which will be of most service to you in helping you to your conclusions" (104).

At the outset of *A Study in Scarlet* we have two narrators – Watson and Holmes – but a third-person narrator unexpectedly intervenes to relate the first five chapters of part 2, "The Country of the Saints," which concerns John and Lucy Ferrier in Mormon Utah many years earlier. Finally, in the concluding chapter the murderer, Jefferson Hope, becomes a fourth narrator, filling in the details that the others have no way of knowing. His narration/interpretation is also, implicitly, a defense intended to clarify what motivated the murder(s). These several narrators help to prevent the reader from relying too heavily on a single perspective, which in *The Hound of the Baskervilles* is associated with a murderous disposition rather than interpretive openness. There, the murderer, Stapleton, is associated with the great rare moth he is chasing, which is significantly a "Cyclopides," a single-eyed Homeric "monster." As Stapleton chases him, Watson notes that his "irregular progress made him not unlike some huge moth himself" (75).

What does Conan Doyle accomplish by dividing the narration among these four voices? In addition to collapsing the difference between narrator and interpreter, and offering the reader several different models of engaging with the supplied data, the four voices allow Doyle to gain time; he is able to delay the telling of the story, which is a crucial feature of the interpretive process that the stories endorse: the postponement of judgment. In *A Study in Scarlet*, the story unfolds piece by piece, since no one narrator knows it all until Watson is able to put the pieces together. The reader is admonished throughout not to hypothesize, not to theorize, not to make judgments prematurely (premature judgment is the literal meaning of "prejudice"). The effect of such a delay – both narrative and interpretive – is threefold: it preserves the sense of mystery; it reminds readers that "sentencing" – both in the sense of deciding penalties and in the sense of framing a story – should be the ultimate (not the initial) stage in a judicial process; and, finally, it reinforces Holmes's instructions to Watson about how to make observations that facilitate accurate deductions.

One of the most important functions of delayed revelation is that it sustains mystery. Mystery stimulates the imagination yet keeps the observer aware of his or her own ignorance and vulnerability, aiding observation by keeping the senses sharp. As Holmes remarks about the case he is investigating in *A Study in Scarlet,* "There is a mystery about this which stimulates the imagination; where there is no imagination there is no horror."[8] Horror is a product of yet another imaginative identification, here with the victim, and identification with the victim reminds observers that they, too, are potentially at risk. The narrator who most effectively promotes mysteriousness is Watson, who regards Holmes himself as a mystery, calling his actions "incomprehensible" (26) and relishing the opportunity to try to learn more about him: "I eagerly hailed the little mystery which hung around my companion, and spent much of my time in endeavouring to unravel it" (14).

In addition to wondering about Holmes and his methods, Watson also exclaims about the mysteriousness of the case Holmes is investigating: "the more one thinks of it the more mysterious it grows" (29). Mystery is the effect that is produced by difficulty of interpretation in a context in which one is potentially vulnerable to the effects of misunderstanding, which is why Holmes is careful to distinguish mystery from strangeness. Strangeness is a symptom or clue that makes interpretation easier: "It is a mistake to confound strangeness with mystery. The most common-place crime is often the most mysterious, because it presents no new or special features from which deductions may be drawn" (49).

One of Watson's most important functions, then, is to draw attention to the mysteriousness and therefore the complexity and danger associated with Holmes and his cases. He does this in part by asking questions, thereby modeling for the reader the importance of active curiosity. When contemplating the circumstances of the murder in *A Study in Scarlet*, he ponders,

> How came these two men – if there were two men – into an empty house? What has become of the cabman who drove them? How could one man compel another to take poison? Where did the blood come from? What was the object of the murderer, since robbery had no part in it? How came the woman's ring there? Above all, why should the second man write up the German word RACHE before decamping? I confess that I cannot see any possible way of reconciling all these facts. (29)

Holmes models a complementary approach to the problem of finding the truth: observe minutely, and practice the art of "backwards reasoning." In order to solve the problems, readers must to learn to practice Holmes' methods as well as Watson's.

Before we consider Holmes as a reader, we should quickly review his credentials as a forensic scientist, because this affects the kind of reader he is. Holmes is a chemist with a pragmatic rather than theoretical bent and a "passion for definite and exact knowledge" (9). As Watson reflects, "Sherlock Holmes's smallest actions were all directed towards some definite and practical end" (27). Holmes's signature characteristic is a hawklike attentiveness to what other people consider trifles: "To a great mind, nothing is little" (40). In Watson's words, "Desultory readers are seldom remarkable for the exactness of their learning. No man burdens his mind with small matters unless he has some very good reason for doing so" (14). Holmes is indefatigable in his pursuit of truth, defining genius as "an infinite capacity for taking pains" (27).

Holmes, then, is a supremely rational, formidably observant, uncon-ventional, and quick-witted analyst who practices what he calls "the scientific use of the imagination" (*HB* 38). This "excessively lean" man, topping six feet in height, combines sharp and piercing eyes with an "extraordinary delicacy of touch" (*SS* 13). Sometimes full of energy, he also has periods in which he lies on the sofa for days on end (Watson suspects him of a narcotic addiction, and this famous addiction complicates any desire the reader might have to idealize him). Holmes' knowledge of a few highly specialized subjects is prodigious – for example, it is noted in *A Study in Scarlet* that he has made a special study of cigar ashes (29) and has found "an infallible test for blood stains" (10). As Watson relates, "within eccentric limits his knowledge was so extraordinarily ample and minute that his observations have fairly astounded me," but, importantly, "His ignorance was as remarkable as his knowledge" (14). Watson is astonished to discover that Holmes knows nothing about Copernicus and the solar system. When he tells Holmes about Copernican theory, Holmes resolves to forget it immediately, which is a pragmatic necessity that nonetheless illustrates the extreme narrowness of Holmes' focus. As Holmes explains, the human brain is like a little empty attic that one must furnish quite deliberately: "Now the skilful workman is very careful indeed as to what he takes into his brain-attic. . . . It is of the highest importance . . . not to have useless facts elbowing out the useful ones" (14).

Conan Doyle portrays Holmes not only as a fine technician who uses the scientific method, but also as a writer and reader of life. Watson happens upon an article that Holmes has written called "The Book of Life." Watson is a reader of Holmes, but Holmes can read life and death like a book, reading even "in the dust" (29). When he uses his tape measure and magnifying glass, he can construct a surprisingly detailed story out of what others simply see as disorder (27). Watson notes that the "quickness of [Holmes'] perceptive faculties" allows him to "see a great deal which was hidden from" Watson (22).

Holmes' article, which is the one thing he actually writes in *A Study in Scarlet*, attempts "to show how much an observant man might learn by an accurate and systematic examination of all that came in his way" (16–17). As Watson recounts, with great skepticism,

> the writer claimed by a momentary expression, a twitch of a muscle or a glance of an eye, to fathom a man's inmost thoughts. Deceit, according to him, was an impossibility in the case of one trained to observation and analysis. His conclusions were as infallible as so many propositions of Euclid. (17)

Holmes writes that he is able to read a person's thoughts (bypassing any lies that person might try to tell) simply by observing his or her body with the requisite attentiveness. Theoretically, the reason this is possible is that everything is connected, which is why Holmes can say that "From a drop of water, . . . a logician could infer the possibility of an Atlantic or a Niagara without having seen or heard of one or the other. So all life is a great chain, the nature of which is known whenever we are shown a single link of it" (17).

Watson's reaction to Holmes' article, before he learns who wrote it, is incredulous and dismissive: he calls it "a remarkable mixture of shrewdness and absurdity," its deductions "far fetched and exaggerated," and he slaps it on the table with the exclamation, "ineffable twaddle" (17). He argues that the theory advocated in the article is not "practical," which Holmes refutes by revealing that he himself practices it successfully in the way he makes his living. What is at stake in this disagreement is their respective ways of reading, and Holmes explains that a reader may learn to read more deductively and analytically by beginning with details that are usually dismissed as insignificant:

> Like all other arts, the Science of Deduction and Analysis is one which can only be acquired by long and patient study, nor is life long enough to allow any mortal to attain the highest possible perfection in it. Before turning to those moral and mental aspects of the matter which present the greatest difficulties, let the inquirer begin by mastering more elementary problems. Let him, on meeting a fellow-mortal, learn at a glance to distinguish the history of the man, and the trade or profession to which he belongs. Puerile as such an exercise may seem, it sharpens the faculties of observation, and teaches one where to look and what to look for. By a man's finger-nails, by his coat-sleeve, by his boots, by his trouser-knees, by the callousities of his forefinger and thumb, by his expression, by his shirt-cuffs, by each of these things a man's calling is plainly revealed. (17)

Unlike most readers, Holmes wipes his mind clean of expectations and hypotheses when he begins to read, beginning an act of interpretation with his mind "entirely free of impressions" (94). As he remarks on another occasion, "It is a capital mistake to theorize before you have all the evidence. It biases the judgment" (22).[9] In order to generate a hypothesis that meets the facts, one must gather facts first and make conclusions at the end. As Holmes points out, most readers proceed the other way round. It is not enough, however, simply to read the situation at hand; one must also know the history of comparable situations, which is why Holmes tells Gregson, one of the Scotland Yard detectives, to "read. There is nothing new under the sun. It has all been done before" (24).

When Holmes instructs Watson to clear his mind of impressions, expectations, and theories in order to observe more acutely, he is explaining how to begin the analytical (as opposed to the synthetic) interpretive process.[10] He explains his method as one that focuses on the result or end of a sequence of events and "reasons backward" from that point. Such reasoning is storytelling in reverse, and when done in an informed manner it is a crucial technique for creative problem-solving. Holmes suggests that most people understand prediction, which is "synthetic" because it weaves different details together into a coherent expectation, much more successfully than they learn its counterpart, analysis, the attempt to unweave (or "loosen," from the Greek *ana-* and *-lyein*, to loosen) a fabric of events in order to understand how it was woven. As Holmes recounts to Watson:

> I have already explained to you that what is out of the common is usually a guide rather than a hindrance. In solving a problem of this sort, the grand thing is to be able to reason backward. That is a very useful accomplishment, and a very easy one, but people do not practise it much. In the everyday affairs of life it is more useful to reason forward, and so the other comes to be neglected. There are fifty who can reason synthetically for one who can reason analytically. (93)

Watson has trouble following, so Holmes tries to make it clearer:

> Most people, if you describe a train of events to them, will tell you what the result would be. They can put those events together in their minds, and argue from them that something will come to pass. There are few people, however, who, if you told them a result, would be able to evolve from their own inner consciousness what the steps were which led up to that result. This power is what I mean when I talk of reasoning backward, or analytically. (93)

The skill that Holmes tries to teach Watson is the under-developed, under-utilized skill of what has come to be called, somewhat mislead-ingly, "criticism" (it is misleading because the word "criticism" connotes "negative evaluation," whereas the point of "criticism" is not to judge but to elucidate and analyze so that readers may make better judgments for themselves). In "The Perfect Critic," T. S. Eliot argues that "criticism" (Holmes' "reasoning backward") and "creation" (Holmes' "synthesis") are the "two directions of sensibility," which are complementary.[11] Eliot makes the case that artists are the best critics because unlike professional critics they aren't unconsciously "creating" when they seem to be analyz-ing, but the part of his argument that is most relevant here is the sug-gestion that the "ordinary emotional person" (like Watson) tends to be unreliable in response to a work of art (the artwork is here analogous to a crime, insofar as both are the result of intentional "acts" designed to create a powerful effect). Eliot contends that "The sentimental person, in whom a work of art arouses all sorts of emotions which have nothing to do with that work of art whatever, but are accidents of personal association, is an incomplete artist" (7). Eliot argues that in such a "critic," the creative and the analytical processes are mixed up, not complementary.

Eliot's example of the kind of reading that opposes and complements the creative, synthetic impulse is Aristotle's *Posterior Analytics*, obviously akin to Holmes' "backward reasoning" (see *The Sacred Wood* 10). Eliot's view of the artist and the critic as complementary phases of a single antiphonal rhythm reflects Wilde's earlier argument in "The Critic as Artist" (articulated by Wilde's character Gilbert) that the antithesis between the critical and the creative is "entirely arbitrary. Without the critical faculty, there is no artistic creation at all, worthy of the name."[12] Gilbert explains that "it is the critical faculty that invents fresh forms. The tendency of creation is to repeat itself" (357). In Conan Doyle's works, Holmes and Watson embody the important collaboration of the critical spirit and the creative spirit, and we see that the critical spirit is, as Wilde has Gilbert insist, much more cultivated and difficult than the creative (or synthetic) one, but the two are optimally equal and interdependent: they should operate as a team, with Holmes doing the observing and thinking and Watson doing the appreciative storytelling.

I have been concentrating so far on the two main narrators of *A Study in Scarlet*, Watson and Holmes, and their relation to one another as interpreters (or readers) and as writers about "the book of life." But they are also importantly related to the fourth narrator, the murderer, who is, in several important respects, the mirror image of Holmes. The reflection of Holmes in the murderer – here significantly named "Hope," accenting Holmes' patience and his faith in justice – is indebted first to the conception of crime as a creative or original act (in its defiance of convention and law).[13] In *A Study in Scarlet,* the connection between crime and art is acknowledged in the title Holmes bestows upon the case, which he borrows from the language of art:

> I might not have gone but for you, and so have missed the finest study I ever came across: a study in scarlet, eh? Why shouldn't we use a little art jargon. There's the scarlet thread of murder running through the colourless skein of life, and our duty is to unravel it, and isolate it, and expose every inch of it. (32)

Art and murder both add color to the highly regulated sameness of a social life governed by laws and conventions.[14]

Generally, the criminal is clearly differentiated from the artist by the irreversible, real-life consequences of his act. In *A Study in Scarlet*, though, the murderer perceives himself as dispensing justice, just like Holmes. Hope says, "You may consider me to be a murderer, but I hold that I am just as much an officer of justice as you are" (92). Hope conceives of himself as the lethal consequences of the sin committed by Drebber and Strangerson when they kidnapped the woman Hope loved and forced her to become one of Drebber's wives. He plans his encounter with Drebber so as to "have the opportunity of making the man who had wronged me understand that his old sin had found him out" (88). Hope feels himself to have supernatural approval for his lifelong pursuit of revenge; as he hunts Drebber down, he can see the faces of the father and daughter Drebber killed "looking at [him] out of the darkness and smiling at [him]" (89). Even Hope's method of killing Drebber incorporates elements of choice and chance that enable him to think of it as divine justice: he asks Drebber to take one of two pills while he takes the other, letting God decide who dies and who lives:

Let the high God judge between us. Choose and eat. There is death in one and life in the other. I shall take what you leave. Let us see if there is justice upon the earth, or if we are ruled by chance. (90)

Watson picks up the idea that earthly courts are simply imperfect imitations of divine justice when he discloses the fact that Hope had died before appearing in front of the magistrates: "A higher Judge had taken the matter in hand, and Jefferson Hope had been summoned before a tribunal where strict justice would be meted out to him" (93).

The last narrator is a third-person omniscient voice who fills in the background of what happened to John and Lucy Ferrier in Utah. As a source of knowledge that could not be gained from a single person's experience, this narrator stands in for books themselves and the specialized information they are able to impart. Holmes has recourse to such knowledge – essential to establishing the context for a story – when he studies the history of crime. As he tells Watson in *The Sign of Four*, knowledge, along with observation and deduction, is one of the "three qualities necessary for the ideal detective" (8). If each of the narrators offers a different position that can be adopted by the reader, then relevant background material is represented in *A Study in Scarlet* by the intervention of the omniscient narrator. When the reader learns to identify not just with a single protagonist but with the antagonist as well, imaginatively entertaining the perspectives of the murderer, the victim, the investigator, and the sympathetic bystander, such flexible self-positioning promotes an appreciation of what Watson refers to as "the many-sidedness of the human mind" (32). As Conan Doyle suggests, it is when we unconsciously accept a single role or privilege and come to believe in it without skepticism that we prepare the ground for injustice.

In apparent contrast, Joyce's *Dubliners* is designed to frustrate those interpretive habits. A reader cannot learn anything meaningful from *Dubliners* by approaching it in the usual vicarious way; if we try, we unconsciously replicate the habits of characters we are quick to dismiss as "paralyzed" and not fully alive. As we have seen, vicarious reading, defined as an instinctive (that is, unthinking) sympathetic identification with author, narrator, or character, produces the same distortion as that created by theorizing before all the facts are known: in Holmes's words, it "biases the judgment." To read less vicariously, one must consciously avoid forming too strong an alliance with the protagonists, without becoming so detached that one becomes judgmental. The difference in the way the reader approaches Conan Doyle's stories in contrast with those of Joyce is reflected in the way we understand the principal partnerships at work in each. In Conan Doyle's work, the main partners are both fictional characters: Watson and Holmes. In *Dubliners*, however, the most significant partnership is between the author and reader. The characters, while important in their own right, also play a more unusual role of *mediating* or facilitating what is potentially an ongoing conversation of the reader with Joyce.

Dubliners, too, is a series of detective stories, but they significantly lack a detective. Readers are presented with a sequence of variably likeable characters who are in some way immobilized by a spiritual deadness. It is up to the reader to detect, by "reasoning backwards" from each collection of facts and observations, what must have happened. The reader as detective is doomed to failure if his or her observations are limited by whatever the protagonist notices or understands, instead of being trained on "the whole story." The stories in *Dubliners* do not involve killing, but they do involve deadness, a deadness of spirit lodged in the self that makes meaningful connection not only unlikely, but virtually impossible. The question is how it got there, how it does its insidiously paralyzing work, and how – if identified and arraigned – that deadness might be transformed into a source of vitality. In both the Holmes stories and in Joyce's, the method of interpretation has a life-or-death urgency to it; in both instances, the investigator's challenge is to discover the means of death.

Joyce envisioned this method of writing as transformative, which is striking in view of the fact that none of his characters undergoes transformation, although one or two are brought to the brink of a new awareness. He described the stories as *epikleti*, invocations to the Holy Ghost to transform ordinary bread and wine into the eternal body and blood of Christ. In other words, he wanted to find a way of infusing mundane objects with an extraordinary power, so that his communication to the reader would have some of the community-building and life-affirming vitality of eucharistic communion. In a letter to Constantine Curran in August 1904, Joyce wrote, "I am writing a series of epikleti – ten – for a paper. I have written one. I call the series *Dubliners* to betray the soul of that hemiplegia or paralysis which many consider a city."[15] As Robert Scholes and A. Walton Litz point out in their notes to *Dubliners, epiklesis* is an invocation to the Holy Ghost used in the Eastern Orthodox Church. As Joyce told his brother Stanislaus, "there is a certain resemblance between the mystery of the mass and what I am trying to do . . . to give people a kind of intellectual pleasure or spiritual enjoyment by converting the bread of everyday life into something that has a permanent artistic life of its own . . . for their mental, moral, and spiritual uplift" (250). *Epiklesis* implies not only transformation, but also "a reproach or imputation." Both meanings are crucial to Joyce's project in *Dubliners*: he may seem to be reproaching his characters for their deadness of spirit, but that very reproach is, looked at another way, a stern plea for the self-recognition that may trigger a transformation. Joyce called *Dubliners* a "nicely polished looking-glass" (June 23, 1906; 277) that he hoped readers would use to see themselves as they really are, rather than as they would like to be seen. This literary mirror reveals flaws in the protagonists not in an effort to shame or depress the reader who identifies with them, but to take him or her to that magical point at which the awareness of the limitations we have *learned* simultaneously offers a reproach and an incentive to change. Moreover, Joyce subjected his own past (and possible future) to the same searingly honest reflections that he holds up to the reader. By representing his own past selves in his fiction, he is making the author the basis of one or more characters; by giving up his own exemption from unflattering representation, he adjures the reader to do the same. He is writing from the position of a fellow traveler, not from a position of superiority, as we can tell by the way he gives two of the more flawed characters his own name (James), and stimulates sympathetic responses to the characters' shortcomings as well as critical ones.

Joyce designed his *epikleti* so that in most cases he is encouraging the *reader* (rather than the character) to search for the hidden vitality that is blocked by the deadening habits of the characters. Only in "An Encounter," "Araby," "A Painful Case," and "The Dead" do the protagonists experience even a flash of self-awareness; in these stories, such flashes are unstable and their implications unclear. The other stories tend to deny the reader any vicarious satisfaction; the main characters never understand what went wrong in their attempts to live more fulfilling lives: Maria in "Clay," Eveline, Little Chandler in "A Little Cloud," Lenehan in "Two Gallants," Farrington of "Counterparts," Mrs Kearney from "A Mother," Mr Kernan of "Grace," the unnamed boy of "The Sisters." Bob Doran of "A Boarding House" understands better than many but is nonetheless rendered helpless to act by his need to play by the rules of society. The characters, then, are unreliable guides. Unexpectedly, the reader must rely on her own economic and political knowledge and be on the lookout for preconceived observations and reactions if she is to reason backward from the stunted life that constitutes the mystery in each successive story.

The uneventful tale that inaugurates *Dubliners*, "The Sisters," offers the subtlest trap for the successfully socialized reader. Although "The Sisters" seems to focus on the informal, parochial tutoring of a young boy by a "retired" priest, it actually provides a prototype of a typical Irish Catholic education and its effects, which it may even be extended to education in general. The effect the story produces on readers is utterly predictable: very few readers win meaningful independence from the boy's confused perspective because they unconsciously identify themselves with him – they feel ambivalent about the priest: they know that he seems strange and that he did some things (such as breaking a chalice and being found laughing in a confession-box in the middle of the night) that probably caused him to be relieved of his duties to his parish. But many readers also empathize with what they perceive to be the priest's crisis of faith, his situation as "a disappointed man" who was "crossed," and they appreciate his voluntary effort to help the boy appreciate the intricacies of church doctrine. Few first-time readers see the eponymous sisters as important; on the contrary, many (like the boy) dismiss them as poorly dressed and ignorant, in the light of their verbal errors ("rheumatic" for "pneumatic," "Freeman's General" for "Freeman's Journal"). Most readers respond to Old Cotter with the boy's impatience, and they finish the story as puzzled as their guide, the boy-narrator. Everything feels unfinished, like the geometrical "gnomon" the boy has trouble understanding on the first page: Old Cotter's sentences, the priest's spiritual development, the boy's education, the story itself.

If we look more closely at the obscured "wrong" or "crime" or "sin" that lies at the heart of the story, we may more easily apply Holmes' method of "reasoning backward" to that wrong, thereby solving the mystery of the story's meaning and why it stands at the gateway of *Dubliners*. The main indication that the priest has somehow wronged the boy comes from the boy's sensation when he is on the threshold of sleep that the priest is trying to confess something to him; the two have changed places, and the priest is asking the boy for absolution.

> In the dark of my room I imagined that I saw again the heavy grey face of the paralytic. I drew the blankets over my head and tried to think of Christmas. But the grey face still followed me. It murmured; and I understood that it desired to confess something. I felt my soul receding into some pleasant and vicious region; and there again I found it waiting for me. It began to confess to me in a murmuring voice and I wondered why it smiled continually and why the lips were so moist with spittle. But then I remembered that it had died of paralysis and I felt that I too was smiling feebly as if to absolve the simoniac of his sin. (3)

Technically, the boy identifies the priest's sin as simony, a worldly trafficking in sacred things, and his disease as paralysis, an immobility of the body that results from lack of local muscle control. Instead of facilitating a sacramental transformation of the ordinary into the divine, the priest as simoniac is guilty of the opposite transformation: he has taken holy mysteries – such as grace or absolution – and made them into ordinary (and marketable) indulgences. Paralysis is meaningful as the disease that killed him because of the way it weakens his power: he loses control over the local muscles on which larger movements depend.[16] Loss of local control is not only a bodily ill, then, it is also a mental and psychological problem that affects readers. One example of a detail easily overlooked is the name of the street where the priest lives – Great Britain Street, which suggests that the Catholic Church in Ireland is complicit with Britain's imperial domination. It is likewise easy to forget that the priest lives over a shop registered as selling "drapery," although what is sold there are primarily umbrellas and children's bootees (3). "Drapery" designates cloth and dry goods, but the word also connotes concealment; the goods, on the other hand, are primarily protective items. Drapery appears in the boy's dream as the long velvet curtains he associates with Persia. What might the priest be hiding or protecting, and why? How might Joyce's purpose be related to that of the other James, the Reverend James Flynn in the story? It is crucial to ask questions as varied as those Watson might ask, and, like Holmes, to notice even apparently minor details.

At the very beginning of the story, the boy ponders the strange sound of three words – "simony," "paralysis," and "gnomon" (this last from

Euclid's treatise on geometry, referring to a parallelogram from one corner of which a smaller parallelogram has been taken, rendering the figure incomplete). The priest died of paralysis, the boy thinks of him as a simoniac, and by extension Joyce seems to be associating him with the incompleteness of a gnomon as well. These charges, while legitimate and meaningful up to a point, are insufficient to explain why the boy subconsciously feels the Father has sinned against him, despite the priest's benevolent intent. These words, then – simony, paralysis, and gnomon – are simply *clues* to the mystery at the heart of the story rather than its solution. The suggestion that the priest is an incomplete, paralyzed human being who has been guilty of some kind of simony (trivialization or commercialization of spiritual mysteries) gives us only a skeletal idea of why the boy feels more liberated than saddened by the priest's death.

The priest's lessons have simultaneously mystified and constrained the boy's relation to "truth." Some of the stories the priest told him were romantic – stories about the catacombs and Napoleon Bonaparte. But most of what he teaches the boy is technical, even scrupulous: he teaches him to pronounce Latin properly, to recite responses to the Mass, to discern fine, even hair-splitting, distinctions between mortal and venial sins. Father Flynn is teaching the boy about the "letter of the law," which killeth, as we find from the unconscious puns concerning death with which the boy's language is sprinkled: "The duties of the priest towards the Eucharist and towards the secrecy of the confessional seemed so *grave* to me that I wondered how anybody had ever found in himself the courage to *undertake* them" (5; my emphasis). Father Flynn has also taught the boy not to try to understand the mystery of faith in personal terms, but to rely on the interpretations of others, especially those of canon law. He has taught him obedience, in the form of deference to his superiors and contempt for those he considers inferior. The price of this obedience is a kind of muteness, a loss of confidence in his own ability to interpret or understand ideas in relation to his own experience. The boy recalls,

> I was not surprised when he [the priest] told me that the fathers of the Church had written books as thick as the *Post Office Directory* and as closely printed as the law notices in the newspaper, elucidating all these intricate questions. Often when I thought of this I could make no answer

or only a very foolish and halting one upon which he used to smile and nod his head twice or thrice. (5)

The labyrinthine complexity of the law that this priest celebrates makes the boy feel stupid, and the priest smiles and nods in apparent approval of the boy's foolish, hesitant responses. Readers often fail to register this fact because it seems so normal to feel helpless before the immense scholarly knowledge of a given subject, but the story suggests that the priest has injured the boy by making him feel that his inadequacy is a cause for shame, and by nonverbally encouraging him to feel better about this shameful inadequacy by taking pleasure in the inadequacy of others. The boy learns to think of all the knowledge he cannot hope to comprehend as proof of his own shortcomings, when in fact it isn't about him at all: it is simply a fact of life that could just as easily be intriguing as daunting.

In the more than nine decades since *Dubliners* was first published, no one has yet to my knowledge argued that the priest wronged the boy by rupturing the intimate connection between what he is being taught and his own experience. We all have accepted the inevitability of such a rupture between knowledge and experience, and such acceptance effectively blinds us – along with the boy himself – to Joyce's dramatization of how such a rupture occurs. We regard this dissociation as natural, not seeing that it constitutes an acceptance of an intermediary place in a systemic hierarchy of knowledge and power. "The Sisters" shows how we are taught to give up our agency and submit to the judgment of others, and it reveals how the acceptance of interpretive helplessness initiates us into a culture of isolation, injustice (for which we compensate by being unjust in turn), and finally despair.

The lesson of "The Sisters" is further illuminated by the story that follows it in *Dubliners*, "An Encounter." Both stories are dominated by "teachers": one a priest, the other commonly identified as a pederast. The reader's blindness sometimes takes the form of sympathy for the blighted lives of these authority figures and sometimes emerges as condescension toward them ("something's gone wrong" with them). However, by emphasizing the emptiness of the priest's faith, and by stressing the potentially threatening queerness of the "old josser" in "An Encounter," we overlook the immense power of both men as normative representations of cultural authority in general, and of cultural *education* in particular. Both men have a profound impact on the boy, without his knowledge or permission. The priest and the pederast are both father figures and teachers, representing two sides of the same Oedipal-cultural configuration: the priest is the one who forbids access to enjoyment and self-enlightenment by demonstrating the great difficulty of understanding the mysteries of church doctrine and discouraging the boy from trying. Instead of appreciation, he teaches denigration, meanness: the boy learns from him to look down on others such as old Cotter and the sisters. The pederast in "An Encounter" embodies the other side of the Father, who encourages the boys to recognize and indulge in the eroticism of fighting boys and touching girls. My point is that these two men personify the same apparently contradictory but actually unified cultural and patriarchal directive, which the boy accordingly learns: you can compensate for your own inadequacies by focusing on the weaknesses of others, alternately deprecating them and enjoying them, punishing them and taking advantage of them. This is a powerful directive, made even more powerful by the priest's death, because an authority figure who dies is more fully internalized.

The connection between the priest and the pederast in the two stories is carefully drawn through the similarity in their garments, their love of books, and the suggestion that their interiors are rotten. Both men are older and dressed in black with a greenish cast. The boy accounts for the patina of the priest's coat as an effect of snuff: "It may have been these constant showers of snuff which gave his ancient priestly garments their green faded look" (4). The pederast, too, is "shabbily dressed in a suit of greenish-black" (16). Both are bookworms whose smiles disclose a decayed mouth. As the boy says of the priest, "When he smiled he used to uncover his big discoloured teeth and let his tongue lie upon his lower lip – a habit which had made me feel uneasy in the beginning of our acquaintance" (5). Similarly, when the pederast smiles, the boy sees "that he had great gaps in his mouth between his yellow teeth" (17). Even when the man makes comments that the boy considers "reasonable," the boy admits that he "disliked the words in his mouth" (18). Joyce's focus on the men's decaying mouths provides a visual image of internal corruption;[17] moreover, by making the mouth the site of that corruption, Joyce associates it not only with their own internal state but also with what they are unconsciously communicating to the boy about themselves: their desire for superiority and their fear of inadequacy.

There are *two* boys in "An Encounter" – the narrator and Mahony – and they react very differently to the pederast. Mahony gets distracted and runs off after a cat, but the narrator is riveted as well as frightened by the man's monologues. The older man tells the narrator that they are alike – both are bookworms, whereas Mahony "goes in for games" (17). By implication, the boy's thirst for knowledge makes him more susceptible to this kind of corruption. After reading these stories, we may well ask whether there is some other, ethical way of teaching desire that does not perpetuate what Joyce calls simony (we would call it materialism) and paralysis, which we know better as apathy.

To answer these questions, let us return to the teaching methods used by both priest and pederast. Both either require or demonstrate a mechanical form of response: the priest teaches the boy to memorize and to learn by rote; the pederast recites his erotic, perhaps even "literary," fantasies about the pleasures of touching girls and whipping boys as if by heart. But what are the desires that they are simultaneously (and automatically) prohibiting and licensing? I would argue that the *desire* here is identical to a fear: it is to see both self and others as inescapably inadequate or, to use the language of religion, irredeemably sinful. The priest teaches the boy to give up hope of understanding the mysteries of the Eucharist, and the story implies that as he learns to despair at the possibility of learning *wisdom* (as opposed to mere knowledge), he confirms his own sense of inadequacy and at the same time learns to focus on the inadequacies and limitations of others: the poor grammar and shoddy dress of the sisters, to take the most obvious example. Similarly, the pederast is sexually *excited* by the badness of boys and girls, which gives him the license to touch them in ways that are hurtful to them but pleasurable to himself (he imagines whipping bad boys and stroking girls who "were not so good as they seemed to be if only one knew," 26). In different ways, both men practice a punitive pedagogy that perpetuates itself by insisting upon the psychological incapacity rather than the worth of the individual. Here, the main effect of this teaching on the boy is that it diminishes his pleasure: the pleasure of learning and the pleasure of disobeying are both tarnished, and he learns to replace the pleasures of adventure and novelty with a compensatory pleasure in the shortcomings of others. As the example of the pederast shows, the habit of pleasuring oneself at the expense of others is the root of abuse. And as we see from Nazi propaganda, this habit can affect groups of people as well as individuals, resulting in a grandiose form of nationalism that glorifies itself by demonizing those who are different.

In "The Sisters," we can see how the priest has altered the boy's way of thinking and feeling by observing that the boy's attitude toward the people around him has changed: he used to see Old Cotter, for example, as "rather interesting" with his stories about the distillery (1), but he has grown "tired of him," and dismisses him as a "Tiresome old fool" (1) and a "Tiresome old red-nosed imbecile" (3) with "beady black eyes" (2). He has to cram his "mouth with stirabout for fear [he] might give utterance to [his] anger" over Old Cotter's suspicions about the dead priest (3). The boy's attitude toward his faith has also changed; he now views "the simplest acts" as complex and mysterious, in need of a scrupulous exegesis that might seem Holmesian, were it not for the fact that its effects obfuscate rather than solve a mystery (5). Even less obtrusively, the boy notices small instances of ignorance or shabbiness in the priest's sisters when he comes with his aunt to pay his respects to the priest's body. He faithfully replicates Eliza's error when she refers to the newspaper as the *Freeman's General* instead of the *Freeman's Journal*, an error that calls her literacy into question, as well as her substitution of "rheumatic" for "pneumatic" wheels, a revealing mistake in its suggestion that the *pneuma* (spirit or air) has become sad (an obsolete meaning of "rheum," which literally refers to a flow, is "tears"; 8, 9). The boy focuses on the clumsy way Nannie's skirt is hooked at the back and on her worn boots (6), experiencing her prayers as "mutterings" that distracted him from his own attempt to pray, but he registers no sympathy when she almost falls asleep downstairs, even when Eliza explains she is "wore out" from all the work of preparing the corpse (8). Nor does he react to the allusion to their straitened circumstances ("as poor as we are – we wouldn't see him want anything," 8); instead, he registers all Eliza's grammatical errors: her references to "them flowers and them two candlesticks" (8), her claim that "the duties of the priesthood was too much for him" (9).

We might also observe the evidence of how the priest himself regarded his sisters. Although he spent time and effort educating the boy, his sisters' errors show that he made no such effort with them, despite the fact that they fed him and cared for him for years (the boy's aunt refers to all their "kindness to him," 8). They seem more like servants than sisters, and one of them is even called "Nannie" as if to underscore her role as caretaker. The contributions of the sisters are as invisible to the priest and the boy as they are to most first-time readers.[18]

When we "reason backward" from these observations, we are able to construct a different story than the one the boy relates. We see a priest who had been acting strangely for an unspecified period of time, who is no longer "of S. Catherine's Church, Meath Street" (4), who has been tutoring a young boy in a way that changes the boy's attitude not only toward the "simplest acts" of the church, but also toward other people. The boy has learned to doubt his own ability to fathom the central precepts of his religion, and simultaneously he has learned to be scrupulous and "mean" in his observation of others. Every time he notices something that demeans someone who is in other respects caring or faithful, he fancies that the dead priest is smiling his approval (see, for example, p. 6). In short, the priest has passed on to the boy not only precision but also smallness of mind, which has interfered with the boy's ability to feel grief or compassion. The teacher has infected his pupil with the "original sin" of feeling unworthy and incapable, which makes him quick to note and disdain the ignorance and shoddiness of even the most devoted caretakers. (Compare Gabriel's attitude to the sisters in "The Dead," whom he mentally refers to as "only two ignorant old women," 193).

In "An Encounter," the pederast addresses human "sin" in a way that justifies not detachment but invasive closeness. Instead of alienating the boy from others, from his own emotions, and from the lessons of his own experience, all in the name of "education," the pederast uses an assumption of the children's innate depravity to justify touching them physically: stroking or whipping them so as to give himself pleasure. The boy narrator, and often the reader, responds in different ways to the two modes of intervening in a child's education. The boy *accepts* the priest's interpretations; he might even be said to learn from him a new way of seeing the world, a view that has made him newly impatient with Old Cotter and allows him to forget, like his mentor, the diurnal constancy of the sisters' devotion. He has "learned" from the priest to secure a place for himself above others by perceiving them to be more incapable of technical precision than he.

In "An Encounter," the boy learns the same lesson from a less respectable teacher — that if he can establish himself as superior he may claim the right to interpret, judge, and punish others — although the pederast imagines expressing his power in physical terms, as the privilege to touch and whip. Listening to the pederast enjoy his superiority over bad boys and girls, the boy catches a brief glimpse of a similar tendency in himself of which he was previously unaware: he has always condescended to his friend Mahony as his inferior. At the end of the story, when he is eager to get away from the pederast, he calls for Mahony. Mahony runs as if to bring him aid, and the narrator is conscience-pricked, "for in [his] heart [he] had always despised him a little" (20).

What are the implications of the way Joyce yokes the priest and the pederast as using a comparable pedagogy, and what can we learn from the apparent approval (or at least ambivalence) with which the narrator responds to that pedagogy when it is presented as a way of thinking instead of a way of touching? Joyce's decision to place "An Encounter" directly after "The Sisters" allows the fantasy of physical touch to illustrate some of the more disturbing implications of the priest's teaching by making them visible: it is not only potentially abusive; there is also a masturbatory pleasure in the contemplation of other people's worthlessness. Readers and critics have historically had trouble understanding the relation between these two stories, interpreting the priest as someone who may have sexually abused the boy.[19] This reading registers the kinship between priest and pederast; however, to read the priest as a pederast is to diminish the abusiveness of his theology by misreading his social and theological indoctrination as physical abuse. The priest does *not* physically abuse the boy – and this is crucial because physical abuse (especially if presented as fantasy and not enacted) is easier to recognize and deplore than indoctrination. "The Sisters" is about the abuse of indoctrination, which is notoriously hard to identify because most readers have been similarly indoctrinated. "Doctrinal" abuse is not identical with sexual abuse, but Joyce's stories suggest by stressing the unworthiness of the uninitiated that doctrinal abuse may be used to license more physically abusive forms of punishment and reward.

Indoctrination is powerful precisely *because* it has been dissociated from anything we can readily see through and deplore, such as physical abuse. This is why the priest insists on teaching the boy the uselessness of trying to interpret sacred mysteries; not only is he seducing the boy to cede his interpretive authority to him, as priest, but he is also gutting the boy's agency and his spirituality in the process. The priest's corruption is that he knows he is "sinning" by simultaneously teaching the boy vanity (that he is more special than other people) and dependence upon himself as an authority. In the boy's dream, the priest's attempted confession to him signifies that both the boy and the priest are unconsciously aware that the priest has wronged him. A similar repressed awareness, laced with self-satisfactory glee, is apparent when the priest is found alone in the confession-box, laughing to himself.

The image of an authority figure named James laughing to himself over others' bewilderment at a complex system of ideas exemplifies many people's vision of Joyce himself.[20] Many who read "The Sisters" see Joyce as akin to Father Flynn, a dead white man whose desire to make an impact on the lives of others grotesquely extends beyond the grave. But in fact "The Sisters" is Joyce's repudiation of that model, and his implicit call for an alternate mode of instruction and inspiration in which readers are not allowed to assume *a priori* that anything is ultimately beyond our comprehension.

What we see if we read "The Sisters" as the Holmes-and-Watson team might approach it is that the title is a clue not only to the priest's blind spot, but also to our own. The title identifies what the priest takes for granted: his sisters' diurnal care and silent support that allowed him to rise above his class, in return for which they received no recognition or reward. This is quite literally a microcosm of a patriarchal society or church, complete with a father and the faithful but neglected nuns who minister to him, who can never be ordained or even fully educated themselves. The sisters are like assumptions in that they provide a foundation for development, but are too often overlooked as the precondition on which everything else depends. In Joyce's story, the sisters exhibit a very different kind of faith than that of their brother: it is simpler, more loving, more tiring, and less rewarding and mysterious. It expresses itself through actions not words. Which kind of faith is closer to the teachings of Christ that the priest claims to understand? Why is it so difficult for well-trained and intelligent readers to see this?

Let's return for a moment to the problem that concerned Milgram in *Obedience to Authority*: "the extreme willingness of adults to go to almost any lengths on the command of an authority" (5), and his surprise at finding that this willingness continued even though his subjects disagreed morally with what they were doing (6). If, as Milgram claimed, "Obedience is the psychological mechanism that links individual action to political purpose" (1), this helps to explain *Dubliners*. That is, Joyce is also interested in the relation between the personal and the political, between the reader's habit of discerning and obeying the author's judgments when reading and the ordinary citizen's habit of conforming to the dictates of church, state, employers, fathers, or teachers. The fundamental lesson Milgram derives from his experiments is equally apparent in *Dubliners*: "ordinary people, simply doing their jobs, and without any particular hostility on their part, can become agents in a terrible destructive process" (6). *Dubliners* is about obedience and disobedience; the boy in "The Sisters" has learned to be faithful to the priest's lessons, despite the fact that such fidelity has cost him his faith in God and humanity. Milgram's study is essentially about the same things: "The force exerted by the moral sense of the individual is less effective than social myth would have us believe"; "Moral factors can be shunted aside with relative ease" when an individual becomes "absorbed in the narrow technical aspects of the task [and] loses sight of its broader consequences" (7).

If "The Sisters" is about the unsatisfactory nature of obedience, "An Encounter" explores the equally disturbing consequences of disobedience. In the story, two boys break away for a day of "miching" (playing hooky) and go in search of "wild sensations" inspired by "chronicles of disorder" (21). They encounter a series of disappointments that climaxes in a potential threat from a masturbating "old josser" they meet in a field. This experience supports the narrator's socialization in that it teaches him the futility and even the danger of disobedience, thereby reinforcing the priest's earlier lessons. In another *Dubliners* story, "Eveline," the protagonist is unable to leave an abusive home environment because she cannot disobey her promises to her mother and Saint Margaret Mary Alacoque to stay. Again and again, the characters in *Dubliners* are seen to obey or disobey. But in no case do any of the characters wittingly choose selective or conscientious disobedience.

Milgram says his subjects were "unable to realize their [humane] values in action" (6); "they failed to realize . . . that subjective feelings are largely irrelevant to the moral issue at hand so long as they are not transformed into action. Political control is effected through action" (10). Again we see the same thing in *Dubliners*; "Eveline" begins with the title character's ruminations about whether she should leave her home. In the end, she stays, not as a result of rational deliberations but through an inability to speak or move. That is, she doesn't *decide* to stay home; she is instead paralyzed, "passive, like a helpless animal. Her eyes gave [her lover] no sign of love or farewell or recognition" (34). Eveline has no idea why she clutches the iron railing as the boat leaves without her; she thought she would escape. She never suspects she is almost totally passive. She pictures the prospect of leaving home not as an act of her own, but as a rescue orchestrated by someone else: her lover, a "very kind, manly, open-hearted" man who has the promising name of "Frank" (31). He may not be a prince, and he may not have even been frank with her, but he has promised her respectability and a new life. Still, Eveline cannot choose because, lacking independent agency, she is ruled by her promise to a higher authority: her mother and Saint Margaret Mary Alacoque. Joyce implies that in real life, this Cinderella figure *cannot* be rescued, even with the magical intervention of love, because she doesn't own herself; she is mortgaged to a system of domestic and religious authority more powerful than romance. Like the subjects in Milgram's experiment, Eveline feels intense conflict, but isn't able to translate into action her belief that she deserves happiness. Instead, like her mother, she is doomed to a "life of commonplace sacrifices closing in final craziness" (33).

Milgram reminds us that "no action of itself has an unchangeable psychological quality. Its meaning can be altered by placing it in particular contexts" (9). We see this, too, operating in "Araby," one of the few *Dubliners* stories in which the protagonist is able to see the contextual frame that determines an act's meaning. "Araby," like "Eveline," is about the ineffectiveness of romance in the larger social context. The larger social context in "Eveline" is familial and religious; in "Araby" it is the world of commerce and imperial domination. The result in both cases is the same: meaningful connection is impossible in such environments. The boy in "Araby" will not be able to express his feeling for the girl he admires by buying her a token from the English, even at an oriental bazaar. In "Araby," too, the fantasy of romance is mere vanity, a phantasm generated by, and climaxing in, a tricked-up multinational marketplace.

As the stories succeed one another, the alienation of the characters from themselves becomes more complete. In "A Painful Case," for example, James Duffy illustrates what happens when special privileges (like those which the priest passed on to the boy in "The Sisters") develop into principles that shape the thoughts and actions of a grown man. The boy in "The Sisters" is unconsciously dismissive, but he still enjoys a sensation of freedom when the priest dies, and he is able to question – dimly – the beneficence of the priest's influence over him. Duffy, who is approximately 40, exhibits an unwaveringly critical distance from himself and others. He is suspicious of his body – "He lived at a little distance from his own body, regarding his own acts with doubtful side-glances" (104) – and he distances his personality as well by treating himself like a character in a fiction; he composes "in his mind from time to time a short sentence about himself containing a subject in the third person and a predicate in the past tense" (104). His life is even, predictable, and exquisitely controlled.

Mr Duffy's isolation is not natural, but learned. He has learned "careful scorn" (107) for humanity, a disdainful superiority that makes him an "outcast from life's feast" (113). When asked why he doesn't write, he replies with disdain,

> To compete with phrasemongers, incapable of thinking consecutively for sixty seconds? To submit himself to the criticisms of an obtuse middle class which entrusted its morality to policemen and its fine arts to impresarios? (107)

Duffy's intellectual isolation is later compromised by love of Mozart's music and by the companionship of a woman, which wears "away the rough edges of his character," emotionalizing "his mental life" (107). His thoughts gradually entangle with those of the woman who urges him "to let his nature open to the full" (106). Her "fervent nature" contrasts sharply with "the strange impersonal voice which he recognized as his own, insisting on the soul's incurable loneliness" (107). But when the woman violates Duffy's loneliness by passionately touching his hand, she excites his severe disapproval. He meets with her one last time, explaining that "every bond is a bond to sorrow," "[bade] her good-bye quickly and left her" (108). When he learns of her death four years later, he outwardly decries her loneliness as a nauseating, contaminating weakness:

> What an end! The whole narrative of her death revolted him and it revolted him to think that he had ever spoken to her of what he held sacred. The threadbare phrases, the inane expressions of sympathy, the cautious words of a commonplace vulgar death attacked his stomach. Not merely had she degraded herself; she had degraded him. (111)

He sternly dismisses this one person with whom he had been intimate as "unfit to live" (112).

But then Mr Duffy's self-approval wavers; he begins to apprehend his own emotional parsimony and meanness, and the isolation that follows from it. He feels the touch of her hand perhaps for the first time, now that it is no longer there (113), and then he *fails* to sense her ghostly presence, experiencing his loss of her with sensual immediacy. The bedrock of his self-approval, "his moral nature," "fall[s] to pieces" as a result of one failed effort to communicate meaningfully or intimately with another (113).

Many readers of *Dubliners* unconsciously replicate the attitudes of one or more of the characters. Most are critical (like Mr Duffy), some are simply bored (like Lenehan in "Two Gallants"), and others nervous (like Gabriel in "The Dead"). Some coyly wait to see what is required of them (like Polly Mooney in "A Boarding House"), and others envision a bold departure from their usual habits (like Eveline). Some go along for the ride (like Jimmy in "A Painful Case"), and others will approach rage or brutality (like Farrington in "Counterparts"). Yet the challenge of being an imaginative reader involves a willingness to play all and none of these roles, to entertain yet ultimately resist the allure of mimicking any one of them; to abandon a moral position that renders us judgmental and rigidly consistent, in order to find a readerly stance that allows us to move from sympathy to critical distance to contextual framing and back again.

Thus the main challenge in reading *Dubliners* is how to get outside the perspective of the main character so that we can see realities to which he or she is blind, but not to detach ourselves from the character's perspective so firmly that we cannot be touched by him or her. This is the challenge of humane interpretation in general: how to exercise cognitive independence without losing the capacity for empathy? How to train ourselves to think and feel at the same time? Why aren't such skills the product of a good education?

If Conan Doyle leads readers to experience unexpected sympathy for murderers and enforces clear limits on our admiration for his great detective, Joyce shows that our judgments – while often stern – are never purely objective unless we retain the flexibility of mind and feeling that is the hallmark of vitality. Flexibility of mind is, in fact, enhanced if we, like Holmes, can learn to reason in reverse, from effect to cause.

Holmes has little to offer in the arena of feeling, however (that comes from Watson). *Dubliners* is, in some ways, a supplement to Holmes' method in that it helps readers also *feel* in more backward ways, although most readers find it easy to ignore or resist these promptings. Joyce does this best through allusions to sentimental but powerful music well-known to Dubliners at the time. "Silent, O Moyle" in "Two Gallants," for example, is a haunting melody emanating from a feminized harp whose "body" is being played by her master. Joyce implies through the song that all Irish are enchanted (a lyrical translation of paralyzed – in medical terms – and oppressed, in political ones) and waiting for a savior to break the spell. Familiar melodies have the power to take listeners back in time, and to frame the actions and inactions of the characters within the larger socio-political context of colonial "learned helplessness." This in turn can soften – but not erase – the reader's judgments against their mean-spirited exploitation of others.

To return to the larger argument of this book, flexibility of thought and feeling is a modernist "solution" to the limited choice of obedience or disobedience, both of which – practiced consistently – hasten the approach of death, at least of mind and soul. Joyce was neither an obedient citizen of the British empire nor a disobedient nationalist rebel, because obedient citizens becomes automata and rebels end up corpses. Selective disobedience, attentive to human and social interaction, was for him an exercise in preserving vitality through movement of thought and feeling.

Social Partnering: The New Woman and the Marriage Question

In *The Sign of Four*, Watson announces that he is engaged to marry Miss Morstan, and Holmes replies: "love is an emotional thing, and whatever is emotional is opposed to that true cold reason which I place above all things. I should never marry myself, lest I bias my judgment" (169). Watson laughs, remarking that he trusts that his own "judgment may survive the ordeal." Holmes does not accept that he is already married to, in the sense of being partnered with, Watson, or that the partnership does not bias his judgment, but enriches it through the addition of

Watson's empathy, curiosity, and willingness to narrate as well as listen to the stories that unfold. Holmes' analytical acuity is made whole through the addition of Watson's willingness to be touched and his ability to narrate the stories from more than one perspective.

Dubliners, in contrast, contains no examples of successful married partnerships. Mr Mooney went after Mrs Mooney with a cleaver, and since then they have lived apart; Little Chandler has married a woman he considers cold and passionless; Mrs Kearney's respect for her husband resembles her respect for the "post office": "though she knew the small number of his talents she appreciated his abstract value as a male" (141). The absence of intimate equal partnerships in *Dubliners* is a symptom and a cause of the characters' enervation. If we are to appreciate the stories fully, we readers must therefore ourselves engage in a partnership with the author in an effort to understand the characters, to bring them to life.

In the 1880s and 1890s, it was becoming increasingly clear that productive, equal partnership between men and women was highly unlikely under the prevailing social conditions. The Woman Question – which Sarah Grand identified with the Marriage Question – was raised in an attempt to change that by discovering "that there are in ourselves, in both sexes, possibilities hitherto suppressed or abused, which, when properly developed, will supply to either what is lacking in the other."[21] Grand was hoping to challenge what might be called the narrative structure of marriage, in which the man's role was to know and speak and the woman's to listen and learn. Instead, she wanted to establish a mutually beneficial dialogue between equally enfranchised partners. The possibility of such dialogue was crucial for the beginning of modernism; as Ann Ardis has argued, "the ongoing controversy over the New Woman and the New Woman novel needs to be factored into our genealogies of high modernism."[22]

The marriage debate of the 1890s expanded awareness of how a hierarchical relationship in which one partner pledged to honor and obey the other differed from a relationship of mutual respect based on questioning, consultation, and choice, an awareness that in time affected the implied contract between author and reader as well. In the late nineteenth century, however, the vision of equal partnership between men and women was still largely utopian. The majority of women were not educated or conditioned by training and habit to be men's equals, to challenge their authority, or even to enter knowledgeably into discussions with them on financial, political, or literary subjects. Similarly, readers were not in the habit of thinking of their own creative and critical abilities as being on a par with those of a writer. Many writers called for "new" women and new readers as well.

The marriage debate of the 1880s and 1890s drew public attention to the destructive effects on women of the institution as it was structured at the time. In 1888, Mona Caird (a "New Woman" novelist) wrote an article on marriage for the *Westminster Review*.[23] In response, the *Daily Telegraph* asked its readers, "Is Marriage a Failure?" and, according to Karl Beckson, received 27,000 replies.[24] In a story called "Virgin Soul" (1895), George Egerton (the pseudonym of Frances Elizabeth Clarke McFall) wrote that "marriage becomes for many women a legal prostitution, a nightly degradation, a hateful yoke under which they age, mere bearers of children conceived in a sense of duty, not love" (cited by Beckson 130). Suffragist Emmeline Pankhurst forbade her followers to marry, calling it, notes Susan Kingsley Kent, a "fraternizing with the enemy."[25] Christabel Pankhurst argued that marriage made women vulnerable to venereal disease (Kent 84), and the actress and writer Florence Farr celebrated the decision of "girls with brains" who refused to marry, thereby declining to "run the risk of living with a man whose love has become a mere habit."[26]

The problem, of course, was that aside from marriage, women had few options for respectable, remunerative employment. Ultimately, the marriage question was an employment question. Especially around 1890, women increasingly objected to the fact that the only reasonably well-paying jobs (with any security) that were open to them were as sex workers, either through marriage or prostitution. Of these two options, only marriage was respectable, but there weren't enough men to go around. Moreover, as a job, marriage often didn't give women sufficient self-respect, independence, or recognition. A married woman had few economic or educational resources of her own, limited freedom of movement, and no possibility of advancement. A respectable woman wasn't even supposed to enjoy sex. Is it any wonder that in the Victorian era, which most of us think of as prim, proper, and repressed, that women – along with quite a few educated men – were furiously angry? The right to engage in remunerative, productive, or gratifying work for which one is well suited is an important human liberty, an indication of citizenship, and the *sine qua non* of partnership. The phenomenon of the "Boston marriage" in the late nineteenth century, when two women lived together without male support (with or without sexual intimacy), was one imaginative attempt to create the conditions for equal partnership.

The New Woman movement was an effort to address pressing questions of female identity, obedience, and employment in a "new" way. Objections to marriage became a kind of shorthand for objections to the overall constraints on women in particular and on passive listeners more generally. No wonder that many writers were, at last, calling for women to be disobedient, to challenge and defy the behaviors expected of them. Sarah Grand was credited with first using the term "new woman" in an article she published in the *North American Review* in March of 1894 (*NWR* and Beckson 141), although the first "New Woman" novel (*avant la lettre*) is generally considered to be Olive Schreiner's *The Story of An African Farm* (1883). Henrik Ibsen (whose plays were caricatured in *Punch* as "Ibscenity") did more than anyone else to shape the image of the New Woman, especially through the productions of *A Doll's House, Hedda Gabler,* and *Ghosts* in 1889 and 1891 (Beckson 138). The popular image of the New Woman emphasized her willingness to smoke in public, ride bicycles, wear "rational dress" (the divided skirt), and generally do whatever she wanted (the danger of a woman who insists on fulfilling her desires was represented by Wilde's Salome, who was called a pathological new woman; Beckson 139).[27] It was easy to criticize New Women as "aggressive, disturbing, officious, unquiet, rebellious to authority and tyrannous" (Eliza Lynn Litton, quoted in Beckson 142). Similarly, New Woman novelists were decried in *All the Year Round* (the weekly journal that had been started by Charles Dickens in 1859) – in terms that sound familiar to women who grew up in the age of "feminism" – as women who "appear to have cultivated the intellect at the expense of all womanly feeling and instinctive delicacy, and to have cast aside all reticence in the mad desire to make others eat as freely as themselves of the forbidden fruit of the tree of knowledge" (Beckson 142).

Thus, New Women found themselves (perhaps unexpectedly) challenging "goodness," if goodness in women had to be synonymous with obedience or passionless purity. They wanted to dismantle the simple, dichotomous and unequal categories of "male" and "female" by presenting each as marbled with the other, and of course they wanted to protest a political situation in which women had no vote in any sense of the word. New women accordingly braved abuse and ostracism if they were "to awake from [their] long sleep and come into [their] kingdom" in "one of the greatest social revolutions of the time" (Farr 16).

What women were fighting for was the right for two partners to participate fully and meaningfully in a relationship. The ideal was to facilitate conversation, not to suffer dictation, which is how this struggle spilled over from a socio-political debate into a literary one. Virginia Woolf took up the argument again on the eve of World War II by reminding her readers in *Three Guineas* that dictators operate in many arenas; a dictator is anyone "who believes that he has the right, whether given by God, Nature, sex or race is immaterial, to dictate to other human beings how they shall live; what they shall do."[28] A person who insists that a woman's world should be restricted to "her family, her husband, her children, and her home" is a dictator, and fear of Hitler made everyone agree that a dictator (at least when he is foreign) "is a very dangerous as well as a very ugly animal." Woolf asserts that women have long had to fight domestic dictators, albeit "secretly and without arms" (53).

Marriage, then, was the battleground on which a war against dictation was being waged. Mona Caird relates the history of marriage as a tale of economic and sexual exploitation:

> the commercial spirit, staid and open-eyed, entered upon its long career, and began to regulate the relations of the sexes. We find a peculiar medley of sensuality and decorum: the mercenary spirit entering into the idea of marriage, women were bought and sold as if they were cattle, and were educated, at the same time, to strict ideas of "purity" and duty. (Caird, *NWR* 190)

Caird helped to publicize the one-sidedness of the marital equation, which replicated in miniature the more general inequality between the sexes. One of the most prominent signs of that inequality was that women, unlike men, were reduced to their sexual utility, which made "strict marriage and prostitution" concurrent (192). Two classes of women were created, "those who submitted to the yoke of marriage on Luther's terms," and those "on the other side of the great social gulf, subject also to stringent laws, and treated also as the property of men (though not of *one* man)" (192).

The connection between marriage and prostitution is examined more closely in George Bernard Shaw's banned play, *Mrs Warren's Profession* (written 1894). Vivie, the daughter of a prostitute, declines marriage for the same reason that she dislikes prostitution: it compromises her freedom to be a complete person rather than a service to be bought. She tells her suitor, "I am much obliged to you for being so definite and business-like. I quite appreciate the offer: the money, the position, Lady Crofts and so on. But I think I will say no, if you don't mind. I'd rather not."[29] Vivie does not condemn her mother for having taken up prostitution in the first place, because she did so in desperate economic circumstances in which she had few alternatives, but she cannot understand why her mother would continue to remain a prostitute once she had earned enough money to do something else. In short, Vivie doesn't believe a woman should sell the rights over herself if she has other choices. Marriage and prostitution are comparable kinds of bargains: the prostitute argues that the wife sells herself too, but with a social sanction that makes her decision seem honorable: "What is any respectable girl brought up to do but to catch some rich man's fancy and get the benefit of his money by marrying him? – as if a marriage ceremony could make any difference in the right or the wrong of the thing!" (39). Vivie is a "New Woman" who, without any moral prejudice in favor of marriage, nonetheless criticizes hypocrisy. She blames her mother not for having entered the sex trade, but for enjoying her enslavement. For this reason, she says her mother is "a conventional woman at heart" (66). Vivie's emancipation consists of her insistence on being "treated as a woman of business, permanently single and permanently unromantic" (57), who earns her living not through sexual services but by doing actuarial calculations in return for the freedom to think and do as she pleases.

At the turn of the twentieth century, the only existing form of partnership between men and women – marriage – was not really a partnership at all, but a form of exploitation. Women were encouraged to believe in the romance of marriage, when in reality marriage was a profession. What made the profession confusing was that the contract between employer and employee was negotiated in such intimate terms. There were two main problems:

1 Women weren't prepared for it. They often entered the married state with no knowledge whatsoever of the realities of sex, childbirth, or household finance.[30]

2 Marriage undermined women's self-respect, because the only respect a married woman could hope to win was "granted solely on condition of her observing certain restrictions of thought and action dictated by" men (Caird, *NWR*, 193). "*Her* honour has reference to someone other than herself . . . however valuable . . . it did not take its rise from a sense of self-respect in woman, but from the fact of her subjection to man" (192).

But with all these drawbacks, marriage was the *only* profession available to women of a certain socio-economic class. As Florence Farr relates, in the England and Wales of 1910, there were four million adult women who were unmarried. The working men told them to go home and do the washing, and one single woman replied, "Well, . . . one million of us are working in a laundry and other work, under half a million of us are amusing ourselves on independent incomes, and the rest of us have to while away life somehow without money or occupation, so we are making a revolution" (Farr 20).

The literature of the 1890s is not challenging to read. The challenge was to the reader, and it was straightforwardly issued by New Women who were urging those who played the passive role in traditional or hierarchical relationships to become more active, or challenging, themselves. To a pantheon that includes Shaw's Vivie Warren, Wilde's Salome, and Ibsen's Nora, George Gissing adds two more strong characters: Mary Barfoot and Rhoda Nunn from *The Odd Women* (1893). These "odd women" help unmarried women attain the necessary qualifications to work outside the home for a living wage. They are deeply concerned by the fact that "there are half a million more women than men" in England, a huge surplus of "*odd* women – no making a pair with them."[31] Mary and Rhoda have made it their mission to improve the lives of single women, but Rhoda is much more intolerant of marriage than Mary. Rhoda, whose last name is appropriately *Nunn*, insists "there will have to be a widespread revolt against the sexual instinct" (61), but Mary is more moderate, counseling her that "by taking up the proud position that a woman must be altogether independent of sexual things, you damage your cause" (60). "Be content to show our girls that it is their duty to lead a life of effort – to earn their bread and cultivate their minds" (61).

Rhoda, even more than Mary, is "one of the new women" – she has "more zeal for womanhood militant" (83). And Rhoda is indeed magnificent; upon meeting her, one of the characters realizes that "It was the first time in her life that she had spoken with a woman daring enough to think and act for herself" (22). She wants to help women become complete human beings who are capable of being partners in business as well as marriage. As she explains, she wants to train women in self-respect in an effort to make marriage honorable for women as well as for men (99).

Gissing treats a troubled marriage as symptomatic of larger social concerns: disrespect for others, intolerance, poor communication, unequal educational opportunities. One of the characters marvels at the capacity of marriage to throw light on so many other social formations:

> What a simple thing marriage had always seemed to him, and how far from simple he had found it! Why, it led him to musings which overset the order of the world, and flung all ideas of religion and morality into wildest confusion. (Gissing 239)

Although Gissing advocates reforming an institution that spells captivity for both sexes, he anticipates Joyce's later stance in *Dubliners* by affirming love as something different from the social institutions founded in its name, such as marriage and religion. When Rhoda falls in love, we learn that "Passion had a new significance; her conception of life was larger, more liberal" (291). Love can exist without loss of independence; in fact, it is an important inspiration for the fullness of being necessary to a productive partnership. Mary imagines a "new type of woman," who would be both developed and balanced, in contrast to those in the present whose "natural growth has been stunted." She describes her as gentle yet strong, pure of heart but wise and well instructed (136), and willing to invade the sphere formerly restricted to men. She pursues her right to self-realization aggressively, in a way that is not only disobedient but also revolutionary: "If a woman is to [be] . . . a human being of powers and responsibilities, she must become militant, defiant. She must push her claims to an extremity" (135–6). Mary insists that "we are working for the advantage of men as well as our own. . . . At any cost – at any cost – we will free ourselves from the heritage of weakness and contempt" (137).

Although it involved intimacy, marriage was often not conducive to female sexual development or satisfaction. Despite the fact that married women might be described as sex workers in that their job was primarily reproductive, many women (unlike Gissing's Rhoda) saw female sexuality as badly underdeveloped or vilified in the late nineteenth century. Olive Schreiner, who, as noted above, wrote the novel that was later considered to have begun the movement (*The Story of an African Farm*, 1883), argued that sexual abstinence was "more terrible" for women than for men, and took bromide to diminish her sexual drive (Kent 145). She wrote to her close friend Havelock Ellis of "the beauty and sacredness and importance of sex" (146). In 1916, Wilma Miekle recorded that the generation of suffragists born between 1870 and 1880 were "earnestly convinced that there was something certainly wonderful and possibly glorious about this mystery called sex and that it was their business to discover it" (Kent 21). These women believed "that sexual problems were the core of feminism" (22). One suffragist slogan proposed "Votes for women, chastity for men" (Kent 86). Florence Farr agreed, arguing of the 13 million spinsters and bachelors in England that "their sexual nature is hardly developed more than a child's" (Farr 37). She controversially recommended "temperance with an occasional orgy" for the health of both men and women (73), contending that "most women are capable of several love affairs" (58), and exhorting her contemporaries to "make allowance for the passionate" (94). Herminia in Grant Allen's popular novel *The Women Who Did* is also passionate; she argues that "The magic link of sex that severs and unites us" makes all the difference.[32]

Such emphasis on the importance of female sensuality was immensely threatening to the status quo, as we can see from the host of negative reviews of Kate Chopin's *The Awakening*. Chopin's novel was called unhealthy because it depicts a woman infected by "the poison of passion";[33] it was dismissed as a "story . . . not really worth telling," with "disagreeable glimpses of sensuality" that were "repellent" (166). It was described as "unwholesome" and "unpleasant" (173), as "gilded dirt" (167) and as "essentially vulgar" (168). The protagonist, Edna, was derided as selfish and capricious (169), her passion tossed off as mere "animal instinct" (167) and her suicide applauded as appropriate and satisfying (168). This about a woman who had acquired a "notion concerning the eternal rights of women" (63) and who with awakening sensuousness (73) "resolved never again to belong to another than herself" (76). "She felt as if a mist had been lifted from her eyes, enabling her to look upon and comprehend the significance of life, that monster made up of beauty and brutality" (80). Casting off the "soul's slavery" of her marriage, Edna removes her clothes "and for the first time in her life she stood naked in the open air" (108). "How strange and awful it seemed to stand naked under the sky! How delicious! She felt like some new-born creature, opening its eyes in a familiar world that it had never known" (109). Chopin's phrasing suggests that the pressure on married women to be sexless also blinded them, making them unfit to read – in the sense of rightly understand – anything, whether books or social formations.

As part of the effort to free women from trained subservience and make them more acute readers of their society and their culture, the New Women also championed intellectual freedom. Intellectualism, like a more fully developed sexuality, was disturbing partly because it was often seen as a threat to motherhood. Florence Farr alludes to a terror of motherhood known as "Americanism" (because in America some women were beginning to refuse motherhood) that was believed to be caused by women's education becoming too purely intellectual (63, 67). In *The Woman Who Did*, Herminia makes fun of the schooling given to young women, referring to it as an experiment "to see just how far you could manage to push a woman's education without the faintest degree of her emancipation" (27).

The campaign for suffrage proved the ability of women to assert themselves in society. Allen's *The Woman Who Did* (1895) and Arthur Wing Pinero's play *The Notorious Mrs Ebbsmith* (1895) are both basically sympathetic to the cause of women's freedom. Allen stresses his heroine's determination "to find out the Truth for myself about everything, and never to be deterred from seeking it, and embracing it . . . and [acting] upon it freely" (35). Her aim is "to develop every fibre of her nature," to see women made fit to *use* the vote – as well as to challenge the indoctrination built into the books they read (28). His heroine even writes a "novel of genius" herself. Allen repeats over and over the mantra that "the truth [has] made [Herminia] free" (36).[34]

Allen is genuinely opposed to monopoly, patriotism, slavery, and capitalism. If his book ends disastrously for the heroine who contests these things, that is partly because, he questionably argues, "Pessimism is sympathy. Optimism is selfishness. All honest art is . . . of necessity pessimistic" (96). Certainly, his heroine suffers a dire fate. Her lover dies of typhoid fever before her baby is born, and she is left homeless, penniless, and friendless "to face the contempt and hostility of a sneering world" (93, 88). Her child, variously known as Dolores (for sorrow) and Dolly (because she refuses to think for herself), rejects the "unpractical Utopianism" of her mother and returns to "moral darkness," worshiping success and respectability (117). The ungrateful child tells her mother that she won't be able to marry with any respectability as long as her mother is alive. The mother obligingly replies that she will "gladly" die for her daughter, and then drinks prussic acid, waiting for "the only friend she had left in the world" (140) – death. Even apparently supportive men – such as writers like Allen – were actually still questioning women's capacity to challenge the status quo successfully.

Although bizarre, disturbing, and melodramatic in its presentation, Grant Allen's portrayal of women who stand up for the principles of freedom does nonetheless pay tribute to independent women, although he leads them to expect a tragic end. Pinero is much more insidious. He pretends to appreciate female independence while actually undermining women who work for emancipation by depicting them as unstable, cowardly, hypocritical, unattractive, cold, and even basely wicked.[35] His play ends up presenting passion and principle as incompatible. It opens in Venice, where an adulterous "new woman" is characterized as stern, uncompromising, "mannish" (136), and "shabby" (142). The thread that unites her with her married lover begins to fray when she proposes that their union would be "much braver, much more truly courageous, if it could" be "devoid of passion" (139), suggesting that principle suffocates passion. The play concludes by celebrating the separation of the lovers: the woman who identified with the People castigates herself for having undone the man who had a seat in the House of Lords. Pinero implies that the ideal of free union is a self-serving sham, and he insists that the principled life must be lived without passion or intimacy. He unveils his "heroine" as hypocritical and corruptible; she is presented as admirable only in defeat, as he chastens this challenging woman and sends her back to reading her Bible.

The New Woman devolved into the vampire at the end of the 1890s and morphed into the militant suffragettes under the Pankhursts in the first years of the new century (Beckson 152–3). The image of the New Woman as a vampire recognized a reality: women's autonomy was and is a threat to male supremacy. New Women, vampires, and suffragettes *take action*; Emmeline Pankhurst's motto was "Deeds, not words" (cited by Beckson 155). The old fear that unrestrained sexuality in women went hand in hand with aggressiveness seemed to be confirmed.

Vitality was threatening in women, in whatever form it expressed itself – passion, ideas, laughter, or anger. Florence Farr complained that one of the hardest things about being a woman in society was the injunction to be serious: "Men may laugh, while women must look shocked" (cited by Beckson 158). It's hard not to hear a faint adumbration of the rules that governed women in Afghanistan under the Taliban, who were not allowed to laugh out loud, sing, or expose even an ankle without reprisal. The idea that any sign of life in a woman is a lamentable excess is memorably illustrated in a review of H.G. Wells' late New Woman novel *Ann Veronica* (1909), in which the reviewer writes,

> the best woman is still the good woman, who maintains her culture by imparting it to her children . . . and who makes her own home a microcosm of Utopia. . . . She will be lovely and lovable in her life, and in her coffin more beautiful than she whose beauty launched a thousand ships and burned the topless towers of Ilium. (cited by Beckson 158)

One question prompted by a review of the marriage debate of the 1890s is this: despite the many advances in women's rights over the last century, advances in education, sexual freedom, and employment options, how readily and comfortably do women (or men) now exercise the option of conscientious disobedience? Have women changed, or merely the conventions that regulate acceptable behavior? Do we still worry that, as Sarah Grand wrote over one hundred years ago, if we challenge convention,

> we shall be afflicted with short hair, coarse skins, unsymmetrical figures, loud voices, tastelessness in dress, and an unattractive appearance and character generally, and then he [man] will not love us any more or marry us[?] And this is one of the most amusing of his threats, because he has said and proved on so many occasions that he cannot live without

us whatever we are. O man! Man! You are a very funny fellow now we know you! (*NWR* 145)

Grand encourages us to celebrate "the glorious womanhood of this age of enlightenment, compared with the creature as she existed merely for man's use and pleasure of old; the toy-woman, the drudge, degraded domestic animal, beast of intolerable burdens."[36] This woman, who may not yet exist in sufficient numbers, would indeed be capable of partnership with the best – the most careful and caring – of men. But she must be willing to make mistakes and to learn from them, and she must be both assertive and vocal, even to the point of excess, if she is to win back the power of deliberative choice over the habit of deferential obedience.

Modernist Coupling

Examples of the two models of coupling discussed above – the master–slave (or parent–child) relation and the partnership of equals – abound in modernist literature, and both models illustrate how the reader might choose at different moments to relate to the author. In Joyce's *Ulysses*, the symbolic parent–child relation between Stephen and Bloom offsets and balances the troubled bond between husband and wife (Bloom and Molly). Both the parent–child and husband–wife pairings can take the form of a master–slave relation, as we see through the references to sado-masochism throughout, but the book declares itself hostile to any stable, institutionalized oppression. In Beckett's *Waiting for Godot* (1952), the master–slave relation is demonstrated by Pozzo and Lucky, and the partnership of opposite equals by Vladimir and Estragon (who call each other by the names of Didi and Gogo). Offstage, two complementary abstractions are defined by what we see onstage: the savior Godot and the two boys who serve him, and the audience, the members of which come to watch Didi and Gogo watch Pozzo and Lucky and wait for something to happen that will retrospectively endow that wait with meaning. The play questions the idealistic view of equal partnership by turning it into a Laurel-and-Hardy comedy act. It reminds us that we aren't really that different from one another after all, because the natural and social constraints that hinder everyone create a ludicrously handicapped sameness. Sexual difference doesn't matter because in a simultaneously practical and philosophical sense it doesn't exist: Didi and Gogo embody a sameness that cannot be eroticized. Everything is the same, and nothing stays the same from one moment or day to the next: as Gogo remarks, "It's never the same pus from one second to the next."[37] Even instances of opposition produce an impression of sameness: although Didi plays with his hat and Gogo with his boots, their concern with opposite extremes of their bodies is nonetheless similar.

Beckett's analysis of the master–slave relation takes the unusual form of Christian comedy. The Christian story would seem to promise that agonizing suffering and humiliation may be reversed by a (posthumous) vindication through resurrection, a hope the tramps parody through their futile proposal to hang themselves on the tree in the hope of an erection. The hope of salvation hinges on a sometimes forgotten feature of the master–slave relation (or its corollary forms, parent–child and God–human): its potential for the roles of master and slave to be reversed. In Christian terms, God becomes a human servant, but the dead servant becomes a god. The potential for reversal is exciting, inspirational, and even erotic, since it presupposes an underlying equality of terms, but it also constitutes an implicit warning against complacency and abuse. The problem, as Beckett's play reminds us, is that such a reversal (understood by some as "salvation") is the exception rather than the rule; what is most likely is that the hope of eventual vindication will be indefinitely deferred, and, as Didi muses, "Hope deferred maketh the something sick" (8; the heart, according to Proverbs 13 : 12). In the race between salvation and death, death is the most likely winner.

Waiting for Godot remains in perfect equipoise between the anticipation of an end and the experience of extended replays, between the desirability and the impossibility of movement. Each partner in the play's two couples supplements and "completes" the other: each is at once redundant and opposite; the only "salvation" in the sense of wholeness that is immediately available is in the interplay among these partners and couples. Their activities – imitating others, abusing others, asking each other questions, doing exercises, or pretending to be a tree – are framed as distractions, since when they think, they see themselves in a "charnelhouse" full of skeletons and corpses (41); they find that vitality is not present even among the living. They see the inert, silent audience watching the play as dead, the auditorium a bog. Didi and Gogo are actors *and* audience, as we see when Didi asks Gogo to save his seat while he goes to the toilet (23). Flexibility of action and response, the interplay of bodies and words, becomes a value in itself.

Like the characters of *Dubliners*, Didi and Gogo dream of mobility in a socio-theatrical context that is paralyzing: both acts end with the same proposal that cannot be enacted: "Well, shall we go?" "Yes, let's go." "*They do not move.*" Like Joyce, Beckett is implicitly asking his audience to do more than passively watch and wait; as the air rings with Pozzo's cries of "help!" the play encourages its blind and dumb auditors to partner differently with the actors, to experiment with more than one role in an excruciatingly repetitive life-script. Although Didi's final speeches have a falsely rhetorical, *recherché* overtone, they nevertheless, with hackneyed eloquence, make the case for resisting the "great dead-ener" of habit (51, 58). And so Didi and Gogo curse, help, kick, and raise their companions by turns; in the end, they play all the parts, while waiting for the much-anticipated, yet sudden, end.

What does it mean, then, to wait for Godot? To wait is to remain stationary in readiness or expectation, but it is also to serve, a word that comes from the Latin *servus,* or slave, which is why it also connotes obedience (*Webster's*). Finally, to wait is to "watch," as an audience watches: to look forward expectantly (etymologically, the word derives from a Germanic root meaning "to watch"). Beckett, fresh from his resistance work during World War II, raises the same question Milgram will ask a decade later:

> [We think that] a person acts in a particular way because he has *decided* to do so. Action takes place in a physical-social setting, but this is merely the stage for its occurrence. The behavior itself flows from an inner core of the person; within the core personal values are weighed, gratification assessed, and resulting decisions are translated into action. (31)

The problem recurs in Beckett's play *Endgame*, where Clov (the servant/son of Hamm) *wants* to refuse to obey Hamm, but he cannot, because, as Hamm points out, he is "not able to."[38] Near the end of the play, Clov says, "There is one thing I'll never understand. Why I always obey you" (75–6), and Hamm suggests, "Perhaps it's compassion." This is also what Milgram's experimental subjects expected to be the case: they "see their reactions flowing from empathy, compassion, and a sense of justice. They enunciate a conception of what is desirable and assume that action follows accordingly. But they show little insight into the web of forces that operate in a real social situation" (30).

Waiting for Godot and *Endgame* are Beckett's efforts to explore what actually prevents people from moving, from disobeying, from acting upon their desires – the same questions Joyce asks in *Dubliners*. Beckett's unexpected answer is that it is the *helpless* dependence upon other people, a dependence that is epitomized in the parent–child or master–slave or author–reader relation, that keeps individuals immobile. *Endgame* suggests that in the end, there is still no such thing as an equal partnership because there are no autonomous players with whom to conjoin. Hamm, too, claims "I was never there. . . . Absent, always. It all happened without me" (74). What holds each bad, lonely actor (or "ham") in place are "nails" – Nagg (German for "nail"), Nell (English "nail"), Clov ("clou" is French for "nail"), Pegg. These nails are all people, but Hamm regards none as his equal; their purpose – like that of the dialogue (58) – is only to keep him in place, and in the case of Clov ("clove"), to add a little spice while "something is taking its course" (32), while Hamm tells the story that defines or creates but also limits him.

Let us posit that what disables us, preventing us from acting in accordance with what might be desirable, is a twofold constraint: the progressive breakdown of our bodies and the way we tell our story. In *Endgame*, bodily disability is presented as a kind of black comedy in a game of attrition that is structured loosely like chess: a man named Hamm is blind and cannot stand, but his name also suggests part of a leg: specifically, the buttock and thigh of a pig. His parents have lost another part of the leg – their shanks – and they are planted in sand in two lidded ashbins at the front of the stage. Clov, the servant, who is also a kind of son and wife, has limited mobility between the main room and the kitchen, and his eyes are getting worse. "Cloven" is the past participle of "cleave," which means both to adhere firmly and to divide as if by a cutting blow (*Webster's*); by implication, Clov will both be Hamm's helplessly faithful, attached servant and the cleaver who will divide them when the time comes for departure. Nails, with their straight shank and their head, become images of human beings: their drive, their ability to enforce attachment, their passivity under the blow of Hamm (here a hammer). Instead of focusing on waiting in the sense of expecting or looking forward, the play emphasizes the etymological aspect of waiting: watching. But the light has sunk (30). The only real "vision" in the play is Clov's dream of order, which helps to explain his willingness to take orders: "I love order. It's my dream. A world where all would be silent and still and each thing in its last place, under the last dust" (57).

Although progressive disability and loss effectively keep the characters incomplete and therefore dependent upon one another (compare Joyce's suggestion in *Dubliners* that people are like the incomplete geometrical figure of a *gnomon*), the characters are even more firmly immobilized by the story they hear and tell. *Endgame* emphasizes the passiveness of obedience. It depicts human progress as a boring and repetitive tale of how a nail becomes a hammer and then a nail again; or a child becomes a parent and then a child again. Beckett suggests that neither the parent nor the child, the teller nor the listener, is a complete being. The fiction that fuels this alternation is the fiction that man can become a creator, a god, in a wasted world, and that his creation will ultimately replace him. This is the gist of the story Hamm tells throughout his life: that on Christmas Eve, a man crawled up to him and asked him for bread for his infant son, and Hamm took pity on him and gave him a job as a gardener, offering "to take him into my service" (53). By implication, Hamm has created himself as godlike, agreeing to enslave the man (Adam) in a waste land they will call Eden. The child – a version of the Christ child ultimately to be "nailed" – will grow up to be Clov, with a name that suggests the French word for "nail," although at some point he will take over from Hamm: "Yes, one day . . . you'll be like me" (36). The problem is that Hamm, like his father Nagg before him and like the Father of all before that, did not answer or was not present for his child's suffering. As Nagg asks, "Whom did you call when you were a tiny boy, and were frightened, in the dark? Your mother? No. Me. We let you cry. Then we moved you out of earshot, so that we might sleep in peace" (56). When Hamm insists that they all "pray to God," God, similarly, refuses to answer, and they exclaim in frustration: "What a hope! . . . Sweet damn all! . . . Nothing doing! . . . The bastard! He doesn't exist!" and Clov answers, "Not yet" (55). The question then becomes: what kind of story might create a responsive god, or a responsive listener, or an actor who was more effective than a mere ham, performing soliloquies alone, in the dark?

When Clov is finally liberated from Hamm's service, a new small boy approaching on the horizon, his emancipation sparks a hope that the next version of the story might run differently, but Clov confesses that it is unlikely, admitting that he feels "too old, and too far, to form new habits" (81). His "emancipation" is anticlimactic, pitiful:

> I open the door of the cell and go. I am so bowed I only see my feet, if I open my eyes, and between my legs a little trail of black dust. I say to myself the earth is extinguished, though I never saw it lit. (81)

Beckett reminds us that the social, historical, and cultural contexts that preclude change are powerful indeed. If we find ourselves, like Lucky, unable to put down our burdens, it is not because we don't want to; it is because we are held in place by the inexorable progress of aging and mortality, by our dependence upon one another, and by the plot of an ongoing story – a given that we are not to challenge. Women may have won the right to play Hamm as well as Clov, but the dream of equal partnership is perhaps awaiting not just a new woman or a new man, but the start of a new – and a more collaborative – story to supplant the old carpenter's tale of the hammer and nails.

Chapter 3 Window Painting
The Art of Blocking Understanding

A mutually respectful partnership between author and reader – mediated by the text – may still yield inequalities of power, but it makes them unstable and reciprocal rather than one-sided. The idea of the author and reader engaging in a virtual conversation (above the heads of the characters) gradually changed the underlying structure of many modernist texts. This is not necessarily or immediately observable in the text itself; instead, the reader is confronted with an unpredictable format, verbal virtuosity, and a prolonged delay before the design and meaning of the whole begins to become apparent. Such delays frustrate and distract the reader, confounding his or her expectations, but they also draw attention to the multiple ways in which the written material can be interpreted. When the partnership works well, the reader will also be more aware of the importance of the unsaid, and even the hidden: what Beckett – in the last novel in his trilogy – called the unnamable.

Although the idea of a hidden or ineffable meaning is hardly new, before modernism such meanings were typically religious, rather than psychic and social. It was Marx and Freud, with their respective work on the class system and the structure of the individual psyche, who gave the public the necessary conceptual tools for reorganizing their understanding of the preceding century. Freud taught us that individuals do not have full access to the "lower" impulses of their psyche, that the self is alien as well as familiar. At the same time, Marx and others drew attention to the dark underside of industrialized society. H.G. Wells, in *The Time Machine* (1895), explores a future in which workers have become the rulers, and the upper classes have devolved into beautiful, childlike creatures upon which workers literally feed. Increased emphasis on the latent but frightening and potentially formidable power of the uncon-scious mind and the political strength inherent in a huge, depersonalized working class called into question two central values: the sufficiency of rational thought and the morality of an aesthetic based on disavowed or deliberately obscured ugliness. Beauty was both celebrated (in the aes-thetic movement) and indicted by social critics as a distraction from an underlying exploitation or abuse.

How, though, could a work of literature – comprised of carefully chosen, artfully arranged words – convey the power of that which was unknown, perhaps unknowable, and in many parts of society unspeak-able? One way modernist writers acknowledged apprehensions that eluded articulation and conscious awareness was by opening "windows" in their texts that offered glimpses or reminders of some other story, image, or impression: literary, mythical, artistic, or musical (as in Wagner's leitmotifs). In this chapter, I am particularly interested in exploring instances in which the alternate view framed by that window takes the form of a painting or work of visual art – this is the way visual revelation embodies an underlying idea or apprehension that cannot be easily admitted or tolerated by the reader. Some of these non-verbal revelations concern physical or sexual behaviors or fantasies not accept-able to conscious awareness or consistent with social respectability. In other cases, such as Wilde's *The Picture of Dorian Gray*, Woolf's *To the Lighthouse*, or Joyce's *A Portrait of the Artist as a Young Man*, what is chal-lenged is the reader's investment in constructing a beautiful, romanti-cized, and self-flattering image of the self (or humanity).

Moments in which an image wordlessly "speaks" to the reader produce a kind of aporia – a moment in which the reader is given pause, rendered uncertain about meaning and intention.[1] According to Socrates, what we call "learning" is actually the process of realizing, remembering, or reformulating something we already know. It became the job of the writer or teacher to "recall" to a reader or student something that he or she already knew, but had not consciously registered or accepted, which effectively disrupted the illusion that he had already mastered the text. Socrates' method is thus one that can be used to challenge learned or inherited social notions – such as the habit of aggrandizing the self at the expense of the other (discussed in chapters 1 and 2). The Socratic method, thus conceived, jerks us from the realm of assumed understand-ing into a world of acknowledged failure or inability to understand, which is also a world of wonder. Only in that state is it possible for the reader to remember something *else* – something he or she already knows – that might spark compassion for or at least understanding of the other. In modernist literature, this effect can be achieved by the various windows that interrupt the book, play, or poem with a "reminder" of some other work of art. The idea is for that other work to prompt the reader to reflect upon – and perhaps alter – the interpretation he or she initially formulated. Our "window" in the text is also therefore a mirror, making the reader more aware of the unconscious ways our own desires and fears shape our "rational" apprehension.

When these reader-directed textual insights occur, they briefly allow us to see the reader as an unconscious artist. In many works, the author is deliberately in collusion with the reader, fully participating in a shared project of falsifying and simplifying the real in order to avoid the shame and effort of a more honest confrontation with the different levels of experience. More rarely, readers are given the opportunity to recognize their romantic expectations and alter them.

A vivid and sympathetic illustration of the kind of self-image most readers unconsciously hope to construct may be found in Dylan Thomas' 1941 poem, "The Hunchback in the Park."[2] Set in Cwmdonkin Park in Swansea, Wales, the poem focuses on a social misfit, an old and solitary hunchback, who sleeps at night in a dog kennel but spends all day – from the time it is opened early in the morning until the closing bell – in the park. Mocked by the children, the hunchback spends his day dreaming, making "from his crooked bones" his own opposite, a figure he could love: "A woman figure without fault/Straight as a young elm." He creates her "That she might stand in the night/After the locks and chains/All night in the unmade park." The word "unmade" briefly situates the reader between two undecidable meanings. On the one hand, the park at night is described like an unmade bed, which emphasizes the erotic nature of the hunchback's desire for the perfect woman he has fashioned. On the other hand, the park is "unmade" in the sense of being un-created; the poet implies that darkness unmakes the reality we see, but the hunchback is able to create an ideal that lives even in the darkness. This is often why readers read books: in an unconscious effort to imagine or realize an alternative self that has none of the inadequacies and disap-pointments of daily existence. At the same time, despite its power to create beauty and comfort, the imagination can also produce dangers:

the truant boys in the park who mock the hunchback, although "innocent as strawberries," are nonetheless making "tigers jump out of their eyes/ To roar on the rockery stones." Self-awareness is a vital part of imagining, because the imagination can fuel aggression against others as readily as it can create fantasies of attachment.

Dylan Thomas' hunchback uses imagination as a means of attaching himself to the human world, but the aestheticizing impulse can also be used to detach oneself. T.S. Eliot's early poem, "*La figlia che piange*" (Italian; Young Girl Weeping), the final poem in *Prufrock and Other Observations* (1917), begins with an epigraph in Latin: "*O quam te memorem virgo . . .*" (O how – by what name – shall I remember you, maiden?).[3] Before reaching the first line of the poem, the reader has been confronted with two foreign languages – Italian and Latin – that open "windows" onto modern and ancient Rome. Eliot associated the Italian phrase with a funeral stele he once tried to locate in Italy, thereby embedding a link between his poem and a commemorative slab for someone dead. The epigraph isn't attributed, so if as readers we want to play our authorial role, we ourselves must track down the reference. It is from the *Aeneid*. Aeneas meets a woman who seems to be a virgin huntress and asks her name (and where he is), not realizing that she is Venus, his own mother, in disguise. Venus hopes to refresh Aeneas by making him fall in love with Dido, although the plan will cost Dido her life.

If we persevere, we will discover that the poem is about nostalgic remembering, imaginatively rewriting the past, and the consequences of each. The subtext of the poem, through the speaker's longing for a maiden (like Dido) whom he has in some sense hurt, warns the reader against the need to create an "aesthetic distance" between ourselves and our experience: such distancing, although beautiful, makes it impossible to conduct a relationship. It also suggests a possible reason why the man insists on a fatal detachment: like Aeneas, he may have been concerned that the woman might keep him from accomplishing his work.

The first stanza of the poem paints a wordless visual image that we later learn is an artificial scene that he imagines himself directing. The speaker begins by speaking imperatively, presumably to the young girl of the title:

> Stand on the highest pavement of the stair –
> Lean on a garden urn –

> Weave, weave the sunlight in your hair —
> Clasp your flowers to you with a pained surprise —
> Fling them to the ground and turn
> With a fugitive resentment in your eyes:
> But weave, weave the sunlight in your hair.

Here, the girl is loosely allied with the reader: the "you" includes us. We paint a mental picture of a young girl doing as she is ordered: elevating herself (by standing at the top of the stairs), looking beautiful (presumably by tossing her head in a way that weaves the sunlight in her hair), embracing her flowers, and then flinging them down in an oblique expression of resentment. The speaker is directing the girl's response to something the man in the scene is presumably saying. Whether this is an imaginative replay of a scene she once performed or whether the speaker is rescripting a scene that didn't go well in real life, we do not know. We also don't know what prompted her resentment and the tears alluded to in the title.

In the next stanza, the tone changes, becoming retrospective rather than imperative, and the addressee differs as well: the speaker is no longer talking to the girl. The intimacy of the preceding stanza is lost as the direct address is supplanted by a cooler reference to the couple in the third person, and we see them as puppets of the narrator's desire to revise the past.

> So I would have had him leave,
> So I would have had her stand and grieve,
> So he would have left
> As the soul leaves the body torn and bruised,
> As the mind deserts the body it has used.
> I should find
> Some way incomparably light and deft,
> Some way we both should understand,
> Simple and faithless as a smile and shake of the hand.

Here, brutality darkens the tone: the decision to leave the girl is a kind of death. The girl's body may have become torn and bruised; she seems to have been exploited. The pronoun "we" leaps out in sudden contrast to the previous designation of the pair as "he" and "she." We are given to believe that the speaker is the man who left, and he wishes he had done so "faithlessly."[4] Here the distance that the speaker would create between the man and the woman constitutes a kind of emotional violence to her.

The man's insistence on detaching himself from the woman has succeeded in a literal sense, but failed in an imaginative one, since the girl continues to haunt his imagination as a vision of foreclosed promise. The third-person plural pronoun now appears as the speaker wonders "how they would have been together," and what he would have lost if they had remained attached. He concludes that the loss would have been minimal, since what he gained through the rupture was merely theatrical and aesthetic (a gesture and a pose):

> She turned away, but with the autumn weather
> Compelled my imagination many days,
> Many days and many hours:
> Her hair over her arms and her arms full of flowers.
> And I wonder how they would have been together!
> I should have lost a gesture and a pose.
> Sometimes these cogitations still amaze
> The troubled midnight and the noon's repose.

The speaker contemplates a moment of intimate possibility that is framed by suggestions of birth and death (flowers and urn). We are privy to his thoughts as he tries to control the girl's reactions; we hear the undertones of guilt and yearning as he imagines ways to rewrite their parting; finally, we are left to contemplate how the man's desire to control the girl has paradoxically put him in *her* power as she continues to compel his imagination. The price of the aesthetic distance he has insisted upon is that his nights are "troubled" with thoughts of what might have been. The speaker – implicitly aligning himself with Aeneas, guilty at the suicide of his lover Dido – wonders if his motives in causing the girl to weep were selfishly artistic. Like the speaker in W.B. Yeats' "The Tower," he might well ask, "Does the imagination dwell the most/ Upon a woman won or woman lost? /If on the lost, admit you turned aside/From a great labyrinth out of pride, /Cowardice, some silly over-subtle thought/Or anything called conscience once . . ."[5] In private lyrical moments, the speakers in both poems forsake their pretence of superiority and confess their guilt and sense of loss, offering highly personal warnings against distancing oneself from the unknown and the intimate out of a fear of losing control. Moreover, *"La figlia che piange"* shows that the beautiful, silent scene the speaker staged in his imagination is a flimsy aesthetic compensation for the complex intimacies he has declined.

In Eliot's poem, something *not* done – and not said – has replaced what could have been a meaningful interpersonal exchange in the writer's memory and in his poem. The kind of art the man practices in Eliot's poem, like that of the hunchback in the park, is designed to substitute and compensate for reality, not to express it. This brings up two ethical questions about the desire for beauty: is beauty – defined as the antithesis of ugliness, age, and corruption – anything other than a nostalgic desire for that which does not seem to change or disturb? If so, does this ally the desire for beauty with a politics that conserves the status quo, even to the point of eliminating threats to it? Second, is beauty associated with attraction (as in Thomas' poem), with repulsion – that which must be viewed from a distance (as in Eliot's poem) – or both? What is the role played by sensual attraction and repulsion in the impulse to demonize others, and to what extent is such attraction or repulsion culturally programmed?

One of the problems with making unfavorable judgments about groups of people on aesthetic grounds is that it is difficult to tell which came first: the judgment or the alleged offense to the senses. It is easy to rationalize prejudice by accusing the offender of repulsiveness, as we see in the "Cyclops" episode of Joyce's *Ulysses*. The narrator – a kind of Cyclops – treats Jews as repulsive by insinuating that they give off a smell that dogs can perceive: "those jewies does have a sort of a queer odour coming off them for dogs." The interrupting narrator in the chapter – who serves as the "other eye" that a Cyclops is missing – defensively responds by associating Jews with a *pleasing* rather than an offensive odour: he renames Bloom "Blumenduft," or flower fragrance.[6] Joyce implies that in the football-match mentality of violence, the offense calls the defense physically repulsive and the defense responds by asserting an impossible attractiveness. A significant weapon in any campaign of degradation, then, is forged from a culturally specific definition of what is aesthetically pleasing.

Wilde's *The Picture of Dorian Gray* (1891) offers an example of a character who practices an "aesthetic" ethics (in which he refuses to speak or even realize anything unpleasant or repulsive) with deadly results. What literally happens is that an artist paints a portrait of Dorian so beautiful that Dorian wants to *become* that portrait and, in a gothic moment, the two change places. However, the subtext of the novel is different: Dorian's determination to keep himself beautiful leads him to destroy the people around him and ultimately himself, thus illustrating the danger of trying to keep one's physical and moral ugliness hidden. The rotten spot in Dorian's moral universe is his desire to appear (and remain) perfect, because his denial of imperfection turns him actively – and even cruelly – against anyone who might reveal a flaw in him or in themselves.[7]

Wilde portrays Dorian's desire to keep ugliness hidden – by refusing to express or communicate it – as a denial of the unconscious. In an earlier version of the story, Wilde attributes this equation of reality with expression to the man who painted Dorian's portrait, Basil Hallward. In a passage Wilde deleted, Basil remarks, "it seems to me that to say a thing is to bring it to pass. Whatever has found expression becomes true, and what has not found expression can never happen."[8] In other words, nothing can be true if it has not been articulated or represented, which suggests that if one can keep something from consciousness, it won't exist, and art can become a mode of denial. But Basil also criticizes anything that does not change: "it is only the transitory that stirs me. What is permanent is monstrous and produces no effect" (182n). As the story turns out, countenances that do not change do indeed become monstrous.

In the book, Wilde draws the reader's attention to the ugly effects of the characters' attempts to use art and beauty to *arrest* time and change. Dorian wants to preserve what he sees, an effort to freeze time directed at himself, not the artwork. The changing portrait reflects the monstrosity of a man who refuses to change, who sees beauty not as truth, but as arrested *youth:* a self-directed lie. He tries to use art to alter reality: "if you don't talk about it, it never happened" (228). The structure of the novel itself mirrors, so to speak, its theme: the book is a mirror that reflects the observer. Wilde writes in the preface: "It is the spectator, and not life, that art really mirrors" (3). At the end of the book, Dorian stabs the portrait, calling it "an unjust mirror, this mirror of his soul that he was looking at" (280). The reader knows better, knows that Dorian's self-hatred is the disavowed shadow of his self-love, a reflection of his unconscious, a powerful repository for the changes the narcissist hides.

Dorian takes Basil's portrait of him into a schoolroom where no one else can see it, thereby destroying its "social" power, for art must be seen if it is to facilitate a dialogue between body and soul, artist and sitter, sitter and spectator, artist and spectator. This, in turn, is how Wilde's novel demands to be read: as a work in which recognition of objective reality opens the door to a fuller range of conversational possibilities.

In order to produce puzzlement in the reader, art must reflect physical and emotional change, becoming more like a human being and less like a decorative object. Dorian's relation to his portrait is a kind of conversation with art that illustrates why art should stimulate a public as well as a private dialogue. The viewer must participate in the construction of meaning and revise that meaning according to the way we see ourselves as being seen by others, often through the medium of artistic representation.

The aesthetic objectification of living people in *Dorian Gray* is largely responsible for the violent deaths of three people: an actress, the painter of the portrait, and its subject. An actress removed from the world by being placed on a pedestal as a "Tanagra figurine" (208–9) may be easily possessed, but such figurines are destined to crack or break. Turning people into objects is a way of killing them. This is what the painter does when he calls his portrait "the real Dorian" (194); Dorian does the same thing by loving himself only as a static work of art ("I am in love with [my image], Basil," 193). It is only through a changing relationship with an "other" – a viewer, a spectator, a lover – that art can come to life; a reader or viewer can bring it to life by participating in the larger conversation that it inspires, considering its implications not only for the individual but also for the larger social body.

"How horribly real ugliness made things!" (240), says Dorian. In contrast, when Sibyl, the actress, falls in love with him, she loses interest in artificial, unchanging reality, telling him, "You taught me what reality really is. . . . I am sick of shadows" (214). But Dorian responds that by refusing to play at being in love, she has "killed" his love; his love was for the imitation. Unlike hers, his reaction to reality is attempted repression – "the secret of the whole thing was not to realize the situation" (264). Avoidance of the hideous springs from a social directive to divide experience into two diametrically opposed halves in order to hide or disavow the aesthetically displeasing half. Dorian's mistake was actively to disown his corruption and to fear its exposure. In T.S. Eliot's early poems, something similar happens to the poetic narrators: they too are exposed against their will. The difference is that their need for privacy, unlike Dorian's, is honest. If Wilde's novel indicates the importance of displaying rather than hiding the self, Eliot's poems demonstrate the painful difficulty of being subjected to the scrutiny of others: Eliot's characters are divided into pieces by the voices and gazes of those who observe them. They experience themselves as reduced to fragments, existing only as they are seen from without: their fingers, faces, hands, eyes, heads are detached, dismembered. They suffer from having been disarticulated or analyzed by others. Like Wilde, Eliot implicitly makes the case for wholeness.

In "The Love Song of J. Alfred Prufrock," the speaker muses that he "should have been a pair of ragged claws / Scuttling across the floors of silent seas." Just as time is divided into discrete moments for social purposes, so, too, there is a parallel dissociation of body parts. The moving hands and faces of clocks slide into the disembodied hands and faces of people waiting for a moment of rest or decisiveness:

> There will be time, there will be time
> To prepare a face to meet the faces that you meet;
> There will be time to murder and create,
> And time for all the works and days of hands
> That lift and drop a question on your plate;
> Time for you and time for me,
> And time yet for a hundred indecisions,
> And for a hundred visions and revisions,
> Before the taking of a toast and tea.

When "real" voices are heard, they represent decision-forcing demands, and they "drown" the speaker's own voice.

In another of Eliot's poems, "Preludes," body parts, representing the fracturing of "individuals" by society, litter the streets, and a man's soul is "trampled by insistent feet / At four and five and six o'clock" (IV).

> One thinks of all the hands
> That are raising dingy shades
> In a thousand furnished rooms. (II)

By evening, the world is peopled with disembodied "short square fingers stuffing pipes" and "eyes/Assured of certain certainties" (IV).

Eliot's "Rhapsody on a Windy Night" ends with a telling rhyme between "life" and "knife," which draws our attention to the way life cuts people into pieces; in the poem, we see people not as whole bodies, but sliced into fragments. Again, people appear not as individuals (which means "incapable of being divided further"), but as body parts; they have been quite literally "disarticulated," or taken apart at the joints. The speaker has seen "eyes in the street/Trying to peer through lighted shutters." Ghettos and polite society alike resemble a nightmare of moving body parts as people are characterized by their horrifying incompleteness. Eliot treats body parts as if they were people, and people are remembered as incomplete bits of clothing or food. A prostitute in "Rhapsody on a Windy Night" appears as "the border of her dress" that is "torn and stained with sand." In "Mr Apollinax," the speaker looks for the head of Mr Apollinax "rolling under a chair" "Or grinning over a screen/With seaweed in its hair." Dowager Mrs Phlaccus and Professor and Mrs Cheetah devolve into "a slice of lemon, and a bitten macaroon."

Like Wilde's, Eliot's characters experience aging as corruption and, in Eliot's "Gerontion," despair. The elderly speaker asks,

> I have lost my passion: why should I need to keep it
> Since what is kept must be adulterated?
> I have lost my sight, smell, hearing, taste and touch:
> How should I use them for your closer contact?

Eliot's old man insists that "Unnatural vices/Are fathered by our heroism," and that "Virtues/Are forced upon us by our impudent crimes." What can art offer in a world of dismemberment, where beauty conceals a hidden terror that is ineluctably tied to the treachery of human society?[9] Eliot implicitly addresses this question in *The Waste Land* (1922), where he suggests that the challenge for reader and writer alike is to embrace the inevitability of fragmentation, to re-member the past, and to learn to speak in different voices, communally as well as individually.

Before discussing the interpretive challenges posed by *The Waste Land*, I would like to revisit the basic question of how and why it constitutes a challenging fiction. *The Waste Land* takes place in a shared cultural nightmare: the devastated aftermath of world war.[10] In the wake of a national or international trauma, speaking directly about the event becomes repellent; the words sound hollow and inadequate. Avoiding the trauma entirely is equally unsatisfying. In response to World War I and a nervous breakdown of his own, Eliot, with the help of Pound's skillful editorial eye, found a way of lyrically capturing a communal response to the spectacle of mass suffering that is precariously poised between despair and a glimmer of (possibly deceptive) hope.

The Waste Land has a reputation for being difficult to read, but what is sometimes overlooked is the meaning of that difficulty. In writing the poem, Eliot has eschewed the familiar forms and easy coherence of a culture that from a postwar perspective appears barbaric rather than civilized. The five sections of Eliot's poem seem at first reading to have little relation to one another; the connections that bind them are emotional and mythical rather than narrative. The poem tells a varied and inconsistent "story" of group response through snippets of individual stories, and more deeply through allusions to the shared ancient stories of mythology. Instead of making a costly and destructive effort to present a beautiful face to the world, as Wilde's Dorian did, Eliot salvages beautiful and horrifying remnants from the ravages of war, searching for relief and the inspiration to keep going. For example, Eliot opens a window onto brutality and the hope of future transformation through a brief description of a painting that depicts "the change of Philomel," her transformation into a nightingale.[11] Art again serves as the wordless expression of the potential of a violated life to mutate into something else.

The story of Philomela is a tale of greed, rape, and mutilation, abuses that are punished and eventually transformed through art. The determination to possess what belongs to someone else against that person's will and to silence any protests serves as a disturbingly personal metaphor for war and its effects. In Ovid's account, Philomela is secretly raped by Tereus, husband of her sister. When she threatens to tell the world, he cuts out her tongue and shuts her away, much as Dorian hid his tell-tale portrait in an attic. She weaves her story into a tapestry – weaving, in an early meaning, signifying the telling of a tale (*text* and *textile* are etymologically related). Philomela and her sister wreak revenge on Tereus, serving his son to him for dinner. In *The Waste Land*, Philomela's story illustrates one way in which the desire to possess and control others violates their very being. Philomela is literally rendered speechless, a mutilation that culminates in retaliatory violence (a domestic war thus mimicking an international one). Yet Philomela also very powerfully reaffirms the power of weaving – tale-telling – and of evoking in the reader (both the sister in Ovid and the reader in *The Waste Land*) the desire to challenge the injustice and thereby complete the story.

In the second section of the poem, "A Game of Chess," the speaker describes the painting of Philomela's metamorphosis as a window on a "sylvan" or wooded landscape that is also, in another sense, a desert:

> Above the antique mantel was displayed
> As though a window gave upon the sylvan scene
> The change of Philomel, by the barbarous king
> So rudely forced; yet there the nightingale
> Filled all the desert with inviolable voice
> And still she cried, and still the world pursues,
> "Jug Jug" to dirty ears. (ll. 97–103)

The gods restore Philomela's voice, making it "inviolable" through the transformative power of art – art that is simultaneously truthful, affecting, and defiant.

The painting of the change of Philomela captures the beauty and horror of something that cannot be said in words. It is in this way comparable to the heart of darkness in Conrad's novel (evoked through the famous exclamation "The horror! The horror!" that Eliot initially chose as the epigraph to *The Waste Land*). E.M. Forster similarly focuses on the power of the unspeakable in *A Passage to India* (1924). In the Marabar Caves an Englishwoman, Adela Quested, has a vision, a sensation of having been raped by India in the form of a man. This is another instance of the issue of possession without consent that equates – here through an inversion – colonial and sexual rape.

Tereus cuts out Philomela's tongue, and since the mouth constitutes the facial correlate of the vagina, this constitutes a second rape.[12] This double wound echoes in two similarly wounded mythical figures alluded to in *The Waste Land*: the Fisher King and Tiresias. The Fisher King suffers from a "thigh wound," a traditional euphemism for sexual impotence, and his weakness lays his land waste.[13] Tiresias, the blind prophet of mythology, whom Eliot identified in his notes as the seer of the entire poem and the person who encompasses all the others, also suffered a dramatic sexual wound – he is blinded. Because he had once been turned into a woman, Juno asked him who receives more pleasure during sexual intercourse, and he chose the woman. She blinded him in punishment, and Jove gave him the gift of insight in partial compensation.[14] Tiresias is the male version of Philomela; he is symbolically castrated by a woman as she was raped and silenced by a man. The understanding of blindness as symbolic castration (as in the story of Oedipus) derives from the resemblance between the eyeballs and the testicles ("testicle" comes from the same root as "testify," the Latin *testis*, or [eye] witness). Like Philomela, Tiresias receives a partial compensation for what he lost: just as she regains her voice through song, he is given the power of second sight. By alluding to myths that obliquely reinforce one another, such as the stories of Philomela, Tiresias, and the Fisher King, Eliot could constellate a group of referents that when read together accents common ideas, such as the social consequences and the potential compensations of sexual wounds.[15] The connections that bind these three figures illustrate Eliot's use of what he called "the mythical method," which designates a way of telling a story on different levels and with different historical and cultural referents at the same time.[16] Pieces of the mythological constructions fit together with pieces of the text to form an alternate picture, adding another dimension to the poem's meaning. In this case, the inability to see or to speak motivates a different kind of seeing and telling – the weaving of a tale – which in turn challenges the reader to hear the silenced voice and see the hidden image, thereby completing (and understanding) Eliot's poem.

If we look through the window opened by *The Waste Land* into myth, we see a sympathy with both men and women that is so acute, and so intimately connected with compassion for individuals everywhere who have been maimed by rapacious covetousness, that it becomes difficult to understand recent denunciations of Eliot's *poetry* as sexist and intolerant (his stated politics are more complicated).[17] Like Forster, Eliot suggests that the sexual wounding of individuals is a microcosmic instance of the social and national rapacity that lies behind imperialism and war.

Now we are in a position to appreciate how intimately sex and violence are connected in the world of this poem, and how Eliot deploys images and music in a fractured, elegiac expression of grief over the domestic and global atrocities motivated by possessiveness.[18] *The Waste Land* is an agonized elegy for World War I. It traces the violence of war and the desire for sexual mastery or ownership to the same root, the thrill of power. Paul Fussell, in *The Great War and Modern Memory*, vividly describes the felt proximity between sexuality and violence, recalling how the language of sexuality overlaps with the language of warfare: assault, thrust, defense, penetration.[19]

Male writers often described war wounds as assaults on their manhood, their sexual potency, as we can see in Hemingway's novel devoted to the aftermath of World War I, *The Sun Also Rises* (1926), in which Jake Barnes is unable to consummate his sexual relationship because of something that happened to him in the war. Wilfred Owen describes the "emasculating" effect of a war wound in "Disabled" (1917– 18),[20] which focuses on a former athlete sitting in a wheelchair, both legs and one arm missing. Owen euphemistically associates his mutilation with a "thigh wound":

> Now, he is old; his back will never brace;
> He's lost his colour very far from here,
> Poured it down shell-holes till the veins ran dry,
> And half his lifetime lapsed in the hot race,
> And leap of purple spurted from his thigh.

The blood spurting from the soldier's thigh recalls a long tradition of thigh wounds (castration) in heroic literature: the Fisher King, Adonis, Osiris, Odysseus, and Attis. The thigh wound is the site of a man's "rape"; it represents a blow against the possibility of reproduction or renewal, and the transformation of a man into a no-man, recalling Tiresias's experience of having been female as well as male.[21] In the wake of the devastation produced by war is impotence, an impotence that is both personal and social, private and public.

In this mythical context in which the psychic, the sexual, and the social are intertwined, a war wound that is simultaneously sexual functions like an aporia, a dead-end: mental, philosophical, and physical, blocking future as well as past life. Such wounds destroy the self and world as it was; if life is to continue, it can only do so by re-membering itself or being remembered by others differently, by undergoing a mutation or transformation. Like the *Metamorphoses*, *The Waste Land* brings the reader, again and again, to experiences of being wounded, assaulted, silenced, rendered impotent, mutilated. It is the reader's job to assemble the fragments, to challenge the fictional tale by making it whole again.

One of the first shocks to the reader of *The Waste Land* comes when an addressee identified only as the "son of man" is asked to come in under the shadow of a red rock and contemplate "fear in a handful of dust" (ll. 26–30). In the very next scene, a man facing a young woman with her arms full of flowers reports a moment of incapacitating but luminous vision: "I could not/Speak, and my eyes failed, I was neither/Living nor dead, and I knew nothing/Looking into the heart of light, the silence" (ll. 38–41). After one character has been awestruck by mortality, and another by something close to immortality, we see the speaker challenge a fellow fighter by asking if the corpse he buried has sprouted, an image that uncannily combines both. The line borrowed from Baudelaire that ends this first section of the poem refers the challenge of facing such shocking conjunctures of the sublime and the horrifying to the "hypocritical" reader, identified as the speaker's double: "You! hypocrite lecteur! —mon semblable, – mon frère!" (l. 76).

Preventing a reader from seeing *through* a poem or story to the meaning beyond it turns the window we have been discussing opaque: it becomes a reflective surface that, by interrupting voyeuristic habits, offers the reader a brief flash of self-awareness. Another way of calming the reader's anguish is musical, which works by wordlessly proceeding through melodic transformations. Eliot alludes to the power of music to soothe despair through repeated references to *The Tempest*, where Prospero calms the tempest he has magically created by commanding Ariel to sing. The song Ariel sings is about the power of death (and, by extension, art) to produce startling transformations:

> Full fathom five thy father lies;
>   Of his bones are coral made;
> Those are pearls that were his eyes;
>   Nothing of him that doth fade

But doth suffer a sea-change
Into something rich and strange. (Act I, Scene II, ll. 396–401)

Ferdinand marvels, "This music crept by me upon the waters, /Allaying both their fury and my passion/With its sweet air" (Act I, Scene II, ll. 391–3). Music, then, lessens grief with its enactment (and here its articulation as well) of the reminder that change is perpetual, that loss is part of a continuing process of transformation.

In a fragmented world in which disconnection seems inevitable, Eliot used running themes, or musical leitmotifs, to unify – through nonsensical, changing repetitions – what would otherwise remain only "A heap of broken images" (l. 22). These musical leitmotifs include the "Twit twit twit/Jug jug jug jug jug jug" of the nightingale, "So rudely forc'd" (ll. 203–5), the "Weialala leia/Wallala leialala" (ll. 277–8, 289–90) of the maidens of the Rhine and the Thames, bewailing the theft of their "gold," and Ariel's song from Shakespeare's *The Tempest*, especially the line, "Those are pearls that were his eyes" (ll. 48, 125). Amid the jumble of musical sounds that comprise the poem, we also hear the (significantly missing) sound of water: "Drip drop drip drop drop drop drop" (l. 358); the sound of the cock signaling morning and betrayal: "Co co rico co co rico" (l. 393), and the thunder speaking in syllables that suggest three Sanskrit words: "DA/*Datta*," "DA/*Dayadhvam*," "DA/*Damyata*" (ll. 401–2, 411–12, 418–19). Through a line from Paul Verlaine's sonnet, "Parsifal," quoted in French – "*Et O ces voix d'enfants, chantant dans la coupole!*" (l. 202) – we can recall the chillingly powerful choral and orchestral effect of Wagner's *Parsifal*, when we actually hear a sound like a choir of children singing from far away as the Grail (and the musical line) slowly descends. Popular and street music also move through the poem: from the ragtime rhythms of a "Shakespeherian Rag" (l. 128) to the raucous lines from an Australian ballad about Mrs Porter and her daughter (ll. 199–201) and "The pleasant whining of a mandoline" "Beside a public bar in Lower Thames Street" (ll. 261, 260).

If *The Waste Land* eschews poetic storytelling, and if it does so partly to avoid a doomed attempt to tell what is unspeakable, it substitutes a different kind of organization: one that is mythical and layered,[22] melodic – comprised of leitmotifs, song medleys, and echoes – and also imagistic. It unfolds as a series of short images and brief dramatic scenes, spliced together without narrative explanation or transition, almost cinematically. Eliot's technique developed out of the Imagist movement begun in 1912 (Ezra Pound defined the image as "that which presents an emotional and intellectual complex in an instant of time"[23]). His scenes supplant one another without comment, unified only by the title of each of the five sections.[24] As a collection of "images," *The Waste Land* can be read only by being divided into its component scenes; only then will it become apparent how those scenes are related.

For example, the second section, "A Game of Chess," falls into two scenes: an exchange between a man and woman as the woman sits at her dressing table (ll. 77–138), and a story told by a woman in a bar at closing time (ll. 139–73).[25] Although both are about experiences of the courtly game of "love" or chess as it moves toward checkmate, and both concern a woman, the two women represent very different social classes. The "lady" of the first scene is a queen on the chessboard of social movement; the woman in the pub is a pawn. The more privileged woman is in conflict with the man: "Speak to me. Why do you never speak. Speak. / What are you thinking of? What thinking? What?" (ll. 112–13). The man doesn't answer, but merely thinks depressed thoughts ("I think we are in rats' alley / Where the dead men lost their bones," ll. 115–16). In contrast, the woman in the bar is in conflict with another woman, the 31-year-old Lil, who, toothless, antique-looking, and worn out from bearing five children, can hardly stand the prospect of her husband coming home from the army. The storyteller in the pub has warned her, "if you don't give it him, there's others will" (l. 149). The queen of the first scene seems ready to "drown" her mate with her perfumes (ll. 88–9), whereas Lil is herself drowning, as we see by the way the section ends with Ophelia's farewell before her death by water in *Hamlet*: "Good night, ladies, good night, sweet ladies, good night, good night" (l. 172). The portrait of a woman whose needs are overpowering, placed against that of a woman whose needs are overpowered, shows that social malaise does not stem from women (they are also victims of it), nor are its effects confined to one class: the problem is systemic.

Another pair of scenes that work together in a similar way appears near the beginning of the first section, "The Burial of the Dead," when a scene in a desert (ll. 19–30) is followed by a scene in a hyacinth garden (ll. 31–42). The contrast between the two scenes is real, but ultimately not meaningful: one landscape lacks water and vegetation, and the other is suffused with them, but both are equally incapacitating. In the desert, a divine voice insists on the inescapable and fearful reality of dryness, shadow, and death:

> you know only
> A heap of broken images, where the sun beats,
> And the dead tree gives no shelter, the cricket no relief,
> And the dry stone no sound of water. Only
> There is shadow under this red rock,
> (Come in under the shadow of this red rock),
> And I will show you something different from either
> Your shadow at morning striding behind you
> Or your shadow at evening rising to meet you:
> I will show you fear in a handful of dust. (ll. 21–30)

The spiritual sterility evoked here seems to be remedied by the wet fertility of the next section, which is framed as a love scene with lines from Wagner's *Tristan und Isolde*. A girl reminds the speaker that he gave her hyacinths – a flower with a famously erotic shape. In a passage cited above, he remembers when they came back from the hyacinth garden, her hair wet and her arms full of flowers: "I could not/Speak, and my eyes failed, I was neither/Living nor dead, and I knew nothing, /Looking into the heart of light, the silence" (ll. 38–41). Whether one looks into the heart of light or the heart of darkness, at sterility or at lush fertility, barrenness prevails, as we hear from the line from *Tristan* that ends the section: "*Oed' und leer das Meer*" (empty and barren the sea).

"The Fire Sermon," as its title implies, is about burning – especially the fires of lust. Fire is followed by a short section on drowning. Again, one is invited to recall the climax of Wagner's *Götterdämmerung*, where the world is destroyed first by fire, then by water. *The Waste Land*, however, accelerates at the end. In "What the Thunder Said" are images of the world's desecration – falling towers, exploding cities, a ruined chapel, and final madness. Yet the text of the poem also explores the possibilities of resurrection, of receiving divine answers to human questions (what the thunder may have commanded is to give, sympathize, and control). The rain that may or may not come, the Grail that may or may not be found, the god(s) that may or may not exist – these prospects remain shadowy. The speaker ends by fishing; symbolically, he is trying to catch something alive beneath the surface of the seen. Answers – as we have seen over and over – are always in motion, elusive. The Fisher King is at once a suffering victim and a potential healer – the Quester – who can effectually restore fruitfulness to the wasted land by asking questions about what is happening, and about the nature of the Grail. The reader is obliquely being asked to become a questioner, a challenger: someone who *must* learn to understand, to interpret, differently. Eliot wrote that "Poets in our civilization, as it exists at present, must be difficult,"[26] because the alternative – to present our challenges as easy and familiar – is a lie, and a dangerous one.

In a sense, Eliot, like Wilde before him, suggests that meaningful intimate relation is precluded by artificial social mechanisms that proscribe life and love in the name of these same values. What society promotes as love is perhaps closer to rape; marriage, like chess, ends in checkmate; self-development is sinful; individuals are mutilated and disarticulated; and compassion is overmatched by indifference and violence. Eliot is bitterly critical of the "age of prudence," asking, "DA / *Datta:* what have we given? / My friend, blood shaking my heart / The awful daring of a moment's surrender / Which an age of prudence can never retract / By this, and this only, we have existed" (ll. 400–5). The music that calms the tempest at the beginning of Shakespeare's play of the same name, the defiant song of a tongueless, raped woman-turned-nightingale, the multiplication of personae in a dramatic world, tapestries that depict violently silenced realities – these are all evocations of a kind of art that might not be as painful and dead as what we call life. Unexpectedly, at the beginning of the twentieth century, Eliot and Wilde agree that art can be alive *because* society is artificial; art can be true and changing because society is static and built on lies, but only if we as readers expose the hidden ugliness of a society that worships and thereby destroys love, youth and beauty.

A Preference for the Tacit

Respect for the power of the unspeakable and for the limits of what could – or should – be said is apparent in much modernist writing, and the writing tries to pass on such respect to the reader by blocking effortless comprehension. In D.H. Lawrence's *The Lost Girl* (1920), the protagonist of the title learns that labeling and regulating everything facilitates "bullying and narrowness":

> What was left unsaid mattered more to Alvina now than anything that was expressed. She began to hate outspokenness and direct speaking-forth of the whole mind. It nauseated her. She wanted tacit admission of difference, not open, wholehearted communication.[27]

More searingly, in William Faulkner's *As I Lay Dying* (1930), Addie Bundren gives voice only after her death to the inadequacy and deceptiveness of words. She describes her realization that words are mere *substitutes* for the intensity of felt experience rather than expressions of it. Words trick and manipulate people:

> That was when I learned that words are no good; that words dont ever fit even what they are trying to say at. When he [Cash] was born I knew that motherhood was invented by someone who had to have a word for it because the ones that had the children didn't care whether there was a word for it or not. I knew that fear was invented by someone that had never had the fear; pride, who never had the pride. . . .

She says that her husband, Anse, "had a word, too. Love, he called it. But I had been used to words for a long time. I knew that that word was like the others: just a shape to fill a lack; that when the right time came, you wouldn't need a word for that anymore than for pride or fear."[28]

Henry James' "The Beast in the Jungle" (1902) demonstrates that not just words but symbols in general try to give a shape to the unknown, thereby closing off experience. John Marcher spends his life waiting for his "rare and strange" destiny – imagined as a powerful beast – that lies in wait for him, and he devotes his entire relationship with the woman in his life to a prolonged speculation about what this secret might be. Through the death of the woman, James shows that words and symbols may also have the effect of displacing and thereby precluding the very developments they prompt one to anticipate. Communication is not something that can be achieved passively, by waiting, watching, or using a powerful word or symbol to organize (or demonize) the unknown. The fearfulness of an encounter with an unrealized possibility is the subject of many of James' most well-known short stories, from "The Turn of the Screw" (1897), where the threat seems external, to "The Jolly Corner" (1906), in which the protagonist comes face to face with the man he might have been, discovering that 'Such an identity fitted his at *no* point . . .'[29]

Beckett's Molloy feels only dismay at the illusion of familiarity that words and naming promote. He tries to live "far from words":

> . . . when the icy words hail down upon me, the icy meanings, . . . the world dies too, foully named. All I know is what the words know, and the dead things, and that makes a handsome little sum, with a beginning, a middle and an end as in the well-built phrase and the long sonata of the dead.[30]

Beckett's trilogy of novels poses the question of how to proceed in the ongoing struggle with words, which name a reality and speak in a voice that is not one's own. In *The Unnamable*, the voice asks whether he should proceed "By aporia pure and simple?" and he warns, "I say aporia without knowing what it means" (291). This paradoxical hope that one might "proceed" via a dead end – without recognizing its meaning as such – is one important way that modernist writers proffer what one doesn't yet know as the only way of gaining self-knowledge. Only an impasse or blockage has the potential to make a reader or speaker aware that what has already been appropriated as his or her own is artificial, alien, and dead. The realization may be intensely uncomfortable, but the corner where a confrontation takes place with the "black stranger" within the self is, James reminds us, a "jolly" one.

The Ambassadors

In a 1533 painting called *The Ambassadors*, Hans Holbein the Younger opens a kind of window onto what cannot be seen in the present moment by including a strange object. That "window," opening onto another reality, also functions as a mirror symbolically reflecting the viewer's highly conditioned, habituated (and therefore "dead") way of perceiving art. Holbein, like the modernist writers four centuries later, aimed to expose and thereby challenge thoughtless or overly literal modes of understanding. Through the use of anamorphosis, an "inverted use of perspective,"[31] he creates, in a glass disc positioned near the feet of the two ambassadors, a distorted image. Regarded from the front, it appears to be an improbably situated decorative object like other objects in the painting; however, if the viewer looks more closely at it from an angle, it appears to be a skull.

In his discussion of the painting, psychoanalyst Jacques Lacan argues that this disc of Holbein's "makes visible for us something that is simply the subject as annihilated" (88). An annihilated subject may be simply dead, but it also aptly designates the successfully socialized viewer. The disc obliquely reflects the viewer as both dead and eyeless, regarding the visible world as something that does not include him or her, from which he or she enjoys the privilege of exemption. Lacan suggests that this is how the conscious subject looks from the perspective of the unconscious (79):

> In Holbein's picture I showed you at once – without hiding any more than usual – the singular object floating in the foreground, which is there to be looked at, in order to catch, I would almost say, *to catch in its trap*, the observer, that is to say, us . . . we are literally called into the picture, and represented here as caught. (92)

Lacan reads the painting as highlighting the vanity of the arts and sciences, which are represented through the objects in the painting that are displayed between the two figures. He contends that we only really "see" our relation to this vanity obliquely, at the moment when we turn away:

> . . . the secret of this picture is given at the moment when, moving slightly away, little by little, to the left, then turning around, we see what the magical floating object signifies. It reflects our own nothingness, in the figure of the death's head. (92)

We are thereby caught in the field of vision, our blindness exposed in the act of looking. Holbein uses an optical distortion to capture what would normally escape from our awareness: an image of the rational, conscious subject as dead and unseeing. Lacan argues that this is also the perspective of psychoanalysis, which "regards the consciousness as irremediably limited," a source of idealization, misreading, and *scotoma*, that which produces a blind or dark spot in the visual field (82). Lacan argues that by reducing itself to the "certainty of being a subject," the mode of being present in the world becomes "active annihilation" (81). Through the one-way process of seeing (without a comparable awareness of being seen) we destroy the vitality of the visible world and render ourselves disabled. This is what several writers of the twentieth century were attempting to convey by inserting a painting within their works: like Holbein's disc, the painting provides a frame for what we do not normally see, what we *cannot* see by retaining a conception of our subjectivity as entire rather than fractured and wounded.

From this perspective we turn our attention to Henry James' *The Ambassadors* (1903). James portrays his 55-year-old protagonist, Lambert Strether, belatedly discovering his own past blindness – and deadness – over the course of three months of consciously trying to see and live all that he could in Paris. Strether's blindness is also, by implication, ours. Throughout, James presents Strether's vision obliquely, or "anamorphically": the reader has to consider what is being said and understood from more than one angle to appreciate its limitations. Similarly, it is necessary for the book itself to be circuitous and prolonged in order for the reader's vision to be blocked as long and as effectively as Strether's: we, too, are blinded by the desire to see something beautiful and inspiring that will reflect its perfection back on us, the invisible perceivers. The book puzzles and teases its reader, ultimately surprising him, along with Strether, "in the function of voyeur," thereby disturbing, overwhelming, and reducing him to a feeling of shame (Lacan 84). Only when, like Strether, the reader glimpses a world other than the one in which he or she has heretofore believed does the text reveal its meaning. The reader experiences himself as unexpectedly caught or seen by the text.

Eliot implicitly – through the use of the Grail myth – suggests that the reader must become a questioner in order to find life in the waste land of a damaged and damaging culture. Through the shadowy knight of the Grail who haunts the background of the poem, Eliot points toward a model for more open, perceptive, and unassuming forms of questioning. James, in contrast, attempts to expose the reader's (and the writer's) complicity in the problems he or she is trying to solve; he does this in *The Ambassadors* by featuring a likeable protagonist who is as handicapped as the average reader, and as unaware of his blindness. Strether is an enthusiastic and appreciative if often mistaken reader of people, situations, motives, and cultures, a role that is reinforced by the narrator's repeated reference to Strether as "our friend."[32] Strether undergoes a metamorphosis: while in America, he was "all cold thought." He is initially described as an attentive but handicapped and inexperienced spectator: his eyes, described as "long-sealed," "were so quiet behind his eternal nippers that they might almost have been absent without changing his face."[33] He has to learn to see, and by seeing to live.[34] In Paris, he learns to read through the bodily senses, which he envisions as "the growing rose of observation, constantly stronger . . . , as he felt, in scent and colour, . . . in which he could bury his nose even to wantonness" (276). The metaphor of observation as a rose emphasizes the naturalness and sensuality of perception. But seeing and even smelling reality does not suffice. Strether still misses the underlying meaning of what he sees.

By focusing on sight, James first emphasizes Strether's imagination (the capacity to form mental pictures), his speculations. In addition to being fed by his growing power of sensual observation, the idealizing nature of Strether's imagination is also reflected by visual art, especially portraits; he instinctively associates almost every character with a beautiful painting. When he meets Little Bilham at the Louvre, he does so while "standing before one of the splendid Titians – the overwhelming portrait of the young man with the strangely-shaped glove and the blue-grey eyes" (85). When Strether first sees Madame de Vionnet's daughter, he experiences her too as a portrait:

> She was fairly beautiful to him – a faint pastel in an oval frame: he thought of her already as of some lurking image in a long gallery, the portrait of a small old-time princess of whom nothing was known but that she died young. (157)

Even Miss Barrace, resorting "to the optical machinery that seemed, like her other ornaments, curious and archaic," suggested "more than ever to her fellow guest the old French print, the historic portrait" (277). Strether's propensity to view life through the beautifying lens of art intensifies when he visits the studio of the painter Gloriani (based on James McNeill Whistler) and delivers his impassioned advice to Little Bilham to "Live all you can; it's a mistake not to," which Little Bilham remembers as an adjuration "to *see* . . . everything I can" (137, 172; emphasis added). Ultimately, Strether conceives an especially "idyllic" painting that will accommodate a revelation of his own when he sights two of the principal characters alone in a boat. Ironically, it is the completion of his mental picture that robs him of his blindness, and robs the art of its "innocent" beauty. James' decision to compare his project with Holbein's painting by using the same title becomes meaningful in that both works paradoxically use a visual image to expose what the viewer has missed.[35]

Strether is literally and figuratively seduced by idealized versions of beauty, art, and experience. The narrator described "Our friend" at the time of his arrival in Europe as suffering from an "odious ascetic suspicion of any form of beauty." Strether assures himself "that he shouldn't reach the truth of anything till he had at least got rid of that" (123). He does succeed in losing his suspicion of the beautiful: the city of Paris, site of so many famous (and not so famous) seductions, seduces him first with its beauty and its art, and then Madame de Vionnet's charm makes the seduction complete. It is Strether's immersion in beauty and art that eventually enables him to see the fuller, less ideal picture, when he suddenly apprehends the truth of the relationship between Madame de Vionnet and Chad, the young American he had been sent to retrieve. Strether is forced to acknowledge the failure of his ambassadorship, as he relinquishes not only his idealism, but also his sensation of youth.

Strether's immersion in the visual becomes complete when he spends an entire day "inside the frame" of a picture by Lambinet that he had seen years ago at a dealer's in Boston:

> The oblong gilt frame disposed its enclosing lines; the poplars and willows, the reeds and river – a river of which he didn't know, and didn't want to know, the name – fell into a composition, full of felicity, within them; the sky was silver and turquoise and varnish; the village on the left was white and the church on the right was grey; it was all there, in short – it was what he wanted: it was Tremont Street, it was France, it was Lambinet. Moreover, he was moving freely about in it. (319)

Strether seems for the moment to be living in an idealized memory of a painting, which underscores his disconnection from what is actual or real ("the memory . . . was sweet," but "If he were to see [the Lambinet] again he would perhaps have a drop or a shock, and he never found himself wishing that the wheel of time would turn it up again," 319). He has utterly capitulated to the illusion that impossible wishes have been fulfilled: "The little Lambinet abode with him as the picture he *would* have bought" (319). Strether surrenders to pure appearance, to the luxuriance of the senses. He had prepared for such abandonment the last time he had seen Madame de Vionnet, when he "asked her to conjure away everything but the pleasant" (322). And now, for an entire day, he had "not once overstepped the oblong gilt frame" (323). Strether did not then realize that the picture was incomplete. Only after conflating the Lambinet painting and the idyllic lake facing him at dinner one evening does he realize that the figures he sees in real life were missing from his mental image: "It was suddenly as if these figures, or something like them, had been wanted in the picture, had been wanted more or less all day" (325). What Strether realizes only in retrospect, as he sits awake all night fitting the pieces together, is "that there had been simply a *lie* in the charming affair" (329).

Let us pause for a minute on that lie, on "the quantity of make-believe involved and so vividly exemplified that . . . disagreed with his spiritual stomach" (331). The lie is the equivalent of Holbein's anamorphic skull that reflects the viewer: it betrays the woundedness, the blindness, in the viewer (as well as the viewed) that motivates the lie. Compare Marlow's revulsion against the lie in Joseph Conrad's *Heart of Darkness* (1902): "You know I hate, detest, and can't bear a lie, not because I am straighter than the rest of us, but simply because it appals me. There is a taint of death, a flavour of mortality in lies – which is exactly what I hate and detest in the world – what I want to forget."[36] Of course, Conrad's novel ends with a scene that dramatically illustrates the value of a "white" lie: its capacity to lighten the burden of truth. Marlow found he could not tell Kurtz's Intended what his last words really were: "It would have been too dark – too dark altogether" (79). Marlow comes to understand *both* the flavour of mortality in lies and their capacity to relieve our encounters with corruption. What Strether has to struggle to realize is that the lie of innocence perpetrated by Chad and Marie was complicit with his own fantasy of their (and therefore his) artistic perfection. James is not critical of the lie, since he understands that a lie – or a fiction – is necessary to survival; it allows one "to believe in anything that from hour to hour" keeps one going (276). The danger of the lie is that one can easily blame it entirely on others, not recognizing it as one's own.

Strether is ultimately confronting an "image" of reality that integrates the beautiful lies – or art – of Europe with the stern morality of Massachusetts. He realizes, regretfully, that intimacy is "much like lying"

(331) in that it is attractive on the surface but obscures a much more complex and adulterated reality. He learns this firsthand when he visits Madame de Vionnet for the last time in the place where she lived. Appreciating "the picture that each time squared itself, large and high and clear, around her" (333), he is allowed to witness the hidden emotions that were belied by her beautiful performances: "the strange strength of her passion was the very strength of her fear" (340). In turn, Madame de Vionnet suggests that Strether's innocence – his "morality" – had also been rooted in fear, a fear of the aesthetic extremes of beauty and ugliness. She points to his propensity to "pull up when things become *too* ugly; or even, I'll say, to save you a protest, too beautiful. . . . Ugly or beautiful – it doesn't matter what we call them" (342–3). When Strether appreciates the extent of the beautiful-and-ugly truth of the relationship between Chad and Madame, he can do nothing but politely withdraw from all intimate relationships of his own, feeling that he is too old to know how to use this new knowledge.

Let us now return to the main theme of *our* story, because *The Ambassadors* is not only about seeing; it is also about reading. What Strether learns has important implications for how we read challenging fiction – including James' late novel, and other modernist works. James makes it clear that the rules for observing paintings may be applied equally well to texts; that every person may be viewed as a work of fiction as well as a subject of a portrait. One character compares another to a "new edition of an old book that one has been fond of – revised and amended, brought up to date, but not quite the thing that one knew and loved" (115). Strether associates Madame de Vionnet with "some fine firm concentrated heroine of an old story, something he had heard, read, something that, had he had a hand for drama, he might himself have written" (180). At one point, Strether himself is described as reading Madame de Vionnet's story in her face:

> Her face, with what he had by this time grasped, told him more than her words; whether something had come into it, or whether he only read clearer, her whole story – what at least he then took for such – reached out to him from it. (252)

The French countryside resembles the Lambinet painting, but also it "would remind him of Maupassant" (320). And when he thinks of the accumulated impressions of his day, they assemble into a whole that he imagines as textual: "Not a single one of his observations but somehow fell into a place in it; not a breath of the cooler evening that wasn't somehow a syllable of the text" (324).

Surely, James is striving to offer a pleasurable fiction to the reader. As we read books, we imagine ourselves in a desirable story. But such fictions may suddenly become strange and unsettling, a phenomenon Strether calls "queer as fiction, as farce" (326), once he accepts that "fiction and fable *were*, inevitably, in the air" (329). In the end, he is forced to realize that the fiction that everything was wonderful was his own, when in fact "He was mixed up with the typical tale of Paris" (333).

Initially, it is the narrator who notes that "Strether's reading of such matters was, it must be owned, confused" (180). Later Strether himself understands: "here was his usual case: he was for ever missing things, through his general genius for missing them" (284). He sees that he has "rather too much" imagination (307), making him "fantastic and ridiculous" (303); he suffers from a "too interpretive innocence" (333), as we can see confirmed by the way he is verbally associated with a lamb through two names that help to define him and his vision: his own first name – Lambert – and the name of the artist of the picture he remembered so fondly – Lambinet. As likeable as he is, Strether is hampered by his passivity as a reader of life. James presents him to us as an example of how *not* to read if we want to follow Strether's passionate advice and "*really* to see" (172). Although Strether is a curious and engaged reader, reading should not simply be reactive and evaluative, consisting primarily of appreciation and criticism, of judgments and opinions. It must also be performative. What Strether did not do was imagine himself in the position of the two powerful women he admired, and so he loses them both. Instead, he allowed himself to act as extensions of them: as their agent, their ambassador. His point of view was too narrow, too restricted, handicapped by his unacknowledged wishes. "He recognized at last that he had really been trying all along to suppose nothing. Verily, verily, his labour had been lost. He found himself supposing innumerable and wonderful things" (331).

One of the aspects of reading that James uses Strether to illuminate is the extent to which the reader will notice only what he or she expects to find, which is in turn linked to what he or she remembers. One of the main functions of the many paintings we see Strether seeing or imagining is that they show him *framing* his perceptions through past experience:

> Too deep almost for words was the delight of these things for Strether; yet as deeply mixed with it were certain images of his inward picture. He had trod this walk in the far-off time, at twenty-five; but that, instead of spoiling it, only enriched it for present feeling and marked his renewal as a thing substantial enough to share. (24)

Strether's "inward picture" gains value in contrast with what the narrator calls his "backward picture," his grey image of the past few decades of his life:

> It was at present as if the backward picture had hung there, the long crooked course, grey in the shadow of his solitude. It had been a dreadful cheerful sociable solitude, a solitude of life or choice, of community; but though there had been people enough all round it there had been but three or four persons *in* it. (62)

When Strether associates the people he meets with portraits in art galleries, he is revealing the extent to which they remain unreal to him, projections of repressed desire for what he had lost or never had. Later, when he accuses others of having "no imagination" (307), he is simply failing to grasp that they have no need to form *mental* pictures because they are living in the present.

Active, curious reading is what Strether describes as "direct dealing" with reality, as opposed to passively "gaz[ing] at it as a picture, quite staying one's own hand" (140). Strether's advice to his new young friend to "live all you can" urges the viewer to become part of the picture: a challenging reader, not a passive voyeur. He describes "the affair of life" as

> at the best a tin mould, either fluted or embossed, with ornamental excrescences, or else dreadfully plain, into which, a helpless jelly, one's consciousness is poured – so that one "takes" the form, as the great cook says, and is more or less compactly held by it. (138)

"Live," he says: "Don't at any rate miss things out of stupidity . . . don't make *my* mistake. For it was a mistake. Live!" (138). To live, one must know how to "read" or interpret the complexities of experience that do not fit one's own mold. To exceed the confines of the tin mold is to walk outside the "oblong gilt frame" of one's inner picture, to come to life.

The importance of mental pictures brings us near to where we began, with *The Picture of Dorian Gray* and the important psychic connection between painting and youth. A painting that arrests time easily signifies youth, or incomplete development. Dorian quite literally used his portrait to preserve his youth; Strether tries not to preserve but to recapture his youth in the art and arts of Paris. Strether tells his friend Maria Gostrey that if he comes to grief through his adventures in Europe the disappointment won't kill him: "No – worse. It will make me old" (206). She replies that nothing will do that, because, as she tells him paradoxically, "The wonderful and special thing about you is that you *are*, at this time of day, youth." Strether agrees, saying that he began to be young when he first arrived in Europe, and that he has stayed young ever since: "I never had the benefit at the proper time . . . I'm making up late for what I didn't have early . . . it's my surrender, my tribute, to youth" (206–7). But he is doing so through the agency of two other characters: "they're my youth" (207). Whereas Wilde shows Dorian literally trying to preserve his youth by becoming a work of art, James is more circumspect and subtle in his treatment of Strether's romance with youth: he intimates that we frame reality as art in a futile but heartfelt effort to pause or reverse the passage of time. This affords a certain compensatory pleasure, but it is not really reading in that it doesn't help an individual come alive or learn to see: on the contrary, it reduces the self to a mere fiction, "a vain appearance" (129).

Life Painting in Joyce

James Joyce saw the relation between people and paintings in much the same way as Henry James, with one important difference: James emphasizes the sensual and aesthetic pleasure of framing other people as works of art; Joyce treats that pleasure as more explicitly erotic. In "The Dead," Gabriel kindles his desire for his wife by seeing her as a painting.

Unconsciously, by "framing" her, Gabriel makes her seem younger and at the same time he transforms her into an object that he might possess. He thinks:

> There was grace and mystery in her attitude as if she were a symbol of something. He asked himself what is a woman standing on the stairs in the shadow, listening to distant music, a symbol of. If he were a painter he would paint her in that attitude. Her blue felt hat would show off the bronze of her hair against the darkness and the dark panels of her skirt would show off the light ones. *Distant Music* he would call the picture if he were a painter.[37]

When she moves out of the frame and turns toward him, "A sudden tide of joy went leaping out of his heart" (213) and desire begins to course in a "warm flood along his arteries" as he recalls private "moments of their life together" (213, 215). Unlike Strether, who had painted an idyllic picture in an effort to deny the underlying sexual connection between his idealized younger friends, Gabriel uses a mental picture to suggest that he knows his wife completely. For a moment, she is only what he sees: an alluring body displayed to his gaze. Gabriel's aestheticizing impulse is a kind of imaginative foreplay that works by turning his beloved into an image he can own. By extension, Joyce suggests that one of the most significant unconscious motivations of readers is voyeuristic and possessive: there is an intense (if often disavowed) pleasure in the prospect of seeing and mastering – understanding in the sense of possessing – a work of art or fiction, and the person or memories it stands for or evokes.[38]

In "The Dead," Gabriel excites himself sexually by viewing a woman as a work of art. In *Ulysses*, Leopold Bloom does so quite explicitly, with greater self-awareness, in the "Nausicaa" episode. This episode, which takes painting as its "art,"[39] is the one that caused the issue of the magazine in which it was first published, *The Little Review*, to be confiscated as obscene. It falls into two parts: the first part is narrated in the sugary and sentimental idiom of Gerty MacDowell, a young woman sitting on the beach who imagines herself as a work of art and a fictional heroine. Leaning back to watch fireworks, Gerty gradually reveals her "understandings" (13.917) to a "gentleman" (Bloom) who is watching her intently, so that "he had a full view high up above her knee . . . and she wasn't ashamed and he wasn't either to look in that immodest way like that because he couldn't resist the sight of the wondrous revealment half offered" (13.728–32). The second part of the chapter consists of Bloom's stream of consciousness after his sexual climax.

Bloom understands that voyeurism – the desire to see someone's secrets without being seen in turn, which is one of the desires behind reading as well – is based on an illusion. The unconscious desire is *not* to see reality, but to be blind, with a blindness (or innocence) reminiscent of youth (Bloom's parting words are "it was lovely. Goodbye, dear. Thanks. Made me feel so young," 13.1272–3). The revelation that excited Bloom in the gathering twilight was only "half offered"; what he actually saw was Gerty's "nainsook knickers" (13.724) and her well-filled hose. He has seen an unrealistic, cosmetically enhanced, still-clothed image, not Gerty's imperfections and her physical handicap. Bloom is grateful that her lameness was not apparent to disturb his fantasy: "Glad I didn't know it when she was on show" (13.775–6). A few minutes later he thinks, "See her as she is spoil all. Must have the stage setting, the rouge, the costume, position, music" (13.855–6). He remembers desiring his wife in much the same idealizing way; he thinks of the evening when he was wooing his wife, kissing her shoulder: "Wish I had a full length oil-painting of her then" (13.1091–2).

Unlike many readers of the episode, Bloom is not ashamed of the moment of understanding and pleasure he shared with Gerty, despite its artificiality. He understands first that the desire for an idealized communion between watcher and watched was mutual. He envisions their attraction as natural magnetism, and he compares his orgasm to a sneeze: "Dress up and look and suggest and let you see and see more and defy you if you're a man to see that and, like a sneeze coming, legs, look, look and if you have any guts in you. Tip. Have to let fly" (13.993–6). He feels only gratitude: "Did me good all the same. . . . For this relief much thanks" (13.939–40). The reader, too, feels a kind of relief. "Beautiful" art, and even popular fiction, purports to give the viewer a glimpse of something secret, when its function is actually to clothe more disturbing realities. It offers readers a respite, a welcome moment of blindness, a sensation of impossible rejuvenation ("My youth. Only once it comes," 13.1102–3).

Joyce invites the reader to recognize his or her own blindness when he uses a strange syllable to punctuate Bloom's internal monologue: "Ba" (13.1117, 1119, 1127, 1143). This syllable is most aptly described as a castrated or raped word: its ending has been removed, producing two opposite effects: nonsense and a potential proliferation of meanings. After the syllable is first introduced, we see Bloom complete it to make the word "bat," using the same logic the reader had to utilize earlier in the book when Bloom thinks of his hat as a "high-grade ha," presumably because that is how the inside of his hatband literally reads after long wear. Bloom's first response to the half-formed "Ba" is "Bat probably. Thinks I'm a tree, so blind" (13.1117–18); he attributes his own blindness to the bat. He even imagines the kind of tree he would be – a weeping willow – and he connects metempsychosis with the Greek belief that "you could be changed into a tree from grief" (13.1118–19). This bat, if he perceives Bloom as a weeping willow, is clearly not as blind as Bloom thinks; on the contrary, he is acutely sensitive to the feelings of loss Bloom is trying to ignore.

Bloom projects other fears onto the bat, as well. When he associates the bat with the "belfry" of the nearby church, imagining him "hanging by his heels" up there when the "Bell scared him out" (13.1121), that linkage evokes the phrase "bats in the belfry," a popular metaphor for mental instability. The fear that others see him as not quite right in the head, like the fear of being blind, is something Bloom manages by repressing it, but it leaks out through his unconscious identification with the bat. The narrative confirms Bloom's anxiety about how others perceive him at the end of the chapter, when it records how Gerty MacDowell "noticed at once that the foreign gentleman that was sitting on the rocks looking was *Cuckoo/ Cuckoo/ Cuckoo*" (13.1301–6).

Bloom's identification with the bat also allows us to glimpse his subconscious sense of himself as simultaneously very young and very old, a "childman weary, [a] manchild in the womb" (17.2317–18). He likens the bat to a small man: "Like a little man in a cloak he is with tiny hands. Weeny bones" (13.1130–1). Beneath the level of consciousness, Bloom seems to have completed the syllable "Ba" in two different ways, as "bat" but also as "baby." The tiny hands and weeny bones of the "little man" reflect an association of the bat – a surrogate for Bloom himself – with Bloom's infant son Rudy, who died when he was eleven days old. In addition, the bat is also a miniature man, importantly connected with the passage of time through his "cloak," which, through its etymology, links the bat back to the belfry and to blindness, thereby completing the circuit of associations. "Cloak" and "clock" derive from the same root, the French *cloche*, or bell (a cloak presumably has something of a bell shape). The buried kinship between a cloak and a clock underscores the connection between Bloom's desire to cloak his suspicion of his wife's infidelity earlier that day and the way that desire was interrupted by his clock, or watch, which stopped at the time of her scheduled meeting with her lover. Finally, Bloom's subconscious mind, directing the stream of language that constitutes his thoughts, also associates the bat with that watch or clock, which also has "tiny hands," directing us to realize that a watch, despite its name, is blind: it is designed to be seen rather than to see. To watch the clock emerges as a version of voyeurism, in that one is observing a face and hands that cannot look back. It is the "blindness" or unawareness of the watched object that makes the voyeuristic relationship sterile and illusory rather than vital and illuminating.

By "castrating" a word, Joyce creates a space for Bloom to fill the gap thereby created in several revealing ways. He has produced a miniature aporia, or dead end, for the conscious mind that paradoxically operates as a portal for the unconscious to express its buried desires and fears. We have observed Bloom's revealing reactions to the incomplete word, but is it also possible to imagine how we ourselves may have responded to it? Joyce seems to have directed our possible responses by featuring several short words that begin with "ba" throughout *Ulysses*. For example, to complete the word as "ball" would bring us back to the beginning of the "Nausicaa" chapter, to the rolling ball that directed Bloom's eyes to Gerty in the first place. More meaningfully, if we register "ba" as the beginning of "bath," that association would link Bloom's masturbation in "Nausicaa" with his earlier plan to "Do it in the bath" that morning (5.504). Most importantly, though, we can see "ba" as a partial expression of the word "bad," which intimates a fear that Bloom can barely tolerate: the apprehension that he is bad: incomplete, castrated, impotent, blind, unstable, unlovable. Bloom draws attention to that construction of "ba" as "bad" by recalling a line from a letter from Martha that he received earlier in the day: "I called you naughty boy because I do not like" (13.1263). The end of Martha's sentence is "that other world" (5.245), by which she clearly means that other "word" – bad? – but her typographical error betrays a deeper fear of the posthumous consequences of badness.

Joyce accents the revelatory power of blindness or darkness (when the blindness is accepted rather than denied) by contrasting it with the potentially destructive effect of the sun, or light. He does this once again through Bloom's stream of consciousness: Bloom imagines the sun as possessive and self-perpetuating – even imperial – when he thinks of the way it imprints its image on the viewer's eyes, so that it affects whatever he or she sees next: "Stare the sun for example like the eagle then look at a shoe see a blotch blob yellowish" (13.1132–3). Bloom's interpretation of the sun's power is significant: he concludes that the sun "Wants to stamp his trademark on everything" (13.1133–4), and he associates the power of light to brand or possess what it touches with a dim memory of the use of light to burn and destroy the enemy in war: "Glass flashing. That's how that wise man what's his name with the burning glass. Then the heather goes on fire . . . Archimedes. I have it! My memory's not so bad" (13.1138–42). What Bloom partly remembers is the legend that Archimedes destroyed the Roman fleet in 212 BC by setting it on fire with a convex glass. By implication, Joyce is asking us to contemplate the idea that light – especially the light of reason – can work like the brightness of gold to inspire a covetous love of all that glitters and a complementary destruction of what threatens it. In contrast, darkness, blindness, and even "badness," can be revelatory as long as the perceiver is willing to own them rather than projecting them onto others. The word "bad" is defined as "failing to meet an acceptable standard"; the very concept is relative rather than absolute, and relative to an established norm. By such a logic, even innovation would be "bad."

It is not the occasional erotic and pleasurable experience of blindness that is a problem, then, but how that experience is understood. Bloom can see the bat as blind, but he cannot easily accept or "see" the blindness or badness in himself. At the end of this episode, Bloom experiences himself as incapable of connection with someone else: he can neither read nor write. When he picks up a piece of paper on the strand and peers at it, he has to give up: "Letter? No. Can't read" (13.1247). A moment later he finds a bit of stick and tries to write a message in the sand with it, but he only gets as far as "I. AM. A." before he effaces the letters with his boot, unwilling or unable to complete the thought, deciding the effort is useless (13.1258, 1264–7). How should Bloom's sentence be completed? I am a . . . bat? A cuckoo? A cuckold? A bad man? Here we can see once again how the truncation of an ending serves to multiply the interpretive possibilities. These incomplete textual utterances also make it possible for the reader to discover his or her own fears and desires in the text, reflected as they are at an oblique angle. The impulses of many readers are narcissistic: desirous of seeing ourselves flatteringly reflected, loath to see ourselves as blind or incapable. At bottom, however, Bloom understands the value of the rare opportunity to "See ourselves as others see us" (13.1058) – a result of looking at art or reading something that resists our desires. When Bloom makes a trip to the National Museum earlier in the day to see if the Greek statues have anuses, he is trying to see art and divinity as less idealized, more real. The ability to see the self from the perspective of something outside the self – apart from desire or fear – is a precondition of non-narcissistic love. It is important to be able to love what is different, because the self is inescapable: as Bloom ruminates, you "Think you're escaping and run into yourself" (13.1110). Those who deny their own blindness or badness will hate that of others, oblivious to the fact that projected hate is merely self-hatred in disguise.

To the Lighthouse

When art blocks voyeuristic or other vision, it creates a momentary blindness to, and respite from, old habits and desires. This is what the artist Lily Briscoe tries to do with her painting in Woolf's *To the Lighthouse* (1927): turn a window into a canvas, to close an aperture leading into an idealized past that would have continued to put pressure on the future. The painting was supposed to be of Mrs Ramsay – Lily's hostess – and Mrs Ramsay's son James as they sit in a window, but in the end it is an abstract expression of the relation between two shadowy masses. When Lily is finally able to decide how to paint that relation, the painting is finished. What makes the painting so difficult is that the challenge of how to connect the two masses refers not only to what Lily sees, but also to the relation between perceiver and perceived. By extension, it also describes the problem of how Woolf might best understand her own connection to her dead mother, on whom Mrs Ramsay was based. As we have seen throughout this analysis, the painter's relation to her subject is a model for the reader's relation to the book: like Lily's painting, *To the Lighthouse* may have to be taken up again after a ten-year interval before the reader can draw that connection between herself and the novel that might allow her to say, as Lily does at the end, "I have had my vision."[40]

In *To the Lighthouse*, the task of aesthetics is once again probed through a painting that is at once a vista and a mirror: the abstract painting of "what she sees" as she looks toward the Ramsays' house. Lily's problem is, in formal terms, "how to connect this mass on the right hand with that on the left" (53). She thinks about making the connection with a horizontal line – "She might do it by bringing the line of the branch across so" – or with a vertical addition: "or break the vacancy in the foreground by an object (James perhaps)" (53), "But the danger was that by doing that the unity of the whole might be broken." Lily confronts the common problem of how to depict two opposite things at the same time, in the same frame:

> For what happened to her, especially staying with the Ramsays, was to be made to feel violently two opposite things at the same time; that's what you feel, was one; that's what I feel was the other, and they fought together in her mind, as now. It is so beautiful, so exciting, this love . . . also it is the stupidest, most barbaric of human passions. (102)

The two "masses" represent not only the tension, even the opposition between the artist and her subject, but also the division in what she sees, a division loosely embodied by Mr and Mrs Ramsay. Mr Ramsay is the principle of disarticulation, represented by a knife, a "beak of brass," an "arid scimitar" (38), an axe or poker, "a famished wolfhound" (200), a "fierce sudden black-winged harpy, with its talons and its beak all cold and hard, that struck and struck at you" (184). Mrs Ramsay, in apparent contrast, is a giver and a nurturer, passionate about dairies ("real butter and clean milk," 103), always (controversially) urging people to marry, and quick to visit the poor and the sick. Lily thinks of Mrs Ramsay's instinct to make sick-visits as one that turned "her infallibly to the human race, making her nest in its heart" (196).

Woolf's portrayal of the Ramsays is so complete because, like Lily when she learns to connect the two masses in her painting, Woolf understands that although the two characters based on her parents are in many ways opposites, they are also united by a strong underlying connection. In their own ways, both are coercive. Lily sees "the astonishing power that Mrs Ramsay had over one. Do this, she said, and one did it. Even her shadow at the window with James was full of authority" (176). (The "ram" in their name may therefore denote not a male sheep, but a propensity to force others.) Lily thinks more than once that "so much depends . . . upon distance" (191); her feeling about Mr Ramsay becomes more sympathetic as he sails out into the bay, but her more difficult challenge is to bring Mrs Ramsay closer, to make her ordinary again, to "realize" her.

Mrs Ramsay becomes briefly real at the end of the novel when her ten-year-old promise to James that he would go to the lighthouse is finally kept, and when Lily is able to "see" her again, not just walking through the fields of death, but knitting at the window as she had done at the beginning of the novel. As Lily paints, she feels Mrs Ramsay draw close, and has

> a sense of someone there, of Mrs Ramsay, relieved for a moment of the weight that the world had put on her, staying lightly by her side and then (for this was Mrs Ramsay in all her beauty) raising to her forehead a wreath of white flowers with which she went. . . . It was strange how clearly she saw her, stepping with her usual quickness across fields among whose folds, purplish and soft, among whose flowers, hyacinths or lilies, she vanished. It was some trick of the painter's eye. For days after she had heard of her death she had seen her thus, putting her wreath to her forehead and going unquestioningly with her companion, a shadow, across the fields. The sight, the phrase, had its power to console. (181)

But Lily's vision is not complete until she apprehends something else that had always evaded her, something that could only be apprehended with "fifty pairs of eyes" (198), with "some secret sense, fine as air, with which to steal through keyholes and surround her where she sat knitting, talking, sitting silent in the window alone" (198). What Lily needed was not a memory of Mrs Ramsay's "astonishing beauty," but "an odd-shaped triangular shadow" thrown over the step. Lily thinks, "One wanted . . . to be on a level with ordinary experience, to feel simply that's a chair, that's a table, and yet at the same time, It's a miracle, it's an ecstasy" (202).

Mrs Ramsay – it was part of her perfect goodness to Lily – sat there quite simply, in the chair, flicked her needles to and fro, knitted her reddish-brown stocking, cast her shadow on the step. There she sat. (202)

For a moment, what was lost has been restored, not only to the heart, but to the eyes. Lily can apprehend two opposite things in the same moment: Mrs Ramsay is both there and not there. This is the magic of fiction.

Part of what makes it possible for Mrs Ramsay to appear and for Mr Ramsay to sail away, putting both parents for a moment in perfect balance, is the fact that the mold that made them has been broken – brilliant men who impose and beautiful women who allow themselves to be imposed upon – by the events of life. Woolf conveys this partly through those who have died (Prue and Andrew) and those who remain (Lily and Mr Carmichael). Prue was the beautiful daughter, a future version of Mrs Ramsay, but she dies in childbirth in her first year of marriage. Andrew was the child with brains, a mathematical genius, the next generation's answer to Mr Ramsay, and he is blown up by a shell in France during the war. Those remaining are Lily and Mr Carmichael, the artist and the poet, who are cut from another pattern altogether. Lily, at 44, has not suffered herself to be imposed upon. As Lily thinks to Mrs Ramsay, "It has all gone against your wishes. . . . Life has changed completely. At that all her being, even her beauty, became for a moment, dusty and out of date" (175). Lily is able to feel a moment of triumph at the thought that Mrs Ramsay would never know that the marriage she herself had arranged had failed, and that Lily herself had "never married, not even William Bankes" (175).

And Mr Carmichael, far from being, like Mr Ramsay, a "lion seeking whom he could devour" (156), was a famous poet, an opium-user, a word-catcher, who comes to stand beside Lily at the end "looking like an old pagan God, shaggy, with weeds in his hair and the trident (it was only a French novel) in his hand" to crown the occasion (208). Lily thinks, "There was an impersonality about him. He wanted very little of other people" (195). For some reason he had never much liked Mrs Ramsay, perhaps because of "her masterfulness, her positiveness, something matter-of-fact in her. She was so direct" (195). Mr Carmichael, unlike Mr Ramsay, is not a needy or intrusive man:

He was an inscrutable old man, with the yellow stain on his beard, and his poetry, and his puzzles, sailing serenely through a world which satisfied all his wants, so that she thought he had only to put down his hand where he lay on the lawn to fish up anything he wanted. (179)

Unlike Mr and Mrs Ramsay, Lily and Mr Carmichael are not interested in romantic love, and lack the coercive kind of authority; in fact, they are more contemplative than active altogether. Lily thinks of herself and Mr Carmichael that "Some notion was in both of them about the ineffectiveness of action, the supremacy of thought" (196). They do not sacrifice others, unlike Mrs Ramsay, who "led her victims . . . to the altar" (101), herself "lavished and spent" by marriage (38). They are artists whose mode of communication is tacit rather than overt or demanding. Their orientation towards truth is multiple-minded rather than single-minded,[41] calm rather than passionate (Lily imagines Mr Carmichael's poetry as "seasoned and mellow," 195); they are more concerned with reality than with beauty, the impersonal than the personal. (As William Bankes once noted about Lily's painting, it reduced mother and child – "objects of universal veneration, and in this case the mother was famous for her beauty" – "to a purple shadow without irreverence" (52).)

In *To the Lighthouse*, what begins framed in a window ends up in the painting, a painting that claims for itself no special status (Lily thinks, "It would be hung in the attics," "it would be destroyed," 208). Mr and Mrs Ramsay are associated with the world of the window, a transparent world, designed to showcase beauty and truth directly, but painfully: he with the "beak" through which he imposes himself upon and cuts through things, she with her complementary insistence on connection, on marrying. This window opens onto the past, despite its promise of prospect; it is a beautiful world, but a deceptive one that will soon erupt into war, exposing the "great lie" of civilization for what it was. The old ideals of female beauty and male brains were blown away, as both violate the privacy of the individual in their different ways. The world of the window would be replaced by the world of the (abstract) painting, and Mr and Mrs Ramsay are succeeded by Lily Briscoe and Mr Carmichael. In place of the astonishingly beautiful mother figure with eight children, we are given the thoughtful, observant painter with the Chinese eyes and puckered face; instead of Mr Ramsay's piercing intellect, we have

Mr Carmichael shuffling in his yellow slippers, sleepily fishing for words in his lawn chair. And amid all the sadness for the departed world of apparent transparency, a world presided over by the rooks Mrs Ramsay has aptly named "Mary and Joseph," we somehow feel that the change is a welcome one, promising greater autonomy and movement.

It is like the change that Wallace Stevens also attributed to world war. In "Asides on the Oboe" (1940), "the metal heroes that time granulates" were replaced by what he calls "the impossible possible philosophers' man, / The man who has had the time to think enough," "responsive / As a mirror with a voice . . . Who in a million diamonds sums us up."[42] The Ramsays are like those "metal heroes" of the past, granulated by the passage of time and the destruction of war, while Lily and Mr Carmichael are avatars of the "central man," an embodiment of the humbler reality of humanity itself, with all its different diamond-like facets. As Stevens tells it,

> One year, death and war prevented the jasmine scent
> And the jasmine islands were bloody martyrdoms.
> How was it then with the central man? Did we
> Find peace? We found the sum of men. We found,
> If we found the central evil, the central good.
> We buried the fallen without jasmine crowns.
> There was nothing he did not suffer, no; nor we.

It is precisely the new feeling that one can "tunnel" behind representations, behind pre-fabricated, deceptive, familiar images, that inspires Lily and gives her the energy to finish her painting. When she imagines Mrs Ramsay, she thinks, "Phrases came. Visions came. Beautiful pictures. Beautiful phrases. But what she wished to get hold of was that very jar on the nerves, the thing itself before it has been made anything. Get that and start afresh; get that and start afresh; she said desperately" (193). Lily wants to get beyond the beauty, with its deceptive surface. Unlike Wilde's painter, Lily, when she looks at her subject (Mrs Ramsay), and sees in her something "clear as the space which the clouds at last uncover," asks,

> Was it wisdom? Was it knowledge? Was it, once more, the deceptiveness of beauty, so that all one's perceptions, half-way to truth, were tangled

in a golden mesh? or did she lock up within her some secret which certainly Lily Briscoe believed people must have for the world to go on at all? (50)

For Mrs Ramsay, for Dorian, for Lambert Strether, beauty hides a secret. The nature of the secrets is quite different, but each has magical power. The secret "chambers of the mind and heart" contain,

> like the treasures in the tombs of kings, tablets bearing sacred inscriptions, which if one could spell them out would teach one everything, but they would never be offered openly, never made public. What art was there, known to love or cunning, by which one pressed through into those secret chambers? What device for becoming, like waters poured into one jar, inextricably the same, one with the object one adored? Could the body achieve it, or the mind, subtly mingling in the intricate passages of the brain? or the heart? Could love, as people called it, make her and Mrs Ramsay one? (51)

Although Lily passionately desires "unity" with Mrs Ramsay, it is precisely the knowledge of Mrs Ramsay's inviolable separateness that feeds that desire, keeping it alive. What Lily loves in her is the near-perfect balance between her warmth and her inscrutability, her capacity for creating a closeness that is at the same time remote: Mrs Ramsay, like the lighthouse, is two things at once, and both look very different at close range than from a distance. Her famed beauty is little more than a distraction from this "completeness."

Once Mrs Ramsay is dead, Lily regards the memory of her beauty even more clearly as a distortion, a kind of lie, ruminating, "beauty was not everything. Beauty had this penalty – it came too readily, came too completely. It stilled life – froze it. One forgot the little agitations; the flush, the pallor, some queer distortion, some light or shadow, which made the face unrecognisable for a moment and yet added a quality one saw for ever after" (177). Lily wants to recapture not the photographic perfection of Mrs Ramsay, but something that has more to do with Mrs Ramsay's effect on Lily. Lily wants to express her "emotions of the body" when Mrs Ramsay is near, and the feeling of complete emptiness that wrings the heart when she is dead. It is a holistic vision of Mrs Ramsay's imperfect, changing, paradoxical presence that Lily wants to convey, much as James Joyce in *Ulysses* wanted to paint a portrait of an "all-round man." Both are more interested in the comprehensiveness of their perspectives, their attempts to see with "fifty pairs of eyes," than in the more superficial consolations of superficial beauty. Lily describes her art as a "combat," an "exacting intercourse" with her ancient enemy, "this truth, this reality, which suddenly laid hands on her, emerged stark at the back of appearances and commanded her attention" (158).

To the Lighthouse chronicles the emergence of a new kind of artist who simultaneously represents a new kind of observer or reader, one who is willing to wrestle with reality over an extended period of time rather than – more easily yet ultimately ungratifyingly – to adorn or pierce it. That reality, moreover, is not represented in the text. What is represented is the struggle to come to terms with it. So that the reader may also experience this struggle, certain important questions in the text remain unanswered: we never learn, for example, whether the final, completing line Lily draws in the centre of her painting is vertical or horizontal, whether she has stressed the connection or the discontinuity of the two masses. Woolf forces the reader to read carefully and patiently until he or she experiences the shock of fresh awareness, a moment of seeing that has not been familiarized by habit or conditioned by the expectations born of experience. "So coming back from a journey, or after an illness, before habits had spun themselves across the surface, one felt that same unreality, which was so startling; felt something emerge. Life was most vivid then" (192).

Krapp's Last Tape

Of course, one can continue to live and read by the old habits, so that life is ordered and predictable, even routine. Beckett provides a comic and pathetic image of what such an existence is like in *Krapp's Last Tape* (1958), in which the title character is making a tape for his sixty-ninth birthday. Every year on his birthday he makes a tape – a chronological narrative of the main events of that year – which he has arranged in numbered spools and boxes. As his name and his ill-advised preference for bananas implies, Krapp is anal-retentive, someone for whom control is very important, but it creates a balancing need for release. For Krapp, such self-medication comes from sex and alcohol. Even thirty years ago he made hopeless resolutions to "drink less" and to have a "less . . . engrossing sexual life" (he says that he has spent approximately forty percent of his waking life on licensed premises).[43] We are given ample evidence of his repeated failures to keep those resolutions.

The poignancy of the play comes through Krapp's belated fascination with a key moment in his life, the moment that he indexes as a "Farewell to – love" (57), part of Krapp's lifelong determination to bury whatever is dark: "the dark I have always struggled to keep under is in reality my most – " (60). But Krapp, cursing, switches off the tape and winds it forward, keeping that revelation dark too. Instead, he listens to a story that he will return to twice more: a description of himself and a woman in a punt after he tells her "I thought it was hopeless and no good going on and she agreed" (61). They get stuck, and he reports,

> [I lay down across her with] my face in her breasts and my hand on her. We lay there without moving. But under us all moved, and moved us, gently, up and down, and from side to side. (60, repeated verbatim on 61 and 63)

The reminiscence ends, and Krapp is back in the present. He reports his own isolation: "Never knew such silence. The earth might be uninhabited" (63). The tape runs on wordlessly.

Krapp lives in an isolation that is almost total, relieved only by the sound of his own voice telling his own life story. His greatest intimacies are with the bananas and bottles that feed him. Beckett emphasizes not narcissistic hate for what is unlike the self, but the pathos of a lifelong conversation with one's own echo (Echo was the lover of Narcissus, who literally wasted away out of love for him until she was nothing more than a voice that lacked all autonomy). Throughout this chapter, we have discussed modernism's distaste for narcissism and the ways in which narcissism forms the root of patriotic and nationalistic ideologies. The fate of those who have loved a narcissistic culture will inevitably be that of Echo. Body will fade into voice, a voice that lacks independence. Beckett de-romanticizes such a resolution as "Krapp." The narcissistic and control-oriented approach to life encourages abuse of others, creates substance-abuse problems for an increasingly isolated self, and renders hopeless the desire to be moved, in contact with someone else, to love ("under us all moved, and moved us").

Chapter 4 Watchman, What of the Night?

As we have seen, it is sometimes helpful to have one's understanding unexpectedly blocked or impeded; otherwise, comprehension becomes little more than an automatic consumption of already familiar and easily acceptable ideas. In this chapter, I would like to explore another metaphor used by modernist writers to suggest a method of delaying and even transforming primarily rational habits of understanding: through darkness. In the "Ithaca" episode of Joyce's *Ulysses*, Bloom recalls his puzzlement over an old riddle: "Where was Moses when the candle went out?" The answer, not given in the text because it is "self-evident," is: in the dark.[1] In darkness, one cannot rely exclusively upon the eyes to see; although the eyes will adjust to darkness in time, apprehension through the ears, smell, and touch is enhanced. One must navigate darkness "feelingly": with the emotional sensitivity associated with sensual perception as well as with the eyes of reason. This is part of the meaning of challenging literature: it is "obscure" literature, a literature of the dark; it must be imaginatively apprehended with all the senses, and with the heart as well as the mind.

The title of the chapter is taken from Djuna Barnes' *Nightwood* (1937), which in turn comes from Isaiah. The protagonist of this dark and difficult "circus" novel, Nora, desperately seeks out a male doctor, surprising him in his nighttime female apparel, to ask him to tell her about the "night." Dr Matthew Mighty-Grain-of-salt-Dante-O'Connor responds with a poetic and eloquent defense of darkness that I discuss in greater detail later in the chapter. In general, though, we can see from his impassioned soliloquy that darkness figures the submerged realities — races, gender orientations, neuroses, even criminals — that are unacceptable to the conscious mind or inconsistent with respectability. The doctor insists that such darkness is a disavowed part of everyone, and the disavowal accounts for much of the sickness of our culture. By extension, in literature darkness stands for the subtext: the patterns of meaning that lie beneath the surface of the text, supporting and subtending what we see on the page. In Isaiah, the nighttime represents vulnerability to attack but also ignorance, affliction, and evil, which is why inquirers go to the watcher, sometimes understood as God or a prophet, to ask him anxiously about the darkness, when it will be over. The watchman replies cryptically that "Morning comes, and also the night. If you will inquire, inquire; come back again" (Isaiah 21: 11–12).[2] As a prophecy, his reply suggests that day and night are equally real and inevitable: we must learn to accept both, and if we want to understand the complex and contradictory nature of reality, we should inquire seriously, carefully, thoughtfully, and do so repeatedly. The watchman is recommending a deeper way of reading, one that encompasses obscurity as well as understanding.

This chapter is structured like the night, which the Romans divided not into hours but into four *vigiliae*, night watches or vigils: Vespera (evening); Conticinium (growing quiet); Intempesta Nox (deepest night); and Gallicinium (cock crowing). I have used these divisions partly to emphasize the close relation between darkness and vigilance: one of the reasons darkness is valuable is precisely because it requires greater vigilance. Each of these sections emphasizes a different aspect of the relation between darkness and modernism: the section entitled "Vespera" (Evening), like Chapter 2 above, explores the importance of balance, of equilibrium between light and darkness, power and impotence, knowledge and ignorance, whites and blacks, men and women. The second section, "Conticinium" (Growing Quiet), shows how this equilibrium may be achieved: through a renaissance of appreciation for the undervalued term. The example I give of such a renaissance is a racial one, featuring the emergence of the New Negro in American literature in the 1920s. The third section, "Intempesta Nox" (deepest night), focuses not on the beauty and importance of darkness but on its threat: specifically, it explores the relation between darkness and the dissolution of identity associated with violence and, less destructively, with eros. The chapter ends with "Gallicinium" (Cock crowing), which, like the first section ("Vespera" or Evening), stresses renewed balance, the reemergence of light into darkness. It constitutes a reminder that no extreme state – whether of brutality, ecstasy, or incomprehension – can be sustained indefinitely; deep inquiry moves towards balance, towards an appreciation of the assurance that, to adapt the words of the watchman, night comes, and also the morning. Modernist literature moves towards the kind of comprehension that encompasses opposite extremes, embracing not only knowledge but also obscurity in the awareness that in time, obscurity too will grow luminous.

Darkness, then, is rich in associations, ranging from the psychological and the social to the historical. During the modernist period in particular, it designated the rising power of what had been oppressed or repressed, but it also aptly described the ugly means used to stifle the emergence of these forces erupting "from below": the long "night" of despair commemorated by Elie Wiesel in his memoir of life in a concentration camp;[3] the sectarian and anti-government violence that became a way of life in India after 1919; the bloody chaos in Ireland under the Black and Tans in 1919, which Yeats evoked through "Those winds that clamour of approaching night," a night that sweats "with terror" when the "nightmare / Rides upon sleep."[4] Darkness might aptly characterize what happened in the Soviet Union, first through Lenin's use of terror to establish a dictatorship, and then through Stalin's "collectivization" – elimination – of over five million peasants, beginning in the fall of 1929 (another 10 million were incarcerated in forced labor camps).[5] The darkness was economic as well, as is reflected by the name of the day when the stock market crashed in the US: Black Tuesday (October 29, 1929). In Spain, the civil war that raged from 1936 to 1939 contributed to the impression that the world was becoming increasingly and terrifyingly dark. The connotation of darkness as the unknown reinforced the sense that social upheaval was allied with psychological madness, as the unconscious challenged the supremacy of "enlightened" rationality. But darkness was also being used in another sense, as something to be asserted with pride: the "kissing, young darkness" associated with black skins at sundown in Zora Neale Hurston's *Their Eyes Were Watching God* (1937), and the "dark men" of Joyce's *Ulysses,* Stephen and Bloom, social outsiders (an intellectual and a Jew) who proceed by feeling and hearing rather than mastering and controlling, thereby unexpectedly pulling ahead in the human race. The chapter ends with Joyce's *Finnegans Wake*, the only book in the history of literature to be addressed primarily to the eyes, ears, memories, and instincts of the reader, to his or her subconscious mind. Its embrace of darkness allows it to touch on such "unspeakable" subjects as incest, sodomy, fratricide, parricide, and the primal scene, but it also, like darkness, unites rather than divides those who enter it. It is a book designed – like ancient scripture – to bring readers together in the effort to read it, rather than encouraging readers to define themselves in opposition to the readings of others. The word "dark" is related to the Old High German word *tarchannen*, to hide, and the Greek *thrassein*, to trouble: books that embrace the dark are ones that try to lance what is troubling and hidden rather than avoid or deny it, a process that requires both vigilance and persistence and relies upon all the senses and emotions as well as the reason. It changes the locus of the enemy from the other to the self, an enemy that everyone shares, and in so doing it encourages the formation of interpretive communities to understand a history of tribal warfare, of discrimination turned lethal through lynching or genocide. If morning comes, and also the night, then the hardest challenge is to change what we do in the dark from fighting to thinking and working together, with pleasure and laughter. This is what challenging fiction enjoins us to learn.

Vespera (Evening)

One of the most groundbreaking changes of the early twentieth century was a sense that the social field was darkening in the beautiful sense of "even-ing": becoming more even. Groups that had been segregated, exploited, and abused were being regarded differently, and they were also finding new opportunities for self-expression. One of the landmark literary events to celebrate this change was the publication of Joyce's *Ulysses* in 1922, which T.S. Eliot had said "destroyed the whole of the nineteenth century."[6] By taking a (cuckolded) half-Jew as its hero, Joyce made a strong counter-statement to the growing admiration for men of steel. His hero is "keyless"; he assumes ownership of nothing, including his wife. He is viewed as an outsider, a "dark" man, in his home country of Ireland. He is not only part-Jewish, he is also part female, presented as "the new womanly man" (15.1798–9). In a nationalist country agitating for freedom from British imperial rule, he is a pacifist, a "toothless terror" (2.429–30) like the stone lions Stephen passes in "Nestor"; aptly named Leopold, as a lion he is harmless. Through his character Stephen, Joyce asserts that being Jewish is not the same as being mercenary. With that one stroke, Joyce frees his own anti-capitalist position from the ugly racist stereotypes of Pound and Eliot: "A merchant, Stephen said, is one who buys cheap and sells dear, jew or gentile, is he not?" (2.359–60).

The hero of *Ulysses*, Leopold Bloom, is emphatically heterodox: he is Hungarian and Irish, Jewish, Protestant, and Catholic. Dressed in black, he emerges as the proverbial "dark horse," whom Joyce backs as the unexpected winner of the human "race," like the horse "Throwaway" that wins the Gold Cup against long odds (20 : 1) on the day on which *Ulysses* takes place (June 16, 1904).[7] Bloom's darkness allows him to represent the darker-skinned people of the Middle East, especially Jews, but it also associates him with blindness – since a "dark man" is an epithet for a blind man – as well as with the allure of obscurity: the territory of that which is more comprehensive than reason. Joyce associates him symbolically with "Averroes and Moses Maimonides, dark men in mien and movement, flashing in their mocking mirrors the obscure soul of the world, a darkness shining in brightness which brightness could not comprehend" (2.138–40). Stephen, Bloom's non-biological "son," celebrates the value of such obscurity when he asks an imaginary reader, "You find my words dark. Darkness is in our souls do you not think?" (3.420–1). And a little earlier, when he is told that the Jews "sinned against the light" and have "darkness in their eyes" that condemns them to wander the earth, Stephen asks in return, "Who has not?" (2.361–3, 373). By associating darkness with sin, Joyce paints everyone dark. This allows him to question the impulse to project our own sins onto others, such as women and Jews, through the charge that Jews sinned against the light and that "A woman brought sin into the world" (2.390). Joyce's sharp-eyed view of everyone as "black" was apparent even in the literary sketches he wrote in high school. These sketches, which have not survived, were called *Silhouettes* after the characters in the first sketch: an onlooker sees two black silhouettes against a lighted window-blind, a man and a woman, one of which hits the other and makes the light go out. As Joyce's brother Stanislaus argued, even these early efforts exemplified a ruthless realism designed to give the lie to the rest of literature, and to the romanticized world of make-believe in which it was set.[8]

For Joyce, whose epic *Ulysses* was devoted to the eventful minutiae of a single day in Dublin and the short night that followed it, and to the subconscious as well as the conscious awareness of its three main characters, evening is within everyone, because darkness is associated with the subconscious that always "makes itself felt" behind the light of reason. *Ulysses* casts social prejudice as cognate with the prevailing attitude toward the psyche: darker peoples, like the unknown, are cast out; they become the "blinds" onto which others project sins to be punished, sometimes with violence. Among other things, *Ulysses* is a book about the unconscious bases of racial (and sexual) prejudice, proposing that individuals make the effort to claim their own darkness, thereby seeing themselves as more evenly divided between good and bad, strong and weak, aware and blind.

Earlier, in the United States, W.E.B. Du Bois had made a similar point about how the legacy of slavery and the experience of oppression affected the black population in America. Unlike whites, gentiles, or successful men, whom Joyce portrayed as disavowing the darker aspects of themselves, Du Bois argued that black people in a predominantly white society had to experience themselves as mixed. In *The Souls of Black Folk* (1903), he suggests that only Negroes were forced to have a double consciousness of dark and light by virtue of being forced to have two identities: that of a Negro and an American.

It is a peculiar sensation, this double-consciousness, this sense of always looking at one's self through the eyes of others, of measuring one's soul by the tape of a world that looks on in amused contempt and pity. One ever feels his twoness, – an American, a Negro; two souls, two thoughts, two unreconciled strivings; two warring ideals in one dark body, whose dogged strength alone keeps it from being torn asunder.[9]

Du Bois emphasizes the struggle of having to maintain two opposed identities, much as William Faulkner would later do in his treatment of the racially mixed Joe Christmas in *Light in August* (1932; originally called *Dark House*). Jean Toomer, in *Cane* (1923), depicts this double consciousness more lyrically, as a plangent, evocative richness of being. The life of Negroes in the rural South – a way of life that was dying – is captured through the dusky confluence of light and dark at evening.

Although it reads as a blend of poetry, drama, prose, and song, *Cane* also reflects a realism as brutal as that of Joyce. That realism is most vividly apparent in the section called "Blood-Burning Moon," in which a black and a white man fight over a beautiful Negro woman: the black man slashes the white man's throat, but the white man's townspeople burn the black man at the stake in an old cotton factory. Brutal realism is the quality in *Cane* that makes it harmonize so closely with the blues, understood as the "impulse to keep the painful details and episodes of a brutal experience alive in one's aching consciousness, to finger its jagged grain and transcend it, not by the consolation of philosophy, but by squeezing from it a near-tragic, near-comic lyricism."[10] Toomer's realism, like Joyce's, comes from a willingness to accept darkness – the brutality of ugly truth – as well as light, and from a heightened appreciation of the moments when the two coexist peacefully, like light and darkness at evening. Dusk becomes for Toomer a lyrical, life-affirming alternative to violent conflict between whites and blacks. He also shifts the metaphor by suggesting that cane – the sugar cane that people are boiling in the Georgia countryside – "*Redolent of fermenting syrup, / Purple of the dusk, / Deep-rooted cane*" – subconsciously calls up Cain, the biblical brother marked on his skin and cursed to wander for having murdered his brother Abel. When writing about his life, Toomer refers to his book *Cane* – once – as *Cain* (145). The error is a meaningful one: sugar cane, Toomer's symbol of the sweetness of black life, also evokes the bitterness of its twin and opposite, Cain, the biblical figure marked and exiled for life for violence against his brother.

Toomer's appreciation of darkness and light together as promoting a sensual richness of being led to controversial arguments when he refused to identify himself as part Negro; he was accused of denying his race (145).[11] Toomer's friend Waldo Frank referred to the book as "evasive, or in any case, indefinite" about "the racial thing"; he noted that a reader would not know *what* Toomer was, and Toomer asks himself, "why should the reader know"? (143). In a letter he wrote to Sherwood Anderson at the end of 1922, Toomer clarifies his reasons for being suspicious of identifying with one extreme of blackness or whiteness at the expense of the other: he argues that such an identification is defensive.

The Negro's curious position in this western civilization invariably forces him into one or the other of two extremes: either he denies Negro entirely (as much as he can) and seeks approximation to an Anglo-Saxon (white) ideal, or . . . he overemphasizes what is Negro. Both of these attitudes have their source in a feeling of (a desire not to feel) inferiority. (150)

Instead, in *Cane*, Toomer highlights the spectral beauty of moments when white and darkness intersect, such as the moment in bed when a dark woman lying next to the speaker "curled like the sleepy waters where the moon-waves start, / Radiantly, resplendently she gleams" (21). Words, too, are described as legible against whiteness, "like the spots on dice" (32). In "Theater," a character is most alive when his face is half in light and half in shadow (52). Whiteness is associated with the familiar sights of cotton, moonshine, the white pulp of the cane. A slim woman's body is appreciatively described as "white as the ash of black flesh after flame" (29). The capital city is brought alive by the infusion of "black reddish blood into the white and whitewashed wood of Washington" (41). Most powerfully, in "Esther," we see a 9-year-old girl who "looks like a little white child" thrilled by an "immense, magnificent, black-skinned Negro" whom she hears speak as a rapturous prophet in her home town. This intersection of blackness and whiteness, at dusk, becomes the most generative experience of her life: "He left his image indelibly on the mind of Esther. He became the starting point of the only living patterns that her mind was to know" (23).

Another aspect of Toomer's novel that links it to Joyce's is its sexual frankness. Such erotic openness flows naturally from an acceptance of darkness. If Joyce's novel was banned for "obscenity" throughout the English-speaking world, Toomer's, according to Du Bois, was the first that "dared to emancipate the colored world from the conventions of sex" (170).[12] Of course, these works are only shocking if seen from a conventionally repressed perspective. Both Joyce and Toomer treat sexual pleasure as a natural and important part of life. In "Fern," the narrator asserts, "That the sexes were made to mate is the practice of the South. Particularly, black folks were made to mate" (17). Sex in *Cane* is like eating or singing at "night's barbecue":

> A feast of moon and men and barking hounds,
> An orgy for some genius of the South
> With blood-hot eyes and cane-lipped scented mouth,
> Surprised in making folk-songs from soul sounds.
>   ("Georgia Dusk," 15)

Toomer does not insist upon a sharp distinction between erotic and sensual pleasure; he describes the "song-lit race" of Negro slaves as "dark purple ripened plums" (14). A woman becomes the evening; Karintha's skin, "carrying beauty, [is] perfect as dusk when the sun goes down" (3). Passion is simply that which fires the body, giving it color and energy, while the "mind, contained above desires of his body, . . . tries to trace origins and plot destinies" (52). It is hardly surprising that both Toomer and Joyce would write books that were not only sensual but also sexually explicit, because what they are talking about is the potential mating of opposite extremes, which can happen pleasurably or through violence. In the most violent story in *Cane*, the burning black man symbolically becomes a version of his white antagonist, named Stone, when his head is seen through the flames as "erect, lean, like a blackened stone" (36). Difference of skin color matters less to Toomer than the shared obduracy, the mutual hardness, of the men of different races. Also like Joyce, Toomer is interested in the way a man's understanding is expanded through his effort to understand the feelings of women. The appreciation of sexual pleasure does not imply a view of women as sexual objects; instead, it is enabled by an appreciation of women as complex individuals in their own right.

Like Joyce, Toomer is attentive to the subconscious and the repressed, hoping like the narrator of *Cane* to find "the truth that people bury in their hearts" (48). For whites, the Negro often figures that buried truth, as we can see most clearly in "Blood-Burning Moon." In this story, the white man's desire for a black woman and his contempt for black men both stem from his dim realization that he could not know them. He thinks, "Was there something about niggers that you couldnt know? Listening to them at church didnt tell you anything. Looking at them didnt tell you anything. Talking to them didnt tell you anything. . . . Nigger was something more" (34). Dusk was attractive as a time when the extremes of light and darkness met – what was allowed and what was denied – and one could see things that most people could not:

> Dusk, suggesting the almost imperceptible process of giant trees, settled with a purple haze about the cane. I felt strange, as I always do in Georgia, particularly at dusk. I felt that things unseen to men were tangibly immediate. It would not have surprised me had I had vision. (19)

Toomer's "vision," like Joyce's, is a vision of a transitory reality, not an abiding moral vision of correctness or damnation. As he wrote to Waldo Frank, "I see myself expressing myself, expressing *life*" (151). For this reason, as Du Bois noted, Toomer's art "carries much that is difficult or even impossible to understand"; in the world of *Cane*, it is hard to see, and "the whole world is a puzzle" (171). But it is a puzzle that Toomer is sharing with a reader whom he invites to help him solve it. In "Fern," he addresses the reader directly as "friend." Insisting that it does not matter if the reader is black or white, he asks his reader what could be done to help Fern: "Your thoughts can help me, and I would like to know. Something I would do for her . . ." (18). The reader is treated as an equal, a partner, a fellow-traveler equally concerned about sadness, despair, brutality, color, loneliness, and beauty. For Toomer, even-ing, in the words of Dylan Thomas, is a time when "darkness, hand in hand with light, / Is blind with tears too frail to taste" ("The Morning, Space for Leda").[13]

Conticinium (Growing Quiet)

The second watch of night occurs when the sounds of day recede. I've chosen this as the heading for literature that celebrates, not the conjunction of light and darkness, but the formerly denigrated beauty of blackness and night. It could as easily have been designated not a "growing quiet," but a "growing loud"; it was only the white voices that were growing quiet in the consciousness of black Americans, especially those of Harlem in the 1920s. More importantly, the emergence of black voices made the violence "grow quieter" for a time as more creative modes of expression became available. The Harlem Renaissance erupted in the wake of the race riots in the "Red Summer" of 1919, which Arnold Rampersad referred to as "the bloodiest anti-black riots in American history."[14] As the emancipation of the late nineteenth century took root, what emerged was not only violence against blacks, but also black pride, a renaissance or new birth of black writing, art, and music.[15] It was the age of the "New Negro": according to the Kansas City *Call,* "The NEW NEGRO, unlike the old time negro 'does not fear the face of day.'" As David Levering Lewis notes in *When Harlem Was in Vogue,* the Chicago

Whip reported that rioters "really fear the Negro is breaking his shell and beginning to bask in the sunlight of real manhood" (24).

In this section, I would like to concentrate on the first part of *The New Negro* anthology (the literary portion), because it was designed to make an assertive public statement about black writing. This anthology, edited by Alain Locke and published at the end of 1925, was put together in the wake of a contest held by *Opportunity* magazine for outstanding creative achievement. According to the editor, the contest and the succeeding anthology were intended

> to encourage the reading of literature both by Negro authors and about Negro life . . . ; to foster a market for Negro writers . . . ; to bring these writers into contact with the general world of letters . . . ; to stimulate and foster a type of writing by Negroes which shakes itself free of deliberate propaganda and protest. (*WHV* 97)

The editor of *Survey* attended a dinner at which a large group of African-American intellectuals and white liberals were present and approached the editor of *Opportunity* with a proposal to devote an entire issue of *Survey Graphic* to what was happening in Harlem, with Alain Locke as editor. After the special issue appeared in March of 1925, Locke expanded it to appear in book form. The anthology included contributions by men, women, blacks, and whites (*WHV* chapter 4, 88–118), and it was designed, as Locke wrote in the "Foreword," to express "a renewed race-spirit that consciously and proudly sets itself apart" (*NN* xxvii). Like modernist writing more generally, *The New Negro* was accused by some of being pretentious and elitist, but as Arnold Rampersad points out, it also exuded with youthful energy "a quality suspiciously like joy" (*NN* xxiii).

The poetry collected in *The New Negro* shows black Americans wearing their blackness proudly, as something majestic and natural like night, fully equal to the day that was associated with whites. Countée Cullen, in "Tableau," describes a new brotherhood of black and white males that mirrors the companionability of day and night:

> Locked arm in arm they cross the way,
> The black boy and the white,
> The golden splendor of the day
> The sable pride of night. (*NN* 130)

For Cullen, the white boy is not only day, but "lightning," whose sword-like brilliance is designed to "blaze the path" of thunder, associated with the black man. James Weldon Johnson, in "The Creation: A Negro Sermon," reminds his readers of the primordial power of blackness out of which the world and stars were created: "as far as the eye of God could see/ Darkness covered everything, / Blacker than a hundred midnights/ Down in a cypress swamp" (*NN* 138). Langston Hughes proclaims that the black people possess the advantage of having walked in the day without fear of the night:

> Being walkers with the dawn and morning
> Walkers with the sun and morning,
> We are not afraid of night,
> Nor days of gloom,
> Nor darkness,
> Being walkers with the sun and morning. (*NN* 142)

Hughes also implores his black brethren not to fear the light either: "Lovely, dark, and lonely one, / Bare your bosom to the sun, / Do not be afraid of light/ You who are a child of night" ("Song," *NN* 143). When Hughes sings America, he proclaims, "I am the darker brother" ("I Too," *NN* 145). He celebrates his power to dance in the sun in "this land where joy is wrong" ("Our Land," *NN* 144), and then to rest in the embrace of a gentle and tender night that is like himself, "Night coming tenderly/ Black like me" ("Dream Variation," *NN* 143). Lewis Alexander appreciates the sensual allure and animal power of night in the *Night* section of his poem "Enchantment." Darkness resembles "Juice flowing from an over-ripe pomegranate," but also "The leopard spotted shade: / inciting fear" (*NN* 149).

Finally, blackness is female as well as male, both motherly and divine in its creative power. James Weldon Johnson compares the God of creation to a caring mammy:

> This Great God,
> Like a mammy bending over her baby,
> Kneeled down in the dust
> Toiling over a lump of clay
> Till He shaped it in His own image. ("The Creation," *NN* 141)

Anne Spencer sees in the heart of an old, overworked black woman a divine, even Pentecostal fire. She addresses this woman, whose face is as "Dark as night withholding a star," as holy:

> Lady, Lady, I saw your heart,
> And altered there in its darksome place
> Were the tongues of flame the ancients knew,
> Where the good God sits to spangle through. ("Lady, Lady,"
> NN 148)

Black female power may be holy, but it is also pictured as demonic in its vibrantly alive refusal to obey oppressive social mores. Again and again black vitality is expressed through a wild dancing and song that is full of color and suggestive of intimacy. Countée Cullen, in "She of the Dancing Feet Sings," makes his speaker chafe against a perfect white heaven as a deadly destination:

> And how would I thrive in a perfect place
> Where dancing would be sin,
> With not a man to love my face,
> Nor an arm to hold me in?
>
> . . .
>
> The wistful angels down in hell
> Will smile to see my face,
> And understand, because they fell
> From that all-perfect place. (NN 131)

Finally, as Michael North has demonstrated in *The Dialect of Modernism*, black speech revitalized the English language, infusing it with words and rhythms that were new to white discourse. American modernists strove to appropriate black dialect at the same time that black writers were striving to go beyond it. The energy of improvisation flowed from jazz into writing, and the steely honesty of blues infused literature with a darker realism. The art of the Harlem Renaissance was being heard and seen in a way that added color and life to American literature. And as the literature grew louder, the violence became quieter – but only temporarily.

The deepest night was associated not with literary accomplishment, though, but with the dissolution of identity and breakdown of categories associated with war, especially the two world wars. In *To the Lighthouse*, published in 1927, Woolf used the metaphor of a profound darkness washing over the "Isle of Skye"[16] to represent the feeling of a world overcome by war, here World War I. Fictionally transferring the setting of her family home, Talland House, from St Ives in Cornwall to the Isle of Skye allowed her to make the house itself a kind of island set on a bigger island, enclosed and isolated, vulnerable to the might of the sea. The name "Skye" donated a metaphorical association with the sky, here being swallowed by darkness. The setting is sharpened by allusions to shipwreck, not only through the lighthouse designed to prevent it, but also through the sunken ships the Ramsays sail over on their trip to the lighthouse (" 'That was where she sunk,' said Macalister's boy suddenly. 'Three men were drowned where we are now,' " 205), as well as through Mr Ramsay's repeated quotation of lines from William Cowper's 1799 poem *The Cast-away*: "we perish'd, each alone: / But I beneath a rougher sea / Was whelmed in deeper gulphs than he" (166). Darkness, shipwreck, drowning: these are the dangers that Cowper used metaphorically to represent his own bouts of madness, and in Woolf's novel, they stretch to encompass the global madness of war.

With a lyrical beauty punctuated by sharp anguish, darkness begins to fall on the world of childhood at the beginning of the central "Time Passes" section. Andrew, coming up from the beach, says "It's almost too dark to see" (125); Prue tells him to put out the light in the hall, and one by one all the lamps are extinguished except that of Mr Carmichael, who, "reading Virgil, kept his candle burning rather longer than the rest" (125). Thus begins a dark night of the world that would last ten years, swallowing up three different members of the Ramsay family:

> So with the lamps all put out, the moon sunk, and a thin rain drumming on the roof a downpouring of immense darkness began. Nothing, it seemed, could survive the flood, the profusion of darkness which, creeping in at keyholes and crevices, stole round the window blinds, came

into bedrooms, swallowed up here a jug and basin, there a bowl of red and yellow dahlias, there the sharp edges and firm bulk of a chest of drawers. Not only was furniture confounded; there was scarcely anything left of body or mind by which one could say "This is he" or "This is she." (125–6)

Such a deep darkness dissolves both material objects and human differences within it.

Precisely because it erodes distinctions, Mrs Ramsay thinks of the dark not as violently destructive, but rather as an emancipation of the soul; it offers her the possibility of movement and freedom through the depths that lie beneath all social life. She retreats with pleasure into her "dark" self:

> To be silent; to be alone. All the being and the doing, expansive, glittering, vocal, evaporated; and one shrunk, with a sense of solemnity, to being oneself, a wedge-shaped core of darkness, something invisible to others . . . this self having shed its attachments was free for the strangest adventures. (62)

The darkness of the mind encompasses all that is below the level of consciousness, of which one may catch occasional glimpses. Mrs Ramsay describes the dark part of herself as very like the unconscious, but it is a communal subconscious as deep as the sea: "Beneath it is all dark, it is all spreading, it is unfathomably deep; but now and again we rise to the surface and that is what you see us by" (62). For Mrs Ramsay, darkness enables connection, movement, freedom:

> This core of darkness could go anywhere, for no one saw it. They could not stop it, she thought, exulting. There was freedom, there was peace, there was, most welcome of all, a summoning together, a resting on a platform of stability. Not as oneself did one find rest ever, in her experience . . . but as a wedge of darkness. (62–3)

Attaching herself to the things she sees, she then looks at the lighthouse – with its strokes of light and wedges of darkness – as a way of realizing herself at a remove: as a rhythmic stroking of beautiful, remorseless, stern, searching beams interrupted by intervals of dark freedom (64–5).

If Mrs Ramsay becomes the lighthouse, something that interrupts and structures the darkness, in "Time Passes" the night grows long until the narrator intervenes to turn it into a pack of cards, dealt steadily by winter. The narrator asks, "what after all is one night?" answering that it is "a short space," with one important qualification: "Night, however, succeeds to night. The winter holds a pack of them in store and deals them equally, evenly, with indefatigable fingers. They lengthen; they darken" (127). At some point, the night starts dealing storm and death:

> The nights now are full of wind and destruction; the trees plunge and bend and their leaves fly helter skelter until the lawn is plastered with them and they lie packed in gutters and choke rain pipes and scatter damp paths . . . [the sleepless person who leaves his bed for the beach in search of answers will find that] no image with semblance of serving and divine promptitude comes readily to hand bringing the night to order and making the world reflect the compass of the soul. The hand dwindles in his hand; the voice bellows in his ear. Almost it would appear that it is useless in such confusion to ask the night those questions as to what, and why, and wherefore, which tempt the sleeper from his bed to seek an answer. (128)

The night has become a yawning abyss, both evoking and denying a higher presence such as God, to which one might address questions. Darkness here is the antithesis of parental care; instead of offering answers or solace, it encloses and conceals the senselessness of loss. "The long night seemed to have set in" (137).

Finally, in *To the Lighthouse* darkness becomes a magnified image of forgetting, of the silence that swallows up the past. Lily – the artist – recalls that Mrs Ramsay welcomed silence as that which most fittingly expresses the darkness of human relationship: silence becomes the aural equivalent of darkness, and, like darkness, it promotes rest. Lily thought that Mrs Ramsay was glad

> to rest in silence, uncommunicative; to rest in the extreme obscurity of human relationship. Who knows what we are, what we feel? Who knows even at the moment of intimacy, This is knowledge? Aren't things spoilt then, Mrs Ramsay may have asked (it seemed to have happened so often, this silence by her side) by saying them? Aren't we more expressive thus? (171–2)

Mrs Ramsay's appreciation for silence, for an acceptance of what Lily calls "the extreme obscurity of human relationship," roughly corresponds to the part of her that is the "wedge-shaped core of darkness" (62). The other part, the flash of light, is connected with Mrs Ramsay's ability to preserve the perfect present moment, an ability that Lily strives to emulate in another mode, through her painting. In thinking of Mrs Ramsay, Lily recalls her appreciation of the moment, her quickness to "bury" the moment in order to save it as a means of illumining that other, vast obscurity of the forgotten past: "The moment at least seemed extraordinarily fertile. She rammed a little hole in the sand and covered it up, by way of burying in it the perfection of the moment. It was like a drop of silver in which one dipped and illumined the darkness of the past" (172).

Lily understands Mrs Ramsay's intensely human "art" as an ability to bring people together, such as Lily and someone she didn't like (Charles Tansley, for example), in order to preserve something positive – a moment of friendship – between them. Lily recalls,

> she brought together this and that and then this, and so made out of that miserable silliness and spite (she and Charles squabbling, sparring, had been silly and spiteful) something – this scene on the beach for example, this moment of friendship and liking – which survived, after all these years, complete, so that she dipped into it to re-fashion her memory of him, and it stayed in the mind almost like a work of art. (160)

Lily's appreciation for Mrs Ramsay's achievement is that it compensates for the fact that "the great revelation perhaps never did come. Instead there were little daily miracles, illuminations, matches struck unexpectedly in the dark" (161). Such matches in the dark, such momentary illuminations of a greater obscurity, arise out of the effort to make "of the moment something permanent" (as in another sphere Lily herself tried to make of the moment something permanent, 161). Against the darkness of past and future there is only the transitory but in its way miraculous illumination of the moment.[17]

To the Lighthouse testified to the great but not interminable darkness of World War I, but another, more ominous darkness began to gather again in the 1930s. As the decade progressed, writers began to appeal more and more emphatically to metaphors of darkness and night. This is apparent even in the titles of important works of the thirties: *Tender is the Night* (F. Scott Fitzgerald), *Nightwood* (Djuna Barnes), *Good Morning, Midnight* and *Voyage in the Dark* (Jean Rhys), *Laughter in the Dark* (Vladimir Nabokov), *Conversation at Midnight* (Edna St Vincent Millay). The impression of a darkening world grows even stronger, however, if we look within the covers of other thirties books: Virginia Woolf's *The Waves*, *The Years*, *Three Guineas*, and *Between the Acts* (set in the thirties, but published in 1941); Samuel Beckett's *Murphy*; and James Joyce's *Finnegans Wake*. The accelerating references to darkness are partly a response to what is happening around the globe – the alarmingly aggressive actions of Japan, Russia, Italy, and Germany, the dismal economic situation, the nightmarish human rights violations that people were dimly aware of happening both on the Left and on the Right. But the fascination with darkness was not – as it might have been – a mere resort to cliché for the purpose of expressing feelings of fear and ignorance. On the contrary, the exploration of a night world signified a new openness to the terrors and pleasures of subterranean life, whether that life was a "circus" world peopled by transvestites and social misfits in a desperate search for love and meaning, as in Djuna Barnes's *Nightwood*, or whether it was the language of the unconscious, half buried in history and dream, as in Joyce's *Finnegans Wake*.

In Faulkner's *As I Lay Dying* (1930), darkness is the principle of dissolution, of un-creation. It undoes identity and expresses grief, especially for the child who irrationally accuses a horse of having killed his mother. He thinks, "It is as though the dark were resolving him out of his integrity, into an unrelated scattering of components – snuffings and stampings, smells of cooling flesh and ammoniac hair; an illusion of a co-ordinated whole of splotched hide and strong bones within which, detached and secret and familiar, an *is* different from my *is*."[18] In sensing a being different from his own through the agency of darkness, the child shows how darkness can represent not only evil but also the mystery of difference. Darkness interferes with the narcissism of likeness, or *liking* only those who are *like* ourselves. It propels us out of the Apollinian world of social individuation into the primal community of Dionysian wholeness.[19]

Ethnic minorities, social misfits, intellectuals, and children appreciated the relief and increased honesty of embracing that deeper, less individuated reality associated with darkness, as did women who felt the disadvantages of living and working in a man's world. In *Good Morning, Midnight* (1939), Jean Rhys – like Woolf in *Three Guineas* – welcomes darkness as a respite from the condition of being an aging female in a daytime reality ruled by money and reason, where women were defined as luxuries: dispensable commodities. For her epigraph, Rhys quotes a poem by Emily Dickinson that personifies the Day (or the Morn) as a man she loves who has cast the speaker off:

> Good morning, Midnight!
> I'm coming home,
> Day got tired of me –
> How could I of him?
>
> Sunshine was a sweet place,
> I liked to stay –
> But Morn didn't want me – now –
> So good night, Day![20]

Dickinson has reversed day and night, saying good morning to night and good night to day, because the sweet male "Morn" didn't want her. The main character of Rhys' strongly autobiographical novel feels similarly outcast from every "sweet place," as she wanders Paris in an attempt to evade becoming totally destitute – or dissolute. Like Orwell's male protagonist in the similarly autobiographical *Down and Out in Paris and London* (1933), Rhys' Sasha needs money; darkness is partly the despair of poverty. She describes "Walking in the night with the dark houses over you, like monsters. If you have money and friends, houses are just houses with steps and a front-door – friendly houses where the door opens and somebody meets you, smiling." To those without money, though, the houses become "Tall cubes of darkness, with two lighted eyes at the top to sneer" (31). Rhys uses houses and rooms to represent the position of individuals in a larger social organization. All Sasha claims to want is a light room, but the room she is told is "very light" is really quite dark, and she concludes in despair that if one were to "tell the truth about this business of rooms, . . . it would bust the roof off everything and undermine the whole social system. All rooms are the same" (38). Insofar as a room represents the situation of the individual who inhabits it, Sasha has discovered through her search for a specific kind of room that society does not accommodate variation.

The darkness that Sasha can never quite succeed in heaving herself out of is that of the human race: at its worst, it is human self-interest, and at its best, it is the obscurity that makes self-delusion possible. It can be the darkness of a stair landing where Sasha can hug a strange man in the belief that everything is in her "arms on this dark landing – love, youth, spring, happiness," everything she thought she had lost (177). And darkness can be simply people, the source of her greatest desire and fear. As she thinks and then explains to René,

> You are walking along a road peacefully. You trip. You fall into blackness. That's the past – or perhaps the future. And you know that there is no past, no future, there is only this blackness, changing faintly, slowly, but always the same.
>
> "You want to know what I'm afraid of? All right, I'll tell you . . . I'm afraid of men–yes, I'm very much afraid of men. And I'm even more afraid of women. And I'm very much afraid of the whole bloody human race. . . ." (172–3)

What has happened on a global scale is being repeated in the private realm of individual consciousness: the dominant conception of human nature has changed. The person being dictated to – by men, by money, by mendicancy – is not any better than those who take advantage of her. The human race is corrupt, and in the darkness of poverty and age even Sasha is prone to delusions of omnipotence. What she cannot do is prolong those delusions; the light in the room comes on, and her "lover" is unmasked as a gigolo, she an aging and indigent alcoholic. Rhys' novel holds out little hope for society from human nature: there is no "room" for individual rest, growth or protest.

Djuna Barnes' *Nightwood* (1937) takes an equally despairing view of human nature as "damned and innocent from the start."[21] It explores the underworlds of Berlin and Paris, examining the impossible love of Nora Flood for a woman named Robin and the hidden, tortured, nighttime femaleness of Dr Matthew-Mighty-grain-of-salt Dante-O'Connor, who calls himself "the god of darkness" (126). Barnes' novel insists, given the untidiness of history and destiny, that we confront our darker sides, for as Matthew says to Felix, "A man is whole only when he takes into account his shadow as well as himself" (119), and in that shadow is both anxiety and divinity (120). The book undertakes an intensely personal and philosophical exploration of darkness that climaxes when Nora comes to Matthew's room in the middle of the night, finding him in a woman's flannel nightgown, a golden wig, with rouged cheeks and painted lashes, and asks him to tell her everything he knows about the night (79). She comes at "the hour when he had evacuated custom" (80), which is part of night's meaning – an evacuation of custom and convention – to talk to him about his favorite topic. He begins his nighttalk by telling her that the night is not premeditated (80), and that through a strange reverse alchemy it changes a person's identity: a man's "identity is no longer his own . . . [and] he neither knows himself nor his outriders. . . . His heart is tumbling in his chest, a dark place!" (81). The doctor begs Nora to "think of the night the day long, and of the day the night through, or at some reprieve of the brain it will come upon you heavily –an engine stalling itself upon your chest, halting its wheels against your heart; unless you have made a roadway for it" (84).

According to Matthew, the darkness epitomizes mortality, doubt, waste, dirt, love, and dream; night is what causes the day to ache (85). History at night is different, because some portion of the night's evil has been committed by the dead (86). Night is a storehouse of everything we refuse to recognize or accept. Most importantly, its darkness can only be combed – never seen or known – by "the great blind searchlight of the heart" (93). Matthew ends his sermon with a warning to Nora about those who "turn the day into night, the young, the drug addict, the profligate, the drunken and that most miserable, the lover who watches all night long in fear and anguish" (94). These are the people who, like Nora's lover Robin, are lost, "blotted out and erased" (95), who leave no mark; they have become nothing. For them, engaged in a self-protective and permanent denial, night has mutated to *nichts*, the German word for nothing, and to the Latin *nox*, root of noxious (from the night). Blindness, ignorance, dissoluteness, death, waste, flesh, and love: for Barnes, these are all aspects of a night that becomes noxious when we sleepwalk through it, as Robin does, or disclaim its power, as Nora tried to do. The night is in each of us, for as the doctor declaims, "There is not one of us who, given an eternal incognito, a thumbprint nowhere set against our souls, would not commit rape, murder and all abominations" (88). However, the perception that the night is evil is a delusion, because according to Matthew there is no such thing as pure evil; evil and goodness are two halves of the same story: "The evil and the good know themselves only by giving up their secret face to face. The true good who meets the true evil . . . learns for the first time how to accept neither; the face of the one tells the face of the other the half of the story that both forgot" (138).

In Samuel Beckett's *Murphy* (1938), darkness is again something that the characters experience as evil only when they have inoculated themselves against experiencing it at all. Murphy survives by giving himself pleasure and setting his mind free, which he can do by strapping himself naked with seven scarves to a rocking chair in a corner "curtained off from the sun."[22] His goal – like that of Joyce and Toomer – is to experience a state of even-ing extremes, a balance between "light and dark that did not clash, nor alternate, nor fade nor lighten except to their communion" (9). Murphy restrains his body in an effort to come alive in his mind, both brightly and darkly. He describes his mind's actual part as "above and bright," and its virtual part as "beneath and fading into dark," but although "It was made up of light fading into dark, of above and beneath," it was not made up

> of good and bad. It contained forms with parallel in another mode and forms without, but not right forms and wrong forms. It felt no issue between its light and dark, no need for its light to devour its dark. The need was now to be in the light, now in the half light, now in the dark. That was all. (108)

Murphy's attitude toward darkness serves as a model for a more ethical relation to evil than a denial of it or even a "heroic" attempt to fight it. Murphy, like the doctor in *Nightwood,* recognizes and accepts the presence of darkness within him, with its dangers and its pleasures.

The dark part of Murphy's mind might be called chaos. Beckett describes it as "a flux of forms, a perpetual coming together and falling asunder of forms . . . without love or hate or any intelligible principle of change. Here there was nothing but commotion and the pure forms of commotion. Here he was not free, but a mote in the dark of absolute freedom" (112). Darkness is pure, emotionless irrationality, a "matrix of surds" (112). As his body sets him increasingly free, Murphy chooses to spend more and more time "in the dark, in the will-lessness, a mote in its absolute freedom" (113).

What, then, is the darkness that Murphy gravitates toward? As it did for Faulkner and Barnes, darkness promotes a dissolution of identity, will, and individuality, inducing a state akin to madness and also, significantly, conducive to erotic bliss. He describes the progress of his nights of lovemaking with Celia musically, as serenade, nocturne, and albada (74). Eventually, though, he loses all connection, becoming an unseen speck in a madman's eyes (250). Like Mother Pegg in *Endgame*, he ultimately dies of the darkness he moved toward, blown up by "excellent gas, superfine chaos" (the words "chaos" and "gas" are related, 253). As one character explains, over the protests of his companion, "We look on the dark side. . . . It is undeniably less trying to the eyes" (215). Extreme darkness, like gas or chaos, leads to annihilation, and looking on the dark side can be an easy way out. On the other hand, as another character comments, "It is only in the dark that one can meet" (234).

Philosophically and imagistically, Beckett uses the image of darkness to work out the connection between intimacy and alienation, being and nothingness, against the silent backdrop of the thirties. In his world, the only "evil" is a kind of tragic incompetence, an inability to tolerate the split in the self, which on a larger stage (not Beckett's) flowers into social divisions. Murphy is addicted to the dark (26), a perverse reflection of a world addicted to light, and of a Nazi world exhorting citizens to strength through joy, but both extremes are finally maladaptive. The Nazi slogan leads to destruction of others, and Murphy's own preference to destruction of self. The only personal and social solution possible is one of which the novel despairs — "the freedom of that light and dark that did not clash, nor alternate, nor fade nor lighten except to their communion" (9, 252).

I've talked about darkness in philosophical and moral terms, and also as a metaphor for a growing social disaster, but it also has rhetorical implications, as a means of connecting a writer and a reader. Those who have read the books I've been discussing know that obscurity is not just a subject addressed in these books; it is also a characteristic of their style. They are all relatively formless in plot, often obscure in their references, apparently disjointed in their treatment of character or setting. The obscurity of these works is part of their political and ethical design: to put readers in the dark. The point of doing so is simply to make readers more aware, to stimulate a motivated groping for new answers rather than a reliance on habit. Barnes, Faulkner, Beckett, Woolf, and Joyce are all in passionate revolt against the widespread optimistic view that we *understand* the vagaries of human nature, or law, or custom, or even language. As Woolf suggests in *The Years* (1937), our literature has failed us. "These little snapshot pictures of people left much to be desired, these little surface pictures that one made, like a fly crawling over a face, and feeling, here's the nose, here's the brow."[23] As the main character has often thought, "We cannot make laws and religions that fit because we do not know ourselves" (282). For other characters, the civilization that seems so smooth, so ordered, is a "primeval swamp" (378), a Conradian "heart of darkness" in which the searcher tries to cut his way toward the light "provided only with broken sentences, single words, with which to break through the briarbush of human bodies, human wills and voices, that bent over him, binding him, blinding him" (411).

Six years earlier, in *The Waves*, Woolf has her writer – Bernard – yearn, not for stories, but for "some little language such as lovers use, broken words, inarticulate words," and for patterns that are always changing. Bernard explains that we need a less transparent language in order to feel "round us the huge blackness of what is outside us, of what we are not."[24] The point of reading is to engage the "central shadow" of the unknown (292, 293). Before beginning Bernard's final section, Woolf describes sea, sky, and land as inundated with "waves of darkness" (237). Darkness covers everything, washing down streets, engulfing single figures, blotting out couples. Darkness here is clearly an agent of erasure, of isolation, of death and dissolution, but it is not something that stories – in their artificial clarity – help us to understand. Woolf asks, through Bernard, how may we understand and combat a creeping death, an egoistic shadow that has long been confused with enlightenment? The central "shadow" for Woolf is that cast by the egotism and rapaciousness of the self. But, in Bernard's words, "how describe the world seen without a self? There are no words" (287). If what the world calls bright and clear is really a deadly shadow, then the only way to experience a renewed sense of life is through an embrace of obscurity, to take upon oneself "the mystery of things" (291). At the end of *The Waves*, Bernard is looking for a change he refuses to call dawn; instead, he calls it the "break of day" (296). Woolf's intention is to "break" day, to remove what Bernard calls "the pressure of the eye, the solicitation of the body, and all need of lies and phrases" (294). Woolf's longing to escape words is, finally, a desire to elude dictation.

In *Between the Acts* (1941), which is set on a June day in 1939, Woolf participates in the widespread despair of the late thirties, a despair about the significance of plots and language as well as about a community and a nation reeling back into a bestial – even primeval – darkness associated with war. In the novel, an annual historical pageant is being staged in an English village. The people who come to watch this pageant are diverted by the past, but *haunted* by the future, which the protagonist, Isa, describes to herself as "The future disturbing our present."[25] The greatest darkness is in the immediate future, and it is bound up with the hatred for Dictators ("The common people hate Dictators," 121). Words are complicit in the harm caused by dictation; as the audience thinks at one point during the pageant, "O Lord, protect and preserve us from words the defilers, from words the impure! What need have we of words to remind us? Must I be Thomas, you Jane?" (190).

The climax of the pageant, and the point of the director's art, is to mimic the effects of darkness, to show the audience its own image, but in pieces: "to snap us as we are, before we've had time to assume . . . And only, too, in parts" (184). The director creates a din that restores chaos and preempts illusions of wholeness and superiority, so that "the barriers which should divide Man the Master from the Brute were dissolved" (184). The moving mirrors held by children reflect people in pieces, challenging their sense of identity as anything other than "orts, scraps and fragments" incapable of building a civilization (188). In pieces, unprotected, unskinned – in darkness – humanity is capable of "immeasurable profundity" (189), a polyphonic musical majesty of divergence, conflict, and resolution. Humanity's only chance at building civilization is by discarding pretension, so that the individual sees herself as "a butt, a clod, laughed at by looking-glasses; ignored by the cows, condemned by the clouds which continued their majestic rearrangement of the celestial landscape; an irrelevant forked stake in the flow and majesty of the summer silent world" (191).

The voice from the loudspeaker tells the audience that they *are* the play, the history, the actors, so that by implication they, in their vanity and conformity, are the counterparts of the dictators they hate and fear. The voice chides, "a tyrant, remember, is half a slave" (187). Yielding to the pressure to conform is the counterpart of active oppression – neither tyrants nor villagers are free, and they are similar insofar as they refuse individual responsibility for their pretensions. Big pretensions, small ones – in the darkness, they're all the same. According to the voice, the "gun slayers" and "bomb droppers" "do openly what we do slyly" (187): they promote an illusion of their own superiority to and difference from others.

Instead of acting the parts conferred on us by our clothes (195), could we, by "thinking differently, . . . think the same" (200)? Who is the author of the pageant we collectively play? What is its meaning and why is it haunted by such a troubling and violent future? The director, Miss LaTrobe, groaning at the failure of her play to convey what she had hoped it would, plans to realize a darker vision next time. "It would be midnight; there would be two figures, half concealed by a rock" (210). She dreams of words arising above mud: "words without meaning – wonderful words" (212).

Between the Acts ends with the inexorable increase of darkness, darkness with a double valence of terror and possibility. This is the darkness of the ancient past and of the near future; in it, "enmity was bared; also love" (219). Isa and her husband will fight and embrace, "as the dog fights with the vixen, in the heart of darkness, in the fields of night" (219). For a moment, "the house had lost its shelter," and "It was the night that dwellers in caves had watched from some high place among rocks." Then the old play begins again – with words, and light, and parts. Like Isa, Woolf suggests that "Surely it was time someone invented a new plot" (215).

I have chosen darkness, or obscurity, as a metaphor to illustrate the conflicting implications of modernism in the thirties because it was used that way by the writers themselves, and because it sums up the tension between opposite tendencies that are both implicit in the same phenomenon. On the one hand, darkness represents evil, especially the kind of evil that Woolf saw shadowing the future in 1939. It represents the evils of poverty and social alienation that Jean Rhys wrote about in *Voyage in the Dark* and *Good Morning, Midnight*, especially the darkness that results from women's social and economic dependence on men. But the acceptance of darkness also represents new possibility, the hope of radical liberation, and a revisionary potential for reconceiving the conventions dominating language and literature along more obscure and politically revolutionary lines. Woolf, Barnes, and Beckett all share a distrust for consoling stories, appreciating the kinship between words and lies, but all also accent the desolation implicit in extreme darkness.

Most of these writers distrusted not only the status quo but also the deceptively easy accessibility of understanding, which is one reason they labored to make their own meanings more obscure. One cannot read Woolf, Beckett, or Barnes without effort, but it *is* possible to read and understand their works – the effort is neither hopeless nor unrewarding. Moreover, their passion for understanding darkness grows out of a powerful and deeply felt response to the atrocities of the thirties – the despair of economic depression, and the threat of totalitarian violence based not on one's responsibility for a criminal action, but on one's status, which is a product of class, ethnicity, religion, and sex. Woolf, for example, knew that the stereotypical thinking that fuels sectarian violence is firmly rooted in the conviction that the oppressor *knows* and *understands* the deficiencies of the denigrated group. She argued in *Three Guineas* (1938) and implied in her novels of the thirties that we can best prevent war *by attacking the delusion of knowledge and mastery*, by embracing darkness. We can prevent war not only by empowering traditionally disenfranchised groups – women, blacks, Jews, Indians – to help us, but also by accepting more responsibility for what we *don't* know. What we *know* serves our personal interest; what we *don't* know serves the greater interests of the survival of civilization. And an awareness of what we *don't know* is only potent if we use it to try to understand more independently, more honestly, and more vigorously how to resist dictation, or what we are told. As Woolf writes in *Three Guineas* (1938), you can use the professions "to have a mind of your own and a will of your own. And you can use that mind and will to abolish the inhumanity, the beastliness, the horror, the folly of war."[26] The surest way "to defend culture and our own intellectual liberty" (88) is at the grass-roots level, "by engaging *and* challenging what we read and hear.

The enemy for Woolf is the Dictator, as well as his counterpart, the obedient and unquestioning listener. The Dictator is what we call him when he is Italian or German, and when we meet him abroad we all agree that he is "a very dangerous as well as a very ugly animal" (53). But Woolf argues that the terrifying Dictators of the thirties were simply larger, foreign versions of the same tendency that poisons the atmosphere for women (and we could add the names of numerous other groups): the Dictator is anyone "who believes that he has the right, whether given by God, Nature, sex or race, . . . to dictate to other human beings how they shall live; what they shall do" (53). Woolf contends that the eggs of Dictators are everywhere – we can shake them out of any newspaper, or find them in people who lecture on English literature (fn. 30, 155–6). "Abroad the monster has come more openly to the surface. There is no mistaking him there. He has widened his scope. He is interfering now with your liberty; he is dictating how you shall live; he is making distinctions not merely between the sexes, but between the races" (102).

What does Woolf propose as a defense against dictation? Obscurity, by which she means suspicion of praise. She recommends financial independence, a refusal to sell one's brain for the sake of money, and a freedom from pride of nationality, and she advises those who would prevent war to "refuse all methods of advertising merit, and [to] hold that ridicule, obscurity and censure are preferable, for psychological reasons, to fame and praise." She asserts that "ease and freedom, the power to change and the power to grow, can only be preserved by obscurity; and that if we wish to help the human mind to create, and to prevent it from scoring the same rut repeatedly, we must do what we can to shroud it in darkness" (114).

Gallicinium (Cock Crowing)

There is a political reason, then, to explain why the writing of people committed to individual human liberty became increasingly difficult to read in the twenties and especially the thirties. The darkness of the mind when it encounters something that it is difficult to understand, something foreign, is a state to be courted, not avoided – it is a test of our ability to engage difference, which is the heart of any true intellectual or moral enterprise. Many modernist writers saw reading as a microcosmically political enterprise, an exercise in resisting totalitarian dictation by an author, who can so easily be authoritarian. This is why Joyce spent seventeen years writing *Finnegans Wake*, the darkest, most foreign, and most carefully designed book ever written. *Finnegans Wake* is a book of the dark, written to mimic the movement of the unconscious mind in sleep, as it ranges across over forty languages and many historical epochs. It is about waste – what is dead and denied – and transgression;

above all, it registers deep suspicion of the values of the enlightenment. As Joyce warns in *Finnegans Wake*, when we court enlightenment, or easy understanding, we accumulate darkness in the threatening sense: "How they succeeded by courting daylight in saving darkness he who loves will see" (321.18–19). For Joyce, there is something supernatural about the power of darkness – he renders the word supernatural as "supernoctural," characterized by intense darkness (598.17). That supernatural quality of darkness (and the weakness and vulnerability of which it makes us aware) is in direct opposition to the Nazi celebration of light and strength, as Joyce reminds us by referring to the Nazi slogan of strength through joy: "Your last words todate in comparative accoustomology are going to tell stretch of a fancy through strength towards joyance . . . where he gets up. Allay for allay, a threat for a throat" [An eye for an eye, a tooth for a tooth], (598.23–6).

Finnegans Wake is the product of Joyce's conviction about the moral importance of encountering darkness – with curiosity, effort, and laughter – with eyes and ears open for any possible meanings or stimuli. As Hugh Kenner once said, Joyce – like many of his counterparts in the thirties –believed that language is the Trojan Horse by which the universe gets into the mind.[27] Why let such a small portion of that vast universe in? What we miss is the more challenging, mysterious, and ultimately human sensation of "shadows shadows multiplicating" (281.17–18). In the darkness of *Finnegans Wake,* readers are apt to complain that "Not a salutary sellable sound is since [sense]" (598.4). Why tell a story that way, "Totalled in toldteld and teldtold in titletell tattle" (597.8–9)?

> Because, graced be Gad and all giddy gadgets, in whose words were the beginnings, there are two signs [sides] to turn to, the yest [yesterday; west] and the ist [today; east], the wright side and the wronged side, feeling aslip and wauking up, so an, so farth. (597.9–12).

With "the torporature . . . returning to mornal" (597.32–3), the temperature returning to normal and our usual torpor returning with the morning, how can we remember to keep our ears open for the way extremes meet, so that we can hear not only the "right" side of a story or conflict, but also the "wronged" side? For "in that european [ear open; European] end meets Ind [the West End meets India; the end meets the orient, or the beginning]" (598.15–16). When "Habit reburns. To flame in you" (614.8–9), it is important to remember that "nought that is has bane [harm, been]" (614.7–8). Nothing that exists now has ever been in exactly the same way in the past; every moment is new. Moreover, nothing that is has bane, or poison, in it. "We've lived in two worlds" (619.11), and, as a result, we all need to develop the double consciousness that one can generate only in the dark.

As Joyce notes in *Ulysses*, it is only after the darkness has taken its course that we can hear the "incipient intimations of proximate dawn" (17.1247–8):

> More active air, a matutinal distant cock, ecclesiastical clocks at various points, avine music, the isolated tread of an early wayfarer, the visible diffusion of the light of an invisible luminous body, the first golden limb of the resurgent sun perceptible low on the horizon. (17.1265–8)

In the words of *Finnegans Wake*, day is different, less comprehensible, more varied, multicolored and many-storied, after "a long, very long, a dark, very dark, an allburt unend, scarce endurable, and we could add mostly quite various and somewhat stumbletumbling night" (598.6–9). Darkness generates humility, and as T.S. Eliot writes in *Four Quartets*, his lyrical meditations in the wake of World War II,

> The only wisdom we can hope to acquire
> Is the wisdom of humility: humility is endless. ("East Coker," II)[28]

The third section of "East Coker" emphasizes the inevitability with which everyone will enter the darkness, "all go into the dark." If we can willingly embrace that darkness, Eliot asserts that it can teach the spirit to wait without cherishing expectations. In "Gerontion," the speaker had asked, "After such knowledge, what forgiveness?" There may be no forgiveness for the atrocities of the twentieth century in which all are complicit, but it is nonetheless possible to "let the dark come upon you":

> I said to my soul, be still, and wait without hope
> For hope would be hope of the wrong thing; wait without love
> For love would be love of the wrong thing; there is yet faith

But the faith and the love and the hope are all in the waiting.
Wait without thought, for you are not ready for thought:
So the darkness shall be the light, and the stillness the dancing.
   ("East Coker," III)

The wisdom of darkness is an embrace of both sides of life, of all the strata of the mind and society, but it is difficult to attain. The challenging literature of modernism obstructed the reader's desires and betrayed his or her learned expectations in order to stimulate different responses: laughter, appreciation for novelty, compassion for human differences and the inevitability of loss, and a profound humility before the atrocities of which we are capable. Eliot repeats in "East Coker" what he claims to have said several times before:

> To arrive where you are, to get from where you are not,
>   You must go by a way wherein there is no ecstasy.
> In order to arrive at what you do not know
>   You must go by a way which is the way of ignorance.
> In order to possess what you do not possess
>   You must go by the way of dispossession.
> In order to arrive at what you are not
>   You must go through the way in which you are not. (III)

In Isaiah, the watchman warns, "Morning comes, and also the night" (Isaiah 21:11). To those who embrace the night, scripture promises to "bring ... the treasures of darkness, and hoards in secret places" (Isaiah 44:3).

Conclusion

Modernist writers took the view that since we understand the world through stories, we needed to change the way stories were told in order to connect with a significantly altered world. Abolition, votes for women, the increasing assimilation of Jews who had formerly lived in ghettos, a more open discussion of homosexuality, changes in marriage law, all represented new freedoms, and new challenges to the status quo. Such changes called into being more complex, dynamic, contradictory, and even seemingly nonsensical stories designed to resist and expose the extent to which interpretation has become a maladaptive habit. Through its challenging forms, but also in its historical context, modernist literature reminds readers to respect the difficulty and unpredictability of reading, and to recall the humility and effort required for sensitive understanding. When on a first encounter readers fail to comprehend numerous strands of elusive but poetic narrative, that experience recalls the illegibility of a multinational world, together with the essential unknowability of the self. If it were possible fully to know or control either the self or the world, each would lose its power to surprise, appall, obscure, amuse, instruct, and delight. Psychologically, respect for the impenetrability of other people's experience also acts as a safeguard against the defensive impulse to project onto others what we find intolerable in ourselves.

If modernism was in part a reaction against powerful social pressures to accept a privileged narrative standard of experience, to defer by default to the voice of authority, to care more about how well a task is performed than how it might affect others, then it is still a relevant movement. The consumerism of western society gives ample evidence that we are still willing to do as we are told: to buy the narrative and pictorial fantasies about our own individual, cultural, sexual, racial, or national superiority to others represented in advertisements, television shows, popular novels, and films. It is even more difficult now than it was a century ago to see how easily consumers are themselves consumed by the economies that regulate their desires along with their spending.

In a consumer culture, books can be commodities, but they can also, more rarely, serve as virtual interlocutors, or partners. Books can hear us, to the extent that our reactions are predictable, and they can also speak to us, but only if we listen; most readers do not realize that their ability to hear is structured by their experience and expectation. When books thwart the reader's demand that they be easy to process without additional time and thought (which means that their authors have anticipated and chosen to ignore that demand), the reader more frequently responds with annoyed dismissiveness than curiosity. Typically, readers don't want to engage in a dialogue with authors, preferring instead to be swept along by someone else's thought, carried away by another person's story. As a result, most popular fiction gives us little practice in thinking skeptically, with a receptivity seasoned by thoughtful resistance, nor does it offer us a self-portrait in which despicable and admirable qualities are intertwined, even inseparable.

It is easy to predict the reactions of a successfully socialized reader to challenging literature: the reader will initially respond with frustration at the book's resistance, to the strategic way it has exceeded or betrayed the reader's expectations. The frustrated reader will then denigrate the resistant object, but once the frustration has subsided, apathy will return. The well-known irony of consumerism is that it paradoxically produces a condition of want in people who have. Consumers seem to want novelty, but the novelty they seek is illusory: most "new" acquisitions bear a strong underlying similarity with the objects (or knowledge) they displace. The disadvantage of most popular literature is that while such literature affords excitement in the present moment, it offers nothing over the long term. The most one can expect from an entertaining book is a temporary diversion. This is why even the best of such books are difficult to remember.

In *Finnegans Wake*, Joyce moves toward the end of the book that does not end by having his chameleon characters, HCE and ALP, assume the form of an address to the reader. We can recognize their presence through the acrostics of their initials: "**H**ave we **c**herished **e**xpectations?

Are we for liberty of perusiveness?"[1] As the yin and yang of the book, HCE and ALP most often embody the mature male and female principles, but here they combine to form the book's voice as it questions and gently chides the reader. HCE asks if we (author and reader alike) have cherished expectations; if so, we will understand that this book has challenged and refused to gratify them. Why? The next question suggests an answer: "Are we for liberty of perusiveness?" If we really value freedom when reading, why do we object so strongly when that freedom is offered? How do our cherished expectations accord with the value we invest in interpretive freedom? Both our expectations, which promise stability, and our liberty to peruse the unexpected, which permits innovation, are crucial to interpretation. The challenge for the conscientious reader is to keep the two in balance.

How, then, can we learn to read more flexibly? One prescription is to rely less heavily on what we see, paying more attention to what we hear and sense; to proceed darkly or "blindly." Blindness enhances the other senses and diminishes the power of expectation. To read more blindly is to read more "feelingly"; it prepares us to anticipate surprises, and it interferes with the subconscious desire to master the text. Second, we might attend more closely to the effects of reading – some of which are delayed, many of which are pleasurable – instead of to the explicit (or didactic) meaning of the text. Third, we could anticipate the desirability of reading a complex book or poem more than once. We could make more of an effort to imagine ourselves in the position of the author, making the choices that now constitute a challenge to us as readers. Finally, we could try to recall the pleasures of darkness, especially its Dionysian power to awaken a need for community with others, and find those pleasures in reading. The point is not to replace the values of day with those of darkness, but to restore equilibrium between the two, using what Wallace Stevens, in "The Idea of Order at Key West," calls the "glassy lights, / The lights in the fishing boats at anchor," to organize and beautify the darkness, "Arranging, deepening, enchanting night." The goal is to find a voice that makes "The sky acutest at its vanishing."[2] Or, if we shift the metaphor to imprisonment and freedom, we might claim that modernist literature has the capacity to accomplish the feat that W.H. Auden attributed to Yeats in his "In Memory of W.B. Yeats": "In the prison of his days, / [to] Teach the free man how to praise."[3]

Notes

Preface

1   James Joyce, *Ulysses*, ed. Hans Walter Gabler with Wolfhard Steppe and Claus Melchior (1922; New York: Random-Vintage, 1986), episode 2, lines 401–3.

2   Ralph Waldo Emerson, "Goethe: Or, the Writer Notes," in *Representative Men: Seven Lectures* (1850; rpt Boston: Houghton Mifflin, 1903), p. 290.

3   This, for example, is the view of John Carey in *The Intellectuals and the Masses: Pride and Prejudice among the Literary Intelligentsia, 1880–1930* (Chicago: Academy Chicago Publishers, 1992):

> The intellectuals could not, of course, actually prevent the masses from attaining literacy. But they could prevent them from reading literature by making it too difficult for them to understand – and this is what they did. The early twentieth century saw a determined effort, on the part of the European intelligentsia, to exclude the masses from culture. In England this movement has become known as modernism. (16–17)

4   Angela Carter, *The Bloody Chamber* (Harmondsworth: Penguin, 1979), p. 93; Carter repeated this line in an interview (published posthumously) with Anna Katsovos: "An Interview with Angela Carter," *The Review of Contemporary Fiction*, 14 (Fall 1004: 11–17).

5   Virginia Woolf, *Three Guineas* (1938; New York: Harvest/Harcourt Brace Jovanovich, 1966), pp. 29–30, 33–4.

6   Wallace Stevens, *Notes toward a Supreme Fiction* in *The Palm at the End of the Mind: Selected Poems and a Play*, ed. Holly Stevens (1967; New York:

Random-Vintage, 1971), p. 224. Hereafter page references will be given in the text.

7   James Joyce, *Finnegans Wake* (1939; New York: Penguin, 1967), p. 62, line 8. Hereafter page and line references will be given in the text.

8   Stephen Dedalus alludes to this phenomenon when expounding his theory of aesthetics to Lynch. He says that once the artist has finished a work, "The artist, like the God of the creation, remains within or behind or beyond or above his handiwork, invisible, refined out of existence, paring his fingernails" (James Joyce, *A Portrait of the Artist as a Young Man*, ed. Seamus Deane (1916; New York: Penguin, 1993), p. 233).

9   See, for example, Margot Norris' commentary on J. Hillis Miller's *The Ethics of Reading*. Miller argued that "An understanding of ethics as a region of philosophical or conceptual invesetigation depends, perhaps surprisingly, on mastery of the ability to interpret written stories" (cited in Margot Norris, *Suspicious Readings of Joyce's Dubliners* (Philadelphia: University of Pennsylvania Press, 2003), p. 3). Norris understands this to mean that "learning to reflect on what we do when we interpret a story may help us to reflect on what we do when, in real life, we are obliged to make judgments in situations that are not easily decidable" (14).

10 "Dort, wo man Bücher verbrennt, verbrennt man am Ende auch Menschen," from his play *Almansor.*

11 In a sense, any book is a letter from an author to the reader, and as Virginia Woolf writes in *Three Guineas,* "Without someone warm and breathing on the other side of the page, letters are worthless" (p. 3).

12 "Memory Sites: Destruction, Loss, and Transformation; A Reflection in Words and Images by Angelika Bammer." This was an exhibition at the Schatten Gallery, Robert W. Woodruff Library, Emory University, September 9–November 9, 2003. See *http://web.library.emory.edu/libraries/schatten/previous/memorysites/home/brochure.pdf.*

13 The historical footage of Joseph Goebbels' speech as the books were burned can be seen and heard on the United States Holocaust Memorial Museum website: *http://www.shmm.org.*

14 Amy Dru Stanley, *From Bondage to Contract: Wage Labor, Marriage, and the Market in the Age of Slave Emancipation* (Cambridge: Cambridge University Press, 1998), p. x.

15 Amy Gutmann, "Introduction," in Charles Taylor, *Multiculturalism and "The Politics of Recognition,"* ed. Amy Gutmann, with commentary by Amy Gutmann, Steven C. Rockefeller, Michael Walzer, and Susan Wolf (Princeton: Princeton University Press, 1992), p. 7.

16   Oscar Wilde, *The Picture of Dorian Gray: Authoritative Texts, Backgrounds, Reviews and Reactions*, ed. Donald L. Lawler (1891; New York: W.W. Norton, 1983), p. 3.

17   Ezra Pound, *Selected Poems*, ed. and intro. T.S. Eliot (1928; London: Faber and Faber, 1948).

Chapter 1   Why Read Challenging Literature?

1   John Carey, for example, in *The Intellectuals and the Masses* (Chicago: Academy Chicago Publishers, 1992), argues that "intellectual" modernist writers expressed contempt for the newly literate mass of middle-class readers, even to the point of "Dreaming of the extermination or steriliza-tion of the mass" (15). Although there are a few specific instances of writers expressing or even advocating such views, Carey's overall argu-ment is based upon a misinterpretation: he chooses to interpret the modernist's sympathy for the outsider as a preference for an intellectual elite, and he reads the modernist attack on *class* – and strictness of clas-sification – as if it were a hatred of "real people" rather than social systems. Carey recasts the modernist fascination with the "*déclassé*" as its opposite – narcissistic elitism, the self-preoccupation of intellectuals.

2   Henry James, "Preface to the New York Edition," in *The Portrait of a Lady* (1881; New York: Norton, 1975), p. 7.

3   The phrase is that of Robert Coles in his response to Simon Wiesenthal in *The Sunflower: On the Possibilities and Limits of Forgiveness* (rev. and expanded edn, New York: Schocken, 1998), p. 129. Hereafter page refer-ences will be given in the text.

4   Michel Foucault, *Discipline and Punish: The Birth of the Prison*, trans. Alan Sheridan (1975; New York: Vintage, 1977). Hereafter page references will be given in the text.

5   Primo Levi, *Survival in Auschwitz: The Nazi Assault on Humanity*, trans. Stuart Woolf (1958; New York: Simon and Schuster, 1986). Hereafter page references will be given in the text.

6   Giorgio Agamben, *Remnants of Auschwitz: The Witness and the Archive*, trans. Daniel Heller-Roazen (New York: Zone Books, 2002). Hereafter page references will be given in the text. J.M. Coetzee, *Elizabeth Costello* (New York: Penguin, 2003).

7   By Stephan Pastis.

8   Virginia Woolf, *A Haunted House: The Complete Shorter Fiction*, ed. Susan Dick (1985; London: Vintage, 2003), p. 78. Hereafter references will be given in the text, preceded by *HH*.

9   Walter Pater, *The Renaissance* (1873; New York: Modern Library, 1928), p. 196.

10   James Joyce, *Finnegans Wake* (1939; New York: Penguin, 1967), p. 597, lines 21–2. Hereafter page and line references will be given in the text.

11   Samuel Beckett, *Waiting for Godot* (1952; New York: Grove Press, 1954), p. 58. Hereafter page references will be given in the text.

12   Virginia Woolf, *The Waves* (1931; New York: Harcourt Brace Jovanovich, 1959), p. 238. Hereafter page references will be given in the text.

13   Wallace Stevens, *Notes toward a Supreme Fiction* in *The Palm at the End of the Mind: Selected Poems and a Play*, ed. Holly Stevens (1967; New York: Random-Vintage, 1971), p. 209.

14   Part V of "East Coker," the second of Eliot's *Four Quartets*, in *The Complete Poems and Plays, 1909–1950* (New York: Harcourt, Brace and World, 1971). Hereafter all quotations from *Four Quartets* are given in the text.

15   Virginia Woolf, *A Room of One's Own* (1929; New York: Harcourt Brace Jovanovich, 1957), pp. 99–100. Hereafter page references are given in the text.

16   Virginia Woolf, *Mrs Dalloway* (1925; New York: Harcourt Brace Jovanovich, 1953), pp. 20–1.

17   Gertrude Stein, *Tender Buttons* (1914; New York: Haskell House, 1970), p. 56.

18   *The Collected Works of W.B. Yeats*, Vol. 1 (*The Poems*), 2nd edn, ed. Richard Finneran (New York: Scribner, 1997). All Yeats poems in this chapter have been taken from this source.

19   From 1900 to 1903, Joyce composed a series of short pieces – both lyrical and dramatic – that he called epiphanies to designate the revelation of the spiritual in the divine. He explained his use of the term in *Stephen Hero*, ed. Theodore Spencer, rev. John J. Slocum and Herbert Cahoon (1944; Norfolk, CT: New Directions, 1963), pp. 210–11. See also Robert Scholes and Richard M. Kain, *The Workshop of Daedalus: James Joyce and the Raw Materials for "A Portrait of the Artist as a Young Man"* (Evanston, IL: Northwestern University Press, 1965).

20   See Virginia Woolf, *Moments of Being: Unpublished Autobiographical Writings*, 2nd edn, ed. Jeanne Schulkind (New York: Harcourt Brace Jovanovich, 1985). For an example of a moment of being, an instant that is irradiated with the vital essence of someone or something, see her story, "Moments of Being: Slater's Pins Have No Points." One particularly vivid illustration is when Fanny Wilmot surprises Miss Craye in a "moment of ecstasy," which makes her image emerge out of the London night as if the night were the "effluence of her spirit":

All seemed transparent for a moment to the gaze of Fanny Wilmot, as if looking through Miss Craye, she saw the very fountain of her being spurt up in pure, silver drops. She saw back and back into the past behind her. . . . She saw Julia open her arms; saw her blaze; saw her kindle. Out of the night she burnt like a dead white star. (*HH* 214)

21 Ezra Pound, "A Few Don'ts by an Imagiste," *Poetry* (Chicago), I, 6 (March 1913).

22 Samuel Beckett, *Endgame* (1957; New York: Grove Press, 1958), p. 1. Hereafter page references will be given in the text.

23 Stevens, *The Palm at the End of the Mind*. All verse by Stevens in this chapter is taken from this source.

24 James Joyce, *Ulysses*, ed. Hans Walter Gabler with Wolfhard Steppe and Claus Melchior (1922; New York: Random-Vintage, 1986), episode 17, lines 1247–8. Hereafter references will be given in the text by episode and line number.

25 Compare Charles Taylor, "The Politics of Recognition," in *Multiculturalism and "The Politics of Recognition,"* ed. Amy Gutmann, with commentary by Amy Gutmann, Steven C. Rockefeller, Michael Walzer, and Susan Wolf (Princeton: Princeton University Press, 1992): "People do not acquire the languages needed for self-definition on their own. . . . We define our identity always in dialogue with, sometimes in struggle against, the things our significant others want to see in us" (32–3).

26 Virginia Woolf, "Mr Bennett and Mrs Brown," in *The Captain's Death Bed and Other Essays* (New York: Harcourt Brace Jovanovich, Inc., 1950), p. 118. Hereafter page references will be given in the text.

27 Hannah Arendt, *Eichmann in Jerusalem: A Report on the Banality of Evil* (New York: Viking, 1963). Theodor W. Adorno, Betty Aron, Maria Hertz Levinson and William Morrow, *The Authoritarian Personality* (New York: Harper, 1950).

28 An example of this kind of "automatic" or obedient reading may be found in Joyce's *Dubliners*, in the story "Clay," when Maria, wearing a blindfold, is playing a divination game and has just put her hand in a "soft wet substance" that the title of the story suggests is clay. If Maria, in trying to scry her future, puts her hand on clay, it implies that what the future holds for her is death, but she doesn't try to understand what has happened by actively interpreting it (and many readers unthinkingly follow her example). Instead, Maria obediently waits for new instructions, never trying to take off the blindfold or to "see" what has happened:

There was a pause for a few seconds; and then a great deal of scuffling and whispering. Somebody said something about the garden, and at last Mrs Donnelly said something very cross to one of the next-door girls and told her to throw it out at once: that was no play. Maria understood that it was wrong that time and so she had to do it over again: and this time she got the prayer-book. (*Dubliners: Text, Criticism, and Notes*, ed. Robert Scholes and A. Walton Litz (1914; New York: Penguin, 1996), p. 101)

29 Stanley Milgram, *Obedience to Authority: An Experimental View* (New York: Harper & Row, 1974), p. 1. Hereafter page references will be given in the text.

30 The experiments were performed in the Department of Psychology at Yale from 1960 to 1963, and Milgram discusses them at length in ibid.

31 See, for example, Paul B. Armstrong, *Play and the Politics of Reading: The Social Uses of Modernist Form* (Ithaca, NY, and London: Cornell University Press, 2005).

32 I don't mean to imply that authority is monolithic, but that obedience is more automatic and consistent than many of us believe. For an earlier exploration of different kinds of authority, see Vicki Mahaffey, *Reauthorizing Joyce* (Cambridge: Cambridge University Press, 1988).

33 *Complete Works of Oscar Wilde*, with an introduction by Vyvyan Holland (New York: Harper and Row, 1966), p. 1081. Hereafter page references will be given in the text.

34 Wilde calls disobedience the original virtue, but knee-jerk disobedience is simply the flip-side of obedience, its mechanical inverse. Wilde was being provocative, but he clearly understood that the original virtue is actually the freedom of *choosing* to be obedient if obedience seemed warranted.

35 In a more recent experiment discussed by Dr Fred Luskin (*Forgive for Good* (San Francisco: HarperCollins, 2002)), participants gave very different accounts of who was responsible for an event depending on whether they adopted the point of view of the offender or the offended, thereby cor-roborating Milgram's findings. Volunteers were asked to respond to a prompt describing a common situation in which one person hurt another and to create a story that filled in the details from their point of view of the offender or the offended. Luskin reports that their stories (which arguably illuminate their assumptions) assigned responsibility differently depending on the point of view that was adopted. The result would seem to show that ordinary people learn to exculpate themselves from respon-sibility. Luskin reports,

The subjects who responded from the point of view of the offended minimized their responsibility for what happened and put blame on the offender. To these subjects, the person who hurt them meant harm, and they themselves were relatively blameless for what happened. Subjects writing from the point of view of the offender . . . placed more responsibility for what happened with the offended and minimized the damage done by their actions. In their stories the hurt was more accidental, and the offended party often did something to put themselves at risk (36).

36 What Wilde called "individualism" is precisely the capacity for thoughtful, conscientious disobedience that I have been discussing. If we think of individualism too idealistically, as a kind of norm in itself (as Americans have learned to do), it obscures Wilde's meaning: Wilde used it to designate the effort to perform a carefully reasoned critique of conformity and its ideological functions. Similarly, when I talk about an "autonomous" subject, I mean to suggest only relative autonomy, the capacity to reflect upon that which has formed us (since human subjects are inevitably shaped by the social systems of which they form a part).

37 Christopher R. Browning, *Ordinary Men: Reserve Police Battalion 101 and the Final Solution in Poland* (New York: HarperCollins, 1992, 1998). Hereafter page references will be given in the text.

38 Compare the situation of these men with that of the dying 21-year-old Nazi who sought forgiveness from Simon Wiesenthal – then an inmate in a concentration camp – for his participation in murdering approximately 250 Jews in Russia by crowding them into a house that they had locked and burned, shooting any who leaped from the windows. In *The Sunflower* (see note 3), Wiesenthal describes the Nazi as a "good boy" who had been "indoctrinated with evil," "a murderer who did not want to be a murderer but who had been made into a murderer by a murderous ideology" (95, 53). The Nazi recounts that they too were given brandy after the action: "Brandy helps one forget" (48). In the preface to the revised edition, Bonny V. Fetterman suggests that the most "vexing" question posed by this story concerns the responsibility of ordinary individuals (which is also Browning's concern). Fetterman asks, "What about the rank-and-file, the faceless individuals who carry out the crimes against other people ordered by their leaders? What about the individual responsibility of ordinary people, blinded or coerced by the reigning political ideology of their day, and of the small number who may regret their actions or repudiate them in a different climate?" (xi).

39 For a view that runs counter to Browning's, see Daniel Jonah Goldhagen, *Hitler's Willing Executioners: Ordinary Germans and the Holocaust* (New York: Alfred A. Knopf, 1996), and Browning's Afterword to *Ordinary Men*.

40 See note 3 above for details of *The Sunflower*.

41 It is easy to confuse the fact that all individuals are equal with the feeling that they are all the same. In the camp, Wiesenthal is careful to specify that "there were no class differences, we were all equals – except for one thing: the times of our appointments with death" (80).

42 Look, however, at the film *Capote*, which suggests that murdering people in a deliberate way may well be comparable to writing with the voyeuristic, detached interest in the lives of murderers that Truman Capote cultivated to write the best-selling book of his career (*In Cold Blood*).

43 Ian Parker calls Milgram's work "an intensely powerful piece of tragicomic laboratory theatre," in Parker, "Obedience," *Granta* 71 (Autumn 2000), p. 121.

44 Zygmunt Bauman, *Modernity and the Holocaust* (Ithaca, NY: Cornell University Press, 1989), p. 166. Hereafter page references will be given in the text.

45 Craig Haney, Curtis Banks, and Philip Zimbardo, "A Study of Prisoners and Guards in a Simulated Prison," 1973, reprinted in Elliot Aronson, ed., *Readings about the Social Animal*, 4th edn (New York: W.H. Freeman and Company, 1984), p. 63. Hereafter page references will be given in the text.

46 The power of belief to "create" a reality with real consequences may well explain why Stephen denies believing in his own theory in the "Scylla and Charybdis" episode of *Ulysses* (9.1067). He prays, "I believe, O Lord, help my unbelief," asking, "help me to believe or help me to unbelieve?" (9.1078–9). If the question is not "to be or not to be," as Hamlet would have it, but to believe or not to believe, then, by implication, being is a byproduct of believing; we are what we believe ourselves to be. The challenge in such a case is to believe *and* to unbelieve ourselves: i.e. to recognize identity as a truthful fiction, a highly partial, theatrical reality.

47 It is interesting to note that Bentham designed the panopticon at the time of the French Revolution; the letters are dated 1787, the blueprint 1791, although his version was never built.

48 See Martin Esslin, *The Theatre of the Absurd* (Garden City, NY: Doubleday, 1961), for a fuller discussion of the performance at San Quentin, directed by Herbert Blau, by the San Francisco Actors' Workshop.

49 Virginia Woolf, *To the Lighthouse* (1927; London: Harcourt Brace Jovanovich, 1955), p. 177. Hereafter page references will be given in the

text. Djuna Barnes uses a similar image in *Nightwood*, when, instead of a tool for observing and controlling others, the moving "eye" that strobes through the night is identified as "the great blind searchlight of the heart" (*Nightwood*, intro. by T.S. Eliot (New York: New Directions, 1937), p. 93). Hereafter page references will be given in the text.

50 In *The Sunflower*, Wiesenthal reports that the Nazis often spoke in an equally mechanical, unthinking way. When the dying Nazi first was riding into Russia with his platoon, he describes one of his comrades as speaking "in the style of a war correspondent. His words were parrotlike, unthinking. His conversation was full of stupid phrases which he had taken from newspapers" (38).

51 The main problem here is not the lack of understanding produced by the proliferation of languages, but the insistence on understanding enforced by physical abuse. Joyce's *Finnegans Wake* is built out of many languages, but it does not pressure its readers to understand or obey; instead, it uses its density of meanings to stimulate readers to develop other, less semantic modes of understanding.

52 Rebecca West, *The Return of the Soldier*, intro. by Samuel Hynes (1918; New York: Penguin, 1998), pp. 87–8.

53 Samuel Beckett, *Collected Shorter Plays* (New York: Grove Press, 1984), pp. 300–1.

54 Samuel Beckett, *Murphy* (1938; New York: Grove Press, 1967), pp. 1–2. Hereafter page references will be given in the text.

55 See note 49 above for details of *Nightwood*. Compare the brute that squats in Bernard in *The Waves* (see p. 18 above).

56 Friedrich Nietzsche, *Beyond Good and Evil*, 1886, in *The Portable Nietzsche*, ed. and trans. Walter Kaufmann (New York: Vintage, 1968), section 153, p. 444. Hereafter parenthetically in the text.

57 Isabel Fonseca, *Bury Me Standing: The Gypsies and their Journey* (New York: Random-Vintage, 1995), p. 253. Hereafter page references will be given in the text.

58 Konnilyn Feig, "Non-Jewish Victims of the Concentration Camps," in Michael Berenbaum, ed., *A Mosaic of Victims* (New York: New York University Press, 1990), p. 162. Hereafter page references will be given in the text.

59 Evelyn LeChene, *Mauthausen* (London: Methuen, 1975), p. 88, cited by Feig, p. 170.

60 See Stephanie Barron, "1937: Modern Art and Politics in Prewar Germany," in Barron, ed., *"Degenerate Art": The Fate of the Avant-Garde in Nazi Germany* (Los Angeles: Los Angeles County Museum of Art, 1991), pp. 12–13. Hereafter page references will be given in the text.

61　In this guise, as the Fisher King, Amfortas is lurking behind the poetic devastation of Eliot's *The Waste Land*.

62　Cited in H. Montgomery Hyde, *Oscar Wilde* (New York: Farrar, Straus and Giroux, 1975), p. 74.

63　L. Perry Curtis, Jr, *Apes and Angels: The Irishman in Victorian Caricature* (Washington: Smithsonian Institution Press, 1971), and Noel Ignatiev, *How the Irish Became White* (New York: Routledge, 1995).

64　Harper Lee, *To Kill a Mockingbird*, 40th anniversary edn (1960; New York: HarperCollins, 1999), p. 281. Hereafter page references will be given in the text.

65　Inga Clendinnen, *Reading the Holocaust* (Cambridge: Cambridge University Press, 1999), p. 98.

66　Raul Hilberg, *The Destruction of the European Jews* (New York: Holmes and Meier, 1985), p. 31.

67　See Voyager CD-Rom version of *Maus*.

68　Art Spiegelman, *Maus: A Survivor's Tale II: And Here My Troubles Began* (New York: Pantheon, 1991), p. 3. Raul Hilberg's classic study, *The Destruction of the European Jews*, teems with additional representations of Jews as a disease or as carriers of disease; his examples date from Martin Luther's book *About the Jews and their Lies* through attempts to pass anti-Semitic legislation in 1890s Germany, and they climax with speeches by Hitler and his henchmen. He gives instances of Jews being called a plague and pestilence, parasites, cholera germs, lice, bloodsuckers, and bacteria, as well as vermin (15–18).

69　Ciaran Carson, *Belfast Confetti* (Winston-Salem, NC: Wake Forest University Press, 1989).

70　Stanley Kubrick uses the same idea in his film *Full Metal Jacket*, in which the American soldiers celebrate their victory over a Vietnamese village by breaking into the Mickey Mouse song.

71　Forster, "English Prose Between 1918 and 1939," in *Two Cheers for Democracy* (1938; New York: Harcourt, Brace and World, Inc., 1951), pp. 274–5. Hereafter page references will be given in the text.

72　See Virginia Woolf, "22 Hyde Park Gate," in *Moments of Being*.

73　Parnell lost his political position – thereby dashing the hope for establishing Home Rule in Ireland through parliamentary (and therefore nonviolent) means in the 1890s – when it was revealed that he had been having an affair with a married woman, Kitty O'Shea. Wilde's life and career were ruined when his homosexual activities were made public during the three legal trials with which he was involved in 1895. He was imprisoned for two years for "gross indecency," and he died soon thereafter. See

Mahaffey, *States of Desire: Wilde, Yeats, Joyce and the Irish Experiment* (New York: Oxford University Press, 1998), pp. 46–9.

74 Letter to Georges Izambard, May 1871.

75 Ezra Pound, *ABC of Reading* (New York: New Directions, 1934), p. 13.

76 Jonathan Franzen, "Mr Difficult: William Gaddis and the Problem of Hard-to-Read Books," *The New Yorker*, September 30, 2002, p. 109.

Chapter 2   Partnering

1 Gertrude Stein, *The Mother of Us All*, 1946, in *Last Operas and Plays*, ed. Carl Van Vechten (New York: Rinehart, 1949), p. 74.

2 George du Maurier, *Trilby*, introduction by Elaine Showalter, notes by Dennis Denisoff (1894; Oxford: Oxford University Press, 1998), p. 65. Hereafter page references will be given in the text.

3 Sir Arthur Conan Doyle, *The Hound of the Baskervilles* (*HB*) (1902; London: Penguin, 1981), p. 31. Hereafter page references will be given in the text.

4 It is illuminating to think of the Holmes mysteries in relation to a form such as the riddle, which is an almost universal literary form. As a particularly intriguing example, consider the Anglo-Saxon riddles found in the *Exeter Book* from the tenth century, which – like the Holmes stories – also seem to function as a test of the listener's (or reader's) knowledge and attentiveness. Not only do riddles demand sharp concentration (and the riddles in the *Exeter Book* are printed without answers), they also inspire wonder and delight at the complexity of the world.

5 Stanley Milgram, *Obedience to Authority: An Experimental View* (New York: Harper & Row, 1974), p. 133. Hereafter page references will be given in the text.

6 Sir Arthur Conan Doyle, *The Sign of Four*, introduction by Peter Ackroyd, notes by Ed Glinert (1890; London: Penguin, 2001), pp. 7, 12. Hereafter page references will be given in the text.

7 "Introduction to Volume I," in Sir Arthur Conan Doyle, *The Complete Sherlock Holmes*, Vol. I, introduction and notes by Kyle Freeman (New York: Barnes & Noble, 2003), p. xxi.

8 Sir Arthur Conan Doyle, *A Study in Scarlet* (*SS*), 1887, in ibid., p. 34. Hereafter page references are given parenthetically in the text.

9 Compare "A Scandal in Bohemia," the first of the Holmes stories to have appeared in the *Strand*, in July 1891. When Watson asks Holmes what

something might mean, Holmes replies, "I have no data yet. It is a capital mistake to theorize before one has data. Insensibly one begins to twist facts to suit theories, instead of theories to suit facts." Sir Arthur Conan Doyle, *The New Annotated Sherlock Holmes*, Vol. I, ed. Leslie S. Klinger (New York: Norton, 2005), p. 11.

10 In "A Scandal in Bohemia," Holmes tries to explain why it is that – until he explains its process – his reasoning repeatedly baffles Watson. Holmes suggests that Watson is kept from observing by the habitual way he sees, declaring,

> "You see, but you do not observe. The distinction is clear. For example, you have frequently seen the steps which lead up from the hall to this room."
>
> "Frequently."
>
> "How often?"
>
> "Well, some hundreds of times."
>
> "Then how many are there?"
>
> "How many? I don't know."
>
> "Quite so! You have not observed. And yet you have seen. That is just my point. Now, I know that there are seventeen steps, because I have both seen and observed." (Ibid., p. 10)

11 T.S. Eliot, *The Sacred Wood: Essays on Poetry and Criticism* (London: Methuen, 1920), p. 16. Hereafter page references will be given in the text.

12 Oscar Wilde, "The Critic as Artist," in *The Artist as Critic: Critical Writings of Oscar Wilde*, ed. Richard Ellmann (Chicago: University of Chicago Press, 1969), p. 355. Hereafter page references will be given in the text.

13 Conan Doyle's contemporary, Oscar Wilde, was a particularly lucid and entertaining commentator on this connection in his essay, "Pen, Pencil and Poison" (ibid.).

14 Wilde made a similar point in his story "The Canterville Ghost" by presenting the ghost as a murderer who is also an artist, painting blood stains on the floor in an effort to produce horror in his audience (*Complete Works of Oscar Wilde*, with an introduction by Vyvyan Holland (New York: Harper and Row, 1966)).

15 Cited in *Dubliners: Text, Criticism, and Notes*, ed. Robert Scholes and A. Walton Litz (1914; New York: Penguin, 1996), p. 253. Hereafter page references will be given in the text.

16 Holmes, too, is constantly stressing how widely observers overlook details they have unconsciously dismissed as trifles. See, for example, his

analysis of an envelope in "The Man with the Twisted Lip" (*Strand*, December 1891). He explains,

> The name, you see, is in perfectly black ink, which has dried itself. The rest is of the grayish colour, which shows that blotting-paper has been used. If it had been written straight off, and then blotted, none of it would be of a deep black shade. This man has written the name, and there has been a pause before he wrote the address, which can only mean that he was not familiar with it. It is, of course, a trifle, but there is nothing so important as trifles. (*The New Annotated Sherlock Holmes*, ed. Klinger, p. 182)

17   Compare the "Circe" episode of *Ulysses*, where Bloom gets a glimpse of the inside of Zoe's mouth and it appears to him as a graveyard full of gold and rotting bones (fillings and decaying teeth): "*The roses* [her lips] *draw apart, disclose a sepulcher of the gold of kings and their mouldering bones*" (James Joyce, *Ulysses*, ed. Hans Walter Gabler with Wolfhard Steppe and Claus Melchior (New York: Random-Vintage, 1986), episode 15, lines 1340–1).

18   Margot Norris suggests a reading of "The Sisters" as

> a naturalistic tale of poverty, ignorance, and sadness that betrays the politics of gender differences. The story of Nannie and Eliza Flynn may well concern two very poor women from the slums of Irishtown . . . who never married and rose to little more than a meager draper's business in Dublin. . . . Meanwhile, their brother managed to receive an education and travel to Rome to attend the Irish college there. . . . Yet instead of transferring their respectability and benefits of this vocation to his sisters, the outcome of their brother's ecclesiastical career was unhappiness, disappointment, and a final dementia that now threatens to further cloud their lives. (*Suspicious Readings of Joyce's Dubliners* (Philadelphia: University of Pennsylvania Press, 2003), p. 24)

19   See ibid., p. 26, for an account of these readings.

20   See my *Reauthorizing Joyce* (Cambridge: Cambridge University Press, 1998), pp. 26–32.

21   Sarah Grand, "The New Aspect of the Woman Question," *North American Review* 158 (March 1894), pp. 270–6. Reprinted in Carolyn Christensen Nelson, ed., *A New Woman Reader: Fiction, Articles, and Drama of the 1890s* (Peterborough, Ont.: Broadview Press, 2001), p. 143. Hereafter cited as *NWR*.

22   Ann L. Ardis, *New Women, New Novels: Feminism and Early Modernism* (New Brunswick, NJ: Rutgers University Press, 1990), p. 169.

23   Mona Caird, "Marriage," *Westminster Review,* 130 (August 1888), pp. 186–201. Reprinted in *NWR.*

24   Karl Beckson, *London in the 1890s: A Cultural History* (New York: W.W. Norton, 1992), p. 134. Hereafter page references will be given in the text.

25   Cited by Susan Kingsley Kent, *Sex and Suffrage in Britain, 1860–1914* (Princeton: Princeton University Press, 1987), p. 84. Hereafter page references will be given in the text.

26   Florence Farr, *Modern Woman: Her Intentions* (London: Frank Palmer, 1910), p. 57. Hereafter page references will be given in the text.

27   The New Woman also influenced several familiar literary characters, such as Hardy's Sue Bridehead; Shaw's Vivie Warren (in *Mrs Warren's Profession*); Gissing's Mary Barfoot and Rhoda Nunn (in *The Odd Women*); and H.G. Wells' Ann Veronica.

28   Virginia Woolf, *Three Guineas* (1938; New York: Harvest/Harcourt Brace Jovanovich, 1966), p. 53. Hereafter page references will be given in the text.

29   George Bernard Shaw, *Mrs Warren's Profession* (1894). In *George Bernard Shaw's Plays,* 2nd edn, ed. Sandie Byrne (New York: Norton, 2002), p. 48. Hereafter page references will be given in the text.

30   This is a complaint explained in some detail by Julia M.A. Hawksley, "A Young Woman's Right: Knowledge," *Westminster Review* 142 (September 1894), pp. 315–18, reprinted in *NWR,* pp. 203–7.

31   George Gissing, *The Odd Women* (1893; New York: W.W. Norton, 1977), p. 37. Hereafter page references will be given in the text.

32   Grant Allen, *The Woman Who Did* (1895; Oxford: Oxford University Press, 1995), p. 35. Hereafter page references will be given in the text.

33   Kate Chopin, *The Awakening: An Authoritative Text, Biographical and Historical Contexts, Criticism,* 2nd edn, ed. Margo Culley (1899; New York: W.W. Norton, 1994), p. 163. Hereafter page references will be given in the text.

34   What makes the book strange is that Allen also thinks that women should be free in order to improve their function as mothers; their passion and intellect should be unshackled and developed for the good of their partners, but especially for the benefit of their children. He suggests that women who are martyrs and moral pioneers (44) will make better mothers, which he identified in an earlier essay as woman's "main function in life" (9). Allen's rather unusual agenda is to change society not for the sake of women themselves (since they pay a very high price for their autonomy), but for the sake of men and children.

35   Carl M. Selle, ed., *The New Drama: The Liars, by Henry Arthur Jones, and The Notorious Mrs Ebbsmith, by Sir Arthur Wing Pinero* (Coral Gables, FL: University of Miami Press, 1963), p. 188. Hereafter page references will be given in the text.

36   In Elaine Showalter, ed., *Daughters of Decadence: Women Writers of the Fin-de-Siècle* (London: Virago, 1993), p. 82.

37   Samuel Beckett, *Waiting for Godot* (1952; New York: Grove Press, 1954), p. 39. Hereafter page references will be given in the text.

38   Samuel Beckett, *Endgame* (1957; New York: Grove Press, 1958), p. 43. Hereafter page references will be given in the text.

Chapter 3   Window Painting

1   An aporia is actually a philosophical puzzle, a logical contradiction that causes an inquirer to admit perplexity. See Plato's "aporetic" dialogues for examples of how Socrates initiates a line of questioning in order to produce a state of aporia in his interlocutor. Socrates describes the effect of aporia in Plato's *Meno*.

2   Dylan Thomas, *Collected Poems 1934–1952* (London: Dent, 1952).

3   T.S. Eliot, *The Complete Poems and Plays, 1909–1950* (New York: Harcourt, Brace & World, 1971). All Eliot's poems in this chapter, including *The Waste Land*, are taken from this source.

4   Ron Bush, in his elegant discussion of the poem, points out that the word "faithless" here, which comes from a line Eliot borrowed from LaForgue, is charged with self-hatred. Bush argues with great persuasiveness for a view that the young girl in the poem is an image of the man's own emotional life, which he has rather brutally abandoned. *T.S. Eliot: A Study in Character and Style* (New York: Oxford University Press, 1984), pp. 11–14.

5   *The Collected Works of W.B. Yeats*, Vol. 1 (*The Poems*), 2nd edn, ed. Richard Finneran (New York: Scribner, 1997).

6   James Joyce, *Ulysses*, ed. Hans Walter Gabler with Wolfhard Steppe and Claus Melchior (1922; New York: Random-Vintage, 1986), episode 12, lines 452–3, 468. Hereafter references will be given in the text by episode and line number.

7   Joyce understood this point clearly, as we can see from his essay on Wilde, in which he says that one can only reach the divine heart through the experience of separation and loss called sin. James Joyce, "Oscar

Wilde: The Poet of 'Salomé'" (1909), in *The Critical Writings of James Joyce*, ed. Ellsworth Mason and Richard Ellmann (Ithaca, NY: Cornell University Press, 1959), p. 205.

8   *The Picture of Dorian Gray: Authoritative Texts, Backgrounds, Reviews and Reactions*, ed. Donald L. Lawler (1891; New York: Norton, 1988), p. 182n.

9   See "Gerontion": as a result of abandonment by the ones we love, we "lose beauty in terror, terror in inquisition."

10   Only once, in the months after the Twin Towers were destroyed in New York, did students intuitively apprehend the emotional subtext of shared grief and distress out of which the voices of the poem speak. Without that feeling of living in the aftermath of disaster to explain and unify its succession of scenes, the poem seems disjointed, heartless, and even self-indulgent in its whirling allusions to other poems, plays, myths, and songs.

11   In some traditions Philomela is changed into a swallow, and her sister Procne into a nightingale, but Eliot prefers to see Philomela as the future nightingale, probably because of the way it makes her muteness then turn into beautiful song.

12   The vision Ovid gives of Philomela's dismembered tongue wriggling to get closer to its mistress' feet graphically illustrates the kinship between sexual and violent rapine. After Tereus, "by sheer force, overcame the struggles of the lonely and defenceless girl, while she vainly called aloud to her father, to her sister, and above all to the gods, for help," Philomela tears her hair, claws at her arms, and charges Tereus with her determination to publish his crime: "If I have the chance, I shall come forward before your people, and tell my story. If I am to be kept shut up in the woods, I shall fill the forests with my voice, and win sympathy from the very rocks that witnessed my degradation." In fearful and angry response, "the fierce tyrant" seizes her as she is pouring out her scorn and struggling to speak:

> he grasped her tongue with a pair of forceps, and cut it out with his cruel sword. The remaining stump still quivered in her throat, while the tongue itself lay pulsing and murmuring incoherently to the dark earth. It writhed convulsively, like a snake's tail when it has newly been cut off and, dying, tried to reach its mistress' feet. Even after this atrocity, they say, though I can hardly bring myself to believe it, that the king in his guilty passion often took his pleasure with the body he had so mutilated.

(Ovid, *The Metamorphoses of Ovid*, trans. Mary M. Innes (Baltimore, MD: Penguin, 1955), Book IV, pp. 148–9)

13   In his notes to the poem, Eliot refers the interested reader to a book by Jessie Weston, *From Ritual to Romance*, for additional information about the myth of the Fisher King, which is a version of the Grail legend (50).

14   Ovid, *Metamorphoses*, Book III, pp. 82–3, quoted in Latin by Eliot in the note to line 218.

15   It is important to note that the four symbols associated with the Grail legend – the cup, the dish, the lance, and the sword – signify male and female sexual differences, because this connection highlights the close relation between the sexual and the spiritual and a union of opposite extremes (which need not involve a physical coupling). The four Grail symbols are associated with the original four suits of the tarot pack, once used to predict the rise and fall of the waters of the Nile, which controlled fertility. They are also the four treasures of Celtic legend, later linked to the death and rebirth of the Christian God through the sword and cup used at the crucifixion.

16   This layering of myths to underscore a common theme – here the unforeseen consequences of a sexual wound – is an example of what Eliot called the "mythical method." In a 1923 review of James Joyce's *Ulysses*, "*Ulysses*, Order and Myth," Eliot contended that

> Psychology (such as it is and whether our reaction to it be comic or serious), ethnology, and *The Golden Bough* have concurred to make possible what was impossible even a few years ago. Instead of the narrative method, we may now use the mythical method. (Reprinted in Peter Faulkner, ed., *The English Modernist Reader, 1910–1930* (Iowa City: University of Iowa Press, 1986), pp. 100–4 (p. 103); originally in *The Dial*, LXXV, 5 (November 1923), 480–3)

The mythical method depends upon an understanding of myth as a kind of universal language that adopted surprisingly similar motifs even in markedly different cultures, as Sir James Frazer had demonstrated in *The Golden Bough*.

17   See, for example, Anthony Julius, *T.S. Eliot, Anti-Semitism and Literary Form* (Cambridge: Cambridge University Press, 1995). For discussions of Eliot's misogyny, see Sandra M. Gilbert and Susan Gubar, *No Man's Land: The Place of the Woman Writer in the Twentieth Century*, Vol. 1: *The War of the*

Words (New Haven: Yale University Press, 1988), who emphasize the places in Eliot's writing where he depicts women as threatening and contaminating, the very source of unspeakable horror (pp. 37, 235–6). Colleen Lamos gives a much more textured account of Eliot's anger against the "feminization" of modern society and the contempt for women writers that he sometimes expresses, linking it to his responses to particular women in his life (especially his mother but also his first wife) as well as to "nostalgic homosociality." Lamos, however, also details the ways in which Eliot's poetry is illuminatingly "errant." As she writes, "for many readers Eliot has become virtually a synecdoche for white male high modernism and its attendant evils" (*Deviant Modernism: Sexual and Textual Errancy in T.S. Eliot, James Joyce, and Marcel Proust* (Cambridge: Cambridge University Press, 1998), p. 56; see also chapters 1 and 2, and especially pp. 26 and 91–108).

18   Eliot does not seem to have questioned the widespread identification of such possessiveness with the Jews, and as a result his depictions of Jews are often degrading. See especially "Burbank with a Baedeker: Bleistein with a Cigar" and "Gerontion."

19   He quotes James Jones' novel, *The Thin Red Line* (1962), to illustrate the soldier's oddly sexual response to danger: "Could it be that *all* war was basically sexual? . . . A sort of sexual perversion? Or a complex of sexual perversions? That would make a funny thesis and God help the race" (Paul Fussell, *The Great War and Modern Memory* (New York and Oxford: Oxford University Press, 1975), pp. 271–2).

20   Wilfred Owen, *The Poems of Wilfred Owen*, ed. Edmund Blunden (New York: Viking Press, 1931).

21   In Shakespeare's *The Passionate Pilgrim*, female genitalia are described as a wound of the sort that Adonis might receive from a boar (IX).

22   One example of the way the poem is "layered" becomes evident when we look at what happens to the river Thames in the poem as it flows through London in the twentieth century. It becomes the Nile, bearing Cleopatra on a barge, at the beginning of "A Game of Chess"; in "The Fire Sermon," it turns into the Thames of three hundred years earlier through its echo of Edmund Spenser's "Prothalamion" – "Sweet Thames, run softly while I end my song" (l. 176); next, it changes into the Rhine of Wagner's *Ring of the Nibelung* at the end of "The Fire Sermon"; and finally it metamorphoses into the Ganges, surrounded by jungle, in "What the Thunder Said" before it turns back into the river over which London Bridge is falling (l. 427). London itself becomes on one level St Augustine's Carthage, but it is also "Jerusalem Athens Alexandria/ Vienna" (ll. 375–6): "Unreal."

23 Ezra Pound, "A Few Don'ts by an Imagiste," *Poetry* (Chicago), I, 6 (March 1913).

24 According to F.S. Flint, *"Imagisme"* adheres to the following principles:

1. Direct treatment of the "thing", whether subjective or objective.
2. To use absolutely no word that did not contribute to the presentation.
3. As regarding rhythm: to compose in sequence of the musical phrase, not in sequence of a metronome. (*"Imagisme,"* *Poetry* (Chicago) I, 6 (March 1913))

25 Although some readers might divide the section into three scenes, with the middle section of dialogue (ll. 111–38), I read these lines as emanating from the electricity generated by the woman brushing her hair before the fire based, on the description of how "her hair/ Spread out in fiery points/ Glowed into words, then would be savagely still" (ll. 108–10). (This image recurs in nightmare form in "What the Thunder Said": "A woman drew her long black hair out tight/ And fiddled whisper music on those strings," ll. 378–9.)

26 T.S. Eliot, *Selected Essays*, 3rd edn (London: Faber and Faber, 1951), p. 289.

27 D.H. Lawrence, *The Lost Girl* (1920; New York: Modern Library, 2003), p. 49.

28 William Faulkner, *As I Lay Dying* (1930; New York: Random-Vintage, 1957), pp. 163–4.

29 Henry James, *The Turn of the Screw and Other Short Fiction* (Toronto: Bantam, 1983), p. 397.

30 *Three Novels by Samuel Beckett: Molloy, Malone Dies, The Unnamable* (New York: Grove Weidenfeld, 1958), p. 31. Hereafter page references will be given in the text.

31 Jacques Lacan, *The Four Fundamental Concepts of Psycho-Analysis*, ed. Jacques-Alain Miller, trans. Alan Sheridan (New York: Norton, 1978), p. 87. Hereafter page references are cited in the text.

32 See Hazel Hutchison, "James's Spectacles: Distorted Vision in *The Ambassadors*," *The Henry James Review*, 26 (2005), pp. 39–51 (pp. 41–2), for a discussion of the extent to which Strether has been linked to the author as well.

33 Henry James, *The Ambassadors*, ed. Leon Edel (1903; Boston: Houghton Mifflin-Riverside, 1960), pp. 25, 22. Hereafter page references will be given in the text.

34 Little Bilham remembers Strether's impassioned speech to him in Gloriani's garden differently from the way Strether delivered it: although Strether urged him to "Live all you can; it's a mistake not to" (137), Little

Bilham reminds Strether later of having advised him to *see*: "Didn't you adjure me, in accents I shall never forget, to see, while I've a chance, everything I can? – and *really* to see, for it must have been that only you meant" (173).

35 For a more extended discussion of the relation between Holbein's painting and James's novel, see Adeline R. Tintner, *Henry James and the Lust of the Eyes: Thirteen Artists in his Work* (Baton Rouge: Louisiana State University Press, 1993), pp. 87–94, and Hutchison, "James's Spectacles."

36 Joseph Conrad, *Heart of Darkness*, ed. Robert Kimbrough (1902; New York: W.W. Norton, 1971), p. 27. Hereafter page references will be given in the text.

37 James Joyce, *Dubliners: Text, Criticism, and Notes*, ed. Robert Scholes and A. Walton Litz (1914; New York: Penguin, 1996), p. 211. Hereafter page references will be given in the text.

38 Joyce again uses the metaphor of portraiture as a way of framing identity – one's own as opposed to that of a love object – in *A Portrait of the Artist as a Young Man*. See my "Framing, Being Framed, and the Janus Faces of Authority," in James C. Carens and Philip Brady, eds, *Critical Essays on James Joyce's A Portrait of the Artist as a Young Man* (New York: G.K. Hall and Co., 1998), pp. 290–315. Redacted from *Reauthorizing Joyce* (Cambridge: Cambridge University Press, 1998), pp. 53–103.

39 Joyce constructed two different "schemata" for his novel – one that he gave to Stuart Gilbert and the other to Carlo Linati – in which every episode was associated with a different art, symbol, bodily organ, time of day, and so on.

40 Virginia Woolf, *To the Lighthouse* (1927; London: Harcourt Brace Jovanovich, 1955), p. 209. Hereafter page references will be given in the text.

41 It is said of Mrs Ramsay, "Her simplicity fathomed what clever people falsified. Her singleness of mind made her drop plumb like a stone, alight exact as a bird, gave her, naturally, this swoop and fall of the spirit upon truth which delighted, eased, sustained – falsely perhaps" (27). Mr Ramsay is equally single-minded, if more brutal about his way of expressing it; Mrs Ramsay responds to him by thinking, "To pursue truth with such astonishing lack of consideration for other people's feelings . . . was to her so horrible an outrage of human decency . . ." (29).

42 Wallace Stevens, *The Palm at the End of the Mind: Selected Poems and a Play*, ed. Holly Stevens (1967; New York: Random-Vintage, 1971).

43 *Krapp's Last Tape,* in Samuel Beckett, *Collected Shorter Plays* (New York: Grove Press, 1984), p. 58. Hereafter page references will be given in the text.

Chapter 4   Watchman, What of the Night?

1 James Joyce, *Ulysses,* ed. Hans Walter Gabler with Wolfhard Steppe and Claus Melchior (New York: Random House, 1986), episode 17, lines 2067–70. Hereafter to be cited in the text by episode and line number. For a more extended discussion of darkness in "Ithaca," see my "Sidereal Writing: Male Refractions and Malefactions in 'Ithaca,'" in Kimberly J. Devlin and Marilyn Reizbaum, eds, *Ulysses: En-Gendered Perspectives: Eighteen New Essays on the Episodes* (Columbia, SC: University of South Carolina Press, 1999), pp. 254–66.

2 *The New Oxford Annotated Bible,* New Revised Standard Version (New York: Oxford University Press, 1991, 1994). Hereafter references will be given in the text.

3 Elie Wiesel, *Night,* trans. Stella Rodway (1958; New York: Bantam, 1982), esp. p. 52.

4 *The Collected Works of William Butler Yeats,* Vol. I (*The Poems*), 2nd edn, ed. Richard Finneran (New York: Scribner, 1977).

5 The name Stalin, which means "steel," helped to underscore the romance with hardness that underwrote the massive violence being deployed by leaders against their own people not only in the Soviet Union, but also in Germany and Italy. Hitler admired Stalin, who was variously known as the "man of Steel, the Granite Bolshevik, the Brass-hard Leninist, the Iron Soldier, the Universal Genius" (Paul Johnson, *Modern Times* (New York: Harper & Row-Perennial, 1983), p. 267). Stalin's attack on the peasantry, which had formed three-quarters of the population, was done secretly, so that most people thought Stalin was fair, honest, even heroic. His second wife shot herself in protest against his treatment of the peasants, and inside Russia the climate of fear produced by the use of secret police was intensified by a virtually unreported famine in 1932–3 that resulted from the peasants burning their grain and slaughtering their livestock rather than give them up (ibid., pp. 261–77).

6 Eliot cited by Lionel Trilling, *The Last Decade: Essays and Reviews 1965–1977* (New York: Harcourt, 1979), p. 28.

7 Instead of betting on a long shot, a "dark" horse, most people go for the favorite out of a desire for certainty and stability, even though the payoff

for doing so is so small. In *Finnegans Wake,* Joyce makes fun of such con-
servatism – which is literally "racial" in that it is concerned with horse
races – when he has Mutt (here Muta) ask, "Haven money on stablecert?
[even haven on a stable-certified horse who represents stability and
certainty]" (*Finnegans Wake* (1939; New York: Penguin, 1967), p. 610,
line 17; hereafter page and line references will be given in the text). An
outsider promises a greater payoff, both in money and in attractiveness
to women, as we see when Jute (here Juva) replies, "Tempt to wom
Outsider!" [ten to one outsider, temptation to woman outside her]"
(610.18).

8   Stanislaus Joyce, *My Brother's Keeper: James Joyce's Early Years,* ed. Richard
Ellmann (Cambridge, MA: Da Capo Press, 1958), pp. 90–3. Note the
similarity between this early sketch and a scene in Joyce's last work,
Finnegans Wake, in which what can be seen on the blind is lovemaking
rather than violence (III.iv).

9   W.E.B. Du Bois, *The Souls of Black Folk,* in *Three Negro Classics* (New York:
Avon, 1965), p. 215.

10 Ralph Ellison, *Shadow and Act,* cited by B.F. McKeever, "Cane as Blues,"
in Jean Toomer, *Cane: An Authoritative Text, Backgrounds, Criticism,* ed.
Darwin T. Turner (New York, Norton, 1988), p. 193. Hereafter cited
parenthetically in the text.

11 Michael North's excellent chapter on William Carlos Williams and
Toomer discusses in greater detail Toomer's "attempt to counter . . . rigid
ideas about race." *The Dialect of Modernism: Race, Language, and Twentieth-
Century Literature* (New York: Oxford University Press, 1994), pp.
162–74.

12 This is an excerpt from W.E.B. Du Bois and Alain Locke, "The Younger
Literary Movement," *Crisis* 27 (February 1924), pp. 161–3.

13 *Dylan Thomas: The Notebook Poems 1930–1934,* ed. Ralph Maud (London:
Dent-Everyman, 1989).

14 Arnold Rampersad, "Introduction," in Alain Locke, ed., *The New Negro*
(1925; New York: Simon and Schuster-Touchstone, 1992), p. xv.
Hereafter cited parenthetically as *NN.*

15 See, for example, David Levering Lewis, *When Harlem was in Vogue*
(1979; New York: Penguin, 1997). Hereafter cited parenthetically as
WHV.

16 Virginia Woolf, *To the Lighthouse* (1927; London: Harcourt Brace
Jovanovich, 1955), p. 7. Hereafter page references will be given in the
text.

17 Compare Woolf's treatment of "moments of being" in "A Sketch of the
Past." *Moments of Being: Unpublished Autobiographical Writings,* 2nd edn, ed.

Jeanne Schulkind (New York: Harcourt Brace Jovanovich, 1985), pp. 72–3.

18 William Faulkner, *As I Lay Dying* (1930; New York: Vintage, 1957), p. 55.

19 See Friedrich Nietzsche, *The Birth of Tragedy, Or: Hellenism and Pessimism*, trans. Walter Kaufmann (1872; New York: Random-Vintage, 1967), for an extended discussion of the difference between Apollinian and Dionysian realities.

20 Jean Rhys, *Good Morning, Midnight* (1939; New York, Norton, 1986). Hereafter page references will be given in the text.

21 *Nightwood*, intro. by T.S. Eliot (New York: New Directions, 1937), p. 121. Hereafter page references will be given in the text.

22 Samuel Beckett, *Murphy* (1938; New York: Grove Press, 1967), p. 1. Hereafter page references will be given in the text.

23 Virginia Woolf, *The Years* (1937; New York: Harcourt Brace Jovanovich, 1959), p. 317. Hereafter page references will be given in the text.

24 Virginia Woolf, *The Waves* (1931; New York: Harcourt Brace Jovanovich, 1959), p. 277. Hereafter page references will be given in the text.

25 Virginia Woolf, *Between the Acts* (1941; New York: Harcourt Brace Jovanovich, 1969), p. 82. (Hereafter page references will be given in the text.) The narrator repeats the point a little later by stressing that "The future shadowed their present" (114).

26 Virginia Woolf, *Three Guineas* (1938; New York: Harcourt Brace Jovanovich, 1966), p. 83. Hereafter page references will be given in the text.

27 Hugh Kenner, "The Portrait in Perspective," reprinted (from *Dublin's Joyce*) in *A Portrait of the Artist as a Young Man: Text, Criticism, and Notes*, ed. Chester G. Anderson (New York: Viking, 1968), p. 421.

28 *The Complete Poems and Plays, 1909–1950* (New York: Harcourt, Brace and World, 1971).

Conclusion

1 James Joyce, *Finnegans Wake* (1939; New York: Penguin, 1967), p. 614, lines 23–4; emphasis added.

2 Wallace Stevens, *The Palm at the End of the Mind: Selected Poems and a Play*, ed. Holly Stevens (1967; New York: Random-Vintage, 1971).

3 W.H. Auden, *Collected Poems* (New York: Vintage, 1991).

Bibliography

Agamben, Giorgio. *Remnants of Auschwitz: The Witness and the Archive*, trans. Daniel Heller-Roazen. New York: Zone Books, 2002.

Allen, Grant. *The Woman Who Did.* 1895; Oxford: Oxford University Press, 1995.

Ardis, Ann L. *New Women, New Novels: Feminism and Early Modernism.* New Brunswick, NJ: Rutgers University Press, 1990.

Armstrong, Paul B. *Play and the Politics of Reading: The Social Uses of Modernist Form.* Ithaca, NY, and London: Cornell University Press, 2005.

Barnes, Djuna. *Nightwood*, intro. by T.S. Eliot. New York: New Directions, 1937.

Barron, Stephanie, ed. *"Degenerate Art": The Fate of the Avant-Garde in Nazi Germany.* Los Angeles: Los Angeles County Museum of Art, 1991.

Bauman, Zygmunt. *Modernity and the Holocaust.* Ithaca, NY: Cornell University Press, 1989.

Beckett, Samuel. *Collected Shorter Plays.* New York: Grove Press, 1984.

———. *Endgame.* 1957; New York: Grove Press, 1958.

———. *Murphy.* 1938; New York: Grove Press, 1967.

———. *Three Novels by Samuel Beckett: Molloy, Malone Dies, The Unnamable.* New York: Grove Weidenfeld, 1958.

———. *Waiting for Godot.* 1952; New York: Grove Press, 1954.

Beckson, Karl. *London in the 1890s: A Cultural History.* New York: W.W. Norton, 1992.

Browning, Christopher R. *Ordinary Men: Reserve Police Battalion 101 and the Final Solution in Poland.* New York: HarperCollins, 1992, 1998.

Bush, Ron. *T.S. Eliot: A Study in Character and Style.* New York: Oxford University Press, 1984.

Carey, John. *The Intellectuals and the Masses: Pride and Prejudice among the Literary Intelligentsia, 1880–1930.* Chicago: Academy Chicago Publishers, 1992.

Carson, Ciaran. *Belfast Confetti*. Winston-Salem, NC: Wake Forest University Press, 1989.

Chopin, Kate. *The Awakening: An Authoritative Text, Biographical and Historical Contexts, Criticism*, 2nd edn, ed. Margo Culley. 1899; New York: W.W. Norton, 1994.

Clendinnen, Inga. *Reading the Holocaust*. Cambridge: Cambridge University Press, 1999.

Conan Doyle, Sir Arthur. *The Complete Sherlock Holmes*. Vol. 1, introduction and notes by Kyle Freeman. New York: Barnes & Noble, 2003.

———. *The Hound of the Baskervilles*. 1902; London: Penguin, 1981.

———. *The New Annotated Sherlock Holmes*, Vol. I, ed. Leslie S. Klinger. New York: Norton, 2005.

———. *The Sign of Four*, introduction by Peter Ackroyd, notes by Ed Glinert. 1890; London: Penguin, 2001.

———. *A Study in Scarlet*, 1884, in *The Complete Sherlock Holmes*. Vol. 1, introduction and notes by Kyle Freeman. New York: Barnes & Noble, 2003.

Conrad, Joseph. *Heart of Darkness*, ed. Robert Kimbrough. 1902; New York: W.W. Norton, 1971.

Curtis, L. Perry, Jr. *Apes and Angels: The Irishman in Victorian Caricature*. Washington: Smithsonian Institution Press, 1971.

Du Bois, W.E.B. *The Souls of Black Folk*. In *Three Negro Classics*. New York: Avon, 1965.

du Maurier, George. *Trilby*, introduction by Elaine Showalter, notes by Dennis Denisoff. 1894; Oxford: Oxford University Press, 1998.

Eliot, T.S. *The Complete Poems and Plays, 1909–1950*. New York: Harcourt, Brace & World, 1971.

———. *The Sacred Wood: Essays on Poetry and Criticism*. London: Methuen, 1920.

———. *Selected Essays*, 3rd edn. London: Faber and Faber, 1951.

Farr, Florence. *Modern Woman: Her Intentions*. London: Frank Palmer, 1910.

Faulkner, Peter, ed. *The English Modernist Reader, 1910–1930*. Iowa City: University of Iowa Press, 1986.

Faulkner, William. *As I Lay Dying*. 1930; New York: Random-Vintage, 1957.

Feig, Konnilyn. "Non-Jewish Victims of the Concentration Camps," in Michael Berenbaum, ed., *A Mosaic of Victims*. New York: New York University Press, 1990.

Fonseca, Isabel. *Bury Me Standing: The Gypsies and Their Journey*. New York: Random-Vintage, 1995.

Forster, E.M. *Two Cheers for Democracy*. 1938; New York: Harcourt, Brace and World, Inc., 1951.

Foucault, Michel. *Discipline and Punish: The Birth of the Prison*, trans. Alan Sheridan. 1975; New York: Vintage, 1977.

Fussell, Paul. *The Great War and Modern Memory*. New York and London: Oxford University Press, 1975.

Gilbert, Sandra M. and Susan Gubar. *No Man's Land: The Place of the Woman Writer in the Twentieth Century*. Vol. 1. *The War of the Words*. New Haven: Yale University Press, 1988.

Gissing, George. *The Odd Women*. 1893; New York: W.W. Norton, 1977.

Haney, Craig, Curtis Banks, and Philip Zimbardo. "A Study of Prisoners and Guards in a Simulated Prison," 1973, reprinted in Elliot Aronson, ed., *Readings about the Social Animal*, 4th edn. New York: W.H. Freeman and Company, 1984.

Hilberg, Raul. *The Destruction of the European Jews*. Student Edition. New York: Holmes and Meier, 1985.

Hutchison, Hazel. "James's Spectacles: Distorted Vision in *The Ambassadors*." *The Henry James Review* 26 (2005), pp. 39–51.

Hyde, H. Montgomery. *Oscar Wilde*. New York: Farrar, Straus and Giroux, 1975.

Ignatiev, Noel. *How the Irish Became White*. New York: Routledge, 1995.

James, Henry. *The Ambassadors*, ed. Leon Edel. 1903; Boston: Houghton Mifflin-Riverside, 1960.

———. *The Turn of the Screw and Other Short Fiction*. Toronto: Bantam, 1983.

Johnson, Paul. *Modern Times*. New York: Harper & Row-Perennial, 1983.

Joyce, James. *The Critical Writings of James Joyce*, ed. Ellsworth Mason and Richard Ellmann. Ithaca, NY: Cornell University Press, 1959.

———. *Dubliners: Text, Criticism, and Notes*, ed. Robert Scholes and A. Walton Litz. 1914; New York, Penguin, 1996.

———. *Finnegans Wake*. 1939; New York: Penguin, 1967.

———. *A Portrait of the Artist as a Young Man*, ed. Seamus Deane. 1916; New York, Penguin, 1993.

———. *Stephen Hero*, ed. Theodore Spencer, rev. John J. Slocum and Herbert Cahoon. 1944; Norfolk, CT: New Directions, 1963.

———. *Ulysses*, ed. Hans Walter Gabler with Wolfhard Steppe and Claus Melchior. 1922; New York: Random-Vintage, 1986.

Joyce, Stanislaus. *My Brother's Keeper: James Joyce's Early Years*, ed. Richard Ellmann. Cambridge, MA: Da Capo Press, 1958.

Kent, Susan Kingsley. *Sex and Suffrage in Britain, 1860–1914*. Princeton, NJ: Princeton University Press, 1987.

Lacan, Jacques. *The Four Fundamental Concepts of Psycho-Analysis*, ed. Jacques-Alain Miller, trans. Alan Sheridan. New York: Norton, 1978.

Lamos, Colleen. *Deviant Modernism: Sexual and Textual Errancy in T.S. Eliot, James Joyce, and Marcel Proust.* Cambridge: Cambridge University Press, 1998.

Lawrence, D.H. *The Lost Girl.* 1920; New York: Modern Library, 2003.

Lee, Harper. *To Kill a Mockingbird,* 40th anniversary edn. 1960; New York: HarperCollins, 1999.

Levi, Primo. *Survival in Auschwitz: The Nazi Assault on Humanity,* trans. Stuart Woolf. 1958; New York: Simon and Schuster, 1986.

Lewis, David Levering. *When Harlem Was in Vogue.* 1979; New York: Penguin, 1997.

Locke, Alain, ed. *The New Negro.* 1925; New York: Simon and Schuster-Touchstone, 1992.

Luskin, Fred. *Forgive for Good.* San Francisco: HarperCollins, 2002.

Mahaffey, Vicki. "Framing, Being Framed, and the Janus Faces of Authority," in James C. Carens and Philip Brady, eds, *Critical Essays on James Joyce's A Portrait of the Artist as a Young Man.* New York: G.K. Hall and Co., 1998, pp. 290–315.

———. *Reauthorizing Joyce.* Cambridge: Cambridge University Press, 1988.

———. "Sidereal Writing: Male Refractions and Malefactions in 'Ithaca'," in Kimberly J. Devlin and Marilyn Reizbaum, eds, *Ulysses: En-Gendered Perspectives: Eighteen New Essays on the Episodes.* Columbia, SC: University of South Carolina Press, 1999, pp. 254–66.

———. *States of Desire: Wilde, Yeats, Joyce and the Irish Experiment.* New York: Oxford University Press, 1998.

Milgram, Stanley. *Obedience to Authority.* New York: Harper and Row, 1974.

Nelson, Carolyn Christensen, ed. *A New Woman Reader: Fiction, Articles, and Drama of the 1890s.* Peterborough: Broadview Press, 2001.

Nietzsche, Friedrich. *The Portable Nietzsche,* ed. and trans. Walter Kaufmann. New York: Vintage, 1968.

Norris, Margot. *Suspicious Readings of Joyce's Dubliners.* Philadelphia: University of Pennsylvania Press, 2003.

North, Michael. *The Dialect of Modernism: Race, Language, and Twentieth-Century Literature.* New York: Oxford University Press, 1994.

Owen, Wilfred. *The Poems of Wilfred Owen,* ed. Edmund Blunden (New York: Viking Press, 1931).

Pound, Ezra. *ABC of Reading.* New York: New Directions, 1934.

———. *Selected Poems,* ed. and intro. T.S. Eliot. 1928; London: Faber and Faber, 1948.

Rhys, Jean. *Good Morning, Midnight.* 1939; New York: Norton, 1986.

Scholes, Robert and Richard M. Kain. *The Workshop of Daedalus: James Joyce and the Raw Materials for "A Portrait of the Artist as a Young Man."* Evanston, IL: Northwestern University Press, 1965.

Selle, Carl M., ed., *The New Drama: The Liars, by Henry Arthur Jones, and The Notorious Mrs Ebbsmith, by Sir Arthur Wing Pinero*. Coral Gables, FL: University of Miami Press, 1963.

Shaw, George Bernard. *George Bernard Shaw's Plays*. Norton Critical Edition, 2nd edn, ed. Sandie Byrne. New York: Norton, 2002.

Spiegelman, Art. *Maus: A Survivor's Tale*. 2 vols. New York: Pantheon, 1973, 1986.

Stevens, Wallace. *The Palm at the End of the Mind: Selected Poems and a Play*, ed. Holly Stevens. 1967; New York: Random-Vintage, 1971.

Thomas, Dylan. *Collected Poems 1934–1952*. London: Dent, 1952.

Tintner, Adeline R. *Henry James and the Lust of the Eyes: Thirteen Artists in his Work*. Baton Rouge: Louisiana State University Press, 1993.

Toomer, Jean. *Cane: An Authoritative Text, Backgrounds, Criticism*, ed. Darwin T. Turner. 1923; New York: Norton, 1988.

West, Rebecca. *The Return of the Soldier*, intro. by Samuel Hynes. 1918; New York: Penguin, 1998.

Wiesel, Elie. *Night*, trans. Stella Rodway. 1958; New York: Bantam, 1982.

Wiesenthal, Simon. *The Sunflower: On the Possibilities and Limits of Forgiveness*, rev. and expanded edn. New York: Schocken, 1988.

Wilde, Oscar. *The Artist as Critic: Critical Writings of Oscar Wilde*, ed. Richard Ellmann. Chicago: University of Chicago Press, 1969.

———. *Complete Works of Oscar Wilde*, with an introduction by Vyvyan Holland. New York: Harper and Row, 1966.

———. *The Picture of Dorian Gray: Authoritative Texts, Backgrounds, Reviews and Reactions*, ed. Donald L. Lawler. 1891; New York: W.W. Norton, 1983.

Virginia Woolf, *The Captain's Death Bed and Other Essays*. New York: Harcourt Brace Jovanovich, Inc., 1950.

———. *A Haunted House: The Complete Shorter Fiction*, ed. Susan Dick. 1985; London: Vintage, 2003.

———. *Moments of Being: Unpublished Autobiographical Writings*, 2nd edn, ed. Jeanne Schulkind. New York: Harcourt Brace Jovanovich, 1985.

———. *Mrs Dalloway*. 1925; New York: Harcourt Brace Jovanovich, 1953.

———. *A Room of One's Own*. 1929; New York: Harcourt Brace Jovanovich, 1957.

———. *Three Guineas*. 1938; New York: Harcourt Brace Jovanovich, 1966.

———. *To the Lighthouse*. 1927; London: Harcourt Brace Jovanovich, 1955.

———. *The Waves*. 1931; New York: Harcourt Brace Jovanovich, 1959.

———. *The Years*. 1937; New York: Harcourt Brace Jovanovich, 1959.

Yeats, W.B. *The Collected Works of W.B. Yeats*, Vol. 1 (*The Poems*), 2nd edn, ed. Richard Finneran. New York: Scribner, 1997.

Index

Adorno, Theodor 34, 35
Aeneas 127
aesthetics 130–1, 161–2, 204n8
Afghanistan 59, 117
Agamben, Giorgio 6, 14, 15
agency
  given up 95
  Milgram 26–7
  responding 29, 31
  spirituality 100–1
aging 134, 187
alienation 191
All the Year Round journal 109
Allen, Grant
  The Woman Who Did 114, 115–16
The Ambassadors (Holbein) 145–7
The Ambassadors (James) 147–54
Americans–Germans xi–xiv
anamorphosis 145–6, 147, 150
Anderson, Sherwood 175–6
apathy/paralysis 97
aporia 125, 217n1
Arendt, Hannah 23, 35
Aristotle 87
Arkansas Gazette xv
art
  beauty 165–7
  To the Lighthouse 160–7
  modernist literature 125
  Nazism 59–60
  reality 131–2

society 143
transformation 135
see also painting
Atwood, Margaret 7
Auden, W.H. 202
Auschwitz 66
author
  darkness images 185–6
  as experimenter 24
  leaving tower 43
  narrator 4–5
  reader viii–ix, 22–3, 70, 76–7, 78, 90,
    107–8, 124
authoritarian personality 34
authority 5
  apparent 27–9, 30
  assigned 38–40
  conflict 38
  conformity 35
  cultural 95–6
  Joyce xix, 101–2
  Józefów massacre 34–5
  questioned 69–70
  reading 79–80

Babel image 45
backwards reasoning 83, 86, 87, 90, 92–3,
    99
balance renewed 170–1, 172, 190
Bammer, Angelika x, xvii
banality of evil 23, 49–50

Barnes, Djuna 67
    Nightwood 54–5, 169–70, 186, 188–9, 211n49
Baudelaire, Charles 139
Bauman, Zygmunt 35, 38, 39
beauty 130, 165–7, 178
Beckett, Samuel
    audience 53
    Catastrophe 53
    Christian comedy 119
    Endgame 19–20, 73–4, 120–1
    frames of reference 36
    immobility of characters 51
    Krapp's Last Tape 167–8
    Malone Dies 15
    master–slave 118
    Molloy 15, 145
    Murphy 53–4, 55, 186, 190–1
    Not I 9
    obedience 120
    Play 9
    unnamable 124
    The Unnamable 15, 145
    see also *Waiting for Godot*
Beckson, Karl 108, 117
Bentham, Jeremy 5–6, 40, 41–2, 210n47
biographical style 11, 17–18, 21–2
Birkenau 58
black Americans 62–3, 174, 175–6
blackness 178, 179, 180–1
blindness 156–7, 158–9, 202
    see also visual
body
    disabled 121–2
    fragmented 133–4
    poverty 53–4
body language 85
Bolshevik Revolution 7
book-burning x–xi, xvi–xvii, 70
Boston marriage 109
Browning, Christopher R. 5, 23
    on Milgram 34–5
    Ordinary Men 31–7
brutality 128–9, 135

Caird, Mona 108, 110
capitalism 7, 23, 62
Capote, Truman 210n42
Carey, John 203n3, 205n1
caricature 75–6
Carson, Ciaran 65
Carter, Angela vii
castration 137, 138
Chaplin, Charlie
    The Great Dictator 3
choice
    denial of 33–4
    individual 28, 32, 37
    interpretation 78, 79
    reader 8
Chopin, Kate 114–15
Christian comedy 119
citizens 28, 63
class 124, 125, 141, 205n1
Coetzee, J.M. 6
Coles, Robert 36
comedy 119, 121–2
communication 45–6, 47–8, 50
compassion 120–1, 137–8
concentration camps 6, 43–4, 49–50, 57–8
conformity 34, 35, 37, 38, 102
Conrad, Joseph 136, 150, 192
consumerism 200–1
Conticinium 170, 178–81
corruption: see decay
Cowper, William 182
criticism 87
cubism 62
Cullen, Countée 179–80

Daily Telegraph 108
Dante Alighieri vii–viii, 6, 44–5, 48, 49
darkness 185–6
    age 187
    blindness 158–9
    of character 188–9
    desolation 194
    evil 189–90
    Finnegans Wake 171–2, 196–8

Four Quartets 198–9
light 170
To the Lighthouse 182–5
of mind 196
obscurity 169, 171, 191–2, 194–6
Toomer 174–5
transformation 169
Ulysses 198
violence 170
The Waves 192
decay 96, 134
deference 118
defragmentation 139
dehumanizing
    graphic novels 64–5
    Nazism xii, 35, 57–8, 66
    Trilby 75
    Zimbardo experiment 40
demonization 34, 98
dependence 121, 123
Depression, Great 23, 62
desolation 194
Dickens, Charles 109
Dickinson, Emily 187
dictatorships 57, 63–4, 195–6
difference
    demonized 98
    dissolved 183
    extermination of 58
    identification 37
    sexual 119
    tacit 144
disobedience 29–30, 31, 106, 208n34,
    209n36
distancing 36–7
Dix, Otto 59
double-consciousness 174
Doyle, Arthur Conan 76, 78
    see also Sherlock Holmes
dreams 12, 46–7, 68
Du Bois, W.E.B. 178
    The Souls of Black Folk 174
Du Maurier, George
    Trilby 74–6

Duberman, Martin xiv
Dubliners (Joyce)
    alternative meanings 73–4
    author–reader 76–7
    backwards reasoning 92–3, 99
    epiklesis 90–1
    gnomon 122
    local control 26
    marriage partnerships 107
    Maunsel edition xvi
    narrator 79
    obedience 100–2
    reading, vicarious 89–90
    self-awareness 91
    stories
        "Araby" 91, 103
        "A Boarding House" 92, 105
        "Clay" 91
        "Counterparts" 91, 105
        "The Dead" 51–2, 91, 99, 105, 154–6
        "An Encounter" 91, 95–8, 99–100,
            102
        "Eveline" 102–3
        "Grace" 92
        "A Little Cloud" 91
        "A Mother" 92
        "A Painful Case" 91, 103–4, 105
        "The Sisters" 92–6, 98–9, 100–2,
            103–4, 216n18
        "Two Gallants" 91, 105, 106
dusk 177–8, 190

echo/narcissism 168
Eckford, Elizabeth xv
education
    cultural 95–6
    social behavior 36
    women 107–8, 115
    Woolf vii
Egerton, George (McFall) 108
Eisenhower, Dwight xv
Eliot, T.S.
    body parts 133–4
    criticism 87

Eliot, T.S. (*cont'd*)
  difficulties of poetry 143
  feminization 220n17
  "*La figlia che piange*" 127–30
  "Gerontion" 134
  Grail myth 147–8
  leitmotifs 140
  "The Lovesong of J. Alfred
      Prufrock" 133
  "Mr Apollinax" 134
  mythical method 137, 140–1,
      219n16
  narrators 133
  "Preludes" 133–4
  racist stereotypes 173
  "Rhapsody on a Windy Night" 134
  sequential life 18–19
  see also Four Quartets; The Waste Land
Ellis, Havelock 114
emancipation 115–16
Emerson, Ralph Waldo vi
employment 108–9
endings 19–20
enlightenment 197
Entarte Kunst exhibition 59–60
epiklesis 90–1
equality in partnerships 66, 74–6, 77–8,
      118–19, 123
erotic bliss 191
Étain village xii–xiii
ethics x, 37, 130–1, 204n9
European nationalisms 62
evaluation 56
evil
  banality of 23, 49–50
  darkness 189–90
  purity 60
  racism xiv–xvi
existentialism 28
experience
  framing 153
  interpretation 154
  knowledge 95
  meaning 17

unreality 167
visual 162–3
experimental writers xvii–xviii, 3–4,
    61
exploitation 110, 111–12, 128–9
Expressionism 62

Farr, Florence 108, 112, 114, 117
Faulkner, William
  As I Lay Dying 144, 186
  Light in August 174
Feig, Konnilyn 58
Fetterman, Bonny V. 209n38
Finnegans Wake (Joyce)
  address to reader 201–2
  awethorrority xix
  blackvoice 52–3
  darkness 171–2, 196–8
  language 15, 186, 211n51
  missed understandings 21
  narrator 55
  pronouns 68
  reading of 17, 69
  right/wrong side 39
  self 10
  uroboros 19
  visual/sound viii
Fisher King 137, 143
Fitzgerald, F. Scott 186
foreignness 59
Forster, E.M. 66, 67
  A Passage to India 136
Foucault, Michel
  Discipline and Punish 5–6, 28, 40–4
Four Quartets (Eliot)
  Burnt Norton 14–15, 19, 51
  The Dry Salvages 16–17, 18–19
  East Coker 13–14, 15, 198–9
  Little Gidding 19, 20
fragmentation
  body 133–4
  categories 182
framing 36, 149, 153, 155, 164–5
Frank, Waldo 175, 178

Franzen, Jonathan 69–70
freedom 115–16, 202
Freeman, Kyle 81
French symbolism 61
Freud, Sigmund 12, 18, 57, 67, 124
Fussell, Paul 138

Gallicinium 170–1, 196–9
Germans–Americans xi–xiv
Germany 43, 57–8, 62, 63
  see also Holocaust; Nazism
Gissing, George
  The Odd Women 112–14
Gnade, Lieutenant 33–4
gnomon 93–4, 122
Goldhagen, Daniel 35
goodness 109–10
Grail myth 147–8, 219n15
Grand, Sarah 107, 109, 117–18
graphic novels 64–5
Green, Ernest xv
Gypsies 57–8

Harlem Renaissance 7, 62, 178–9, 181
Heine, Heinrich x
Hemingway, Ernest 138
heroes 18
heroines 77
Hiroshima 67
Hitler, Adolf 57–8, 70
Holbein, Hans, the Younger
  The Ambassadors 145–7
Holmes, Sherlock: *see* Sherlock Holmes
  (Doyle)
Holocaust 23, 34, 57–8, 67
Homer
  Odyssey 70
homosexuality 6–7, 58
hope 46
horror 82, 214n14
Hughes, Langston 180
human rights 186
Hurston, Zora Neale 171
hypocrisy 139

Ibsen, Henrik 61, 109
identification
  cross-racial xiv
  difference 37
  Nazism 37
  partial 36–7
  skin color 175–6
  subconscious 157–8
  surveillance 42
identity, dissolving 182, 190–1
image/reality 150–1
imagination 82, 83–4, 126–7
Imagist movement 141
impotence, sexual 137
independence 113–14
India 171
indoctrination 35
industrialized society 124
Intempesta Nox 170, 182–96
interconnectedness 56–7
intercultural relationships 68
internalization 27, 41, 56
interpretation 8
  body language 85
  choice 78, 79
  experience 154
  Holmes 85–6
  obedience 76
  reader 43–4
  strangeness 82–3
intimacy 191
inverted commas 42
Ireland 7, 62, 171
Isaiah 169–70, 199
isolation 45–6, 104–5

James, Henry
  The Ambassadors 10, 147–54
  "The Beast in the Jungle" 144
  Holbein 149, 150
  intercultural relationships 68
  "The Jolly Corner" 144, 145
  narrator 4, 152
  "The Turn of the Screw" 144

Jewishness, defined 57–8, 66
Johnson, James Weldon 180
Joyce, James
  authority 101–2
  cartoon about 7–8
  influence of 172–4
  inner thoughts of characters 67
  inverted commas 42
  Irish and Hebrew peoples 62
  melody 106
  people/paintings 154–6
  A Portrait of the Artist as a Young Man 125
  readers xvii
  supernatural 197
  transformative writing 90
  see also Dubliners; Finnegans Wake; Ulysses
Joyce, Stanislaus 173
Józefów massacre 32–3, 34–5, 37
Judenjagd 34
justice, divine 88–9

Kafka, Franz xvi
Kenner, Hugh 197
Kent, Susan Kingsley 108
Kierkegaard, Søren 55
knowledge/experience 95

Lacan, Jacques 146–7
Lamos, Colleen 220n18
language 47–8, 53–4, 211n51
Laski, Harold J. 30
Lawrence, D.H.
  The Lost Girl 143–4
  "The Snake" 54
learning 125–6
Lee, Harper
  To Kill a Mockingbird 63–4, 66
leitmotifs 61, 125, 140
Lenin, V.I. 171
Levi, Primo 34, 43–4, 44–50, 45–6
  Survival in Auschwitz 6, 15, 44–50
Lewis, David Levering 178–9
light/darkness 170
The Little Review 155

Little Rock, Arkansas xiv–xv
Litz, A. Walton 90–1
Locke, Alain 179
[L]omazy massacre 33–4
love 113–14
Luke's Gospel 3
Luskin, Fred 208–9n35
lyric poetry 8

McFall, Frances Elizabeth Clarke 108
marriage
  caricature 75–6
  Dubliners 107
  exploitation 111–12
  New Woman movement 107–8
  partnerships 78, 106–18
  prostitution 108–9, 110–11
  as servitude 74
  sex working 114
  Stein 74
Marx, Karl 57, 124
Marxism 62
master–slave partnerships 118
materialism 97
meaning viii, ix, 14–15, 17
melody 106
memorial art xvi
Mickey Mouse 65
Miekle, Wilma 114
Milgram, Stanley 5
  agency 26–7
  compassion 120–1
  Obedience to Authority 23–31, 101–2
  researcher/subject relationship 66
Millay, Edna St Vincent 186
mirror images 88, 91, 126
modernism, end of 57–67
modernist literature
  art 125
  difficulties 3, 143, 203n3, 205n1
  feelings/language 53–4
  interconnectedness 56–7
  interpretation 8
  narcissism 168

narrator absent vii–viii
reader vi–vii, 200
reality 52
strangeness 4
time 9–13
unspeakable 143–4, 172
Modigliani, Amedeo 59
motherhood 115, 216n34
mouth 96, 136–7, 215n17
music 62, 139–40
mystery 82–3
mythical method 137, 140–1, 219n16

Nabokov, Vladimir 186
narcissism 160, 168
narrative structure 4–5, 10–11, 18, 21–2
narrator
 absent vii–viii
 author 4–5
 Dubliners 79
 Eliot 133
 Finnegans Wake 55
 gaze 20–1
 James 4, 152
 To the Lighthouse 184
 omniscience 36, 57, 89
 Sherlock Holmes stories 80–2, 88–9
 sleeping 10–11
nationalisms 62
Nazism
 art 59–60
 book-burning x–xi, xvi–xvii
 dehumanizing xii, 35, 57–8, 66
 homosexuality 58
 identification 37
 indoctrination 35
 Mickey Mouse 65
 Modernism 59
 pain 97–8, 99–100
 transgression 60
The New Negro 178–9
New Woman movement 6–7
 equality 77
 goodness 109–10

 in literature 216n27
 marriage 78, 107–8, 109
 vampire 117
New Woman novel 61
New Yorker 69
Nietzsche, Friedrich 55, 56
nightmares 46–7
nonconformists 34
Nordau, Max 59
Norris, Margot 215n18
North, Michael 181
North American Review 109

obedience
 Beckett 120
 deference 118
 distancing 36–7
 Dubliners 100–2
 interpretation 76
 Luskin 208–9n35
 mechanical 44
 narrowness 94–5
 passivity 122
 psychological mechanism 101–2
 reading 36, 207–8n28
 social inculcation 77
 Waiting for Godot 29, 120, 122
obedience experiments: see Milgram,
  Stanley
objectifying 155
obscurity 169, 171, 191–2, 194–6
omniscience of narrator 36, 57, 89
optimism rejected 191–2
order, as term 26
Orwell, George
 Down and Out in Paris and London 53–4,
  187
Ovid 135–6, 218–19n12
Owen, Wilfred 138

pain/pleasure 97–8, 99–100
painting 154–6, 161–2
 see also art
Pankhurst, Christabel 108

Pankhurst, Emmeline 108, 117
panopticon 5–6, 40, 41–2, 57, 210n47
paralysis 93, 97, 102–3
Parnell, Charles Stewart 67, 212n73
partnerships
    author–reader 90, 107–8, 124
    equality in 66, 74–6, 77–8, 118–19,
        123
    Holmes–Watson 78, 80–7
    marriage 78, 106–18
    master–slave 118
    The Sign of Four 106–7
    Ulysses 66
passivity 23–4, 36, 102–3, 122
Pater, Walter 10
Pentecost 48, 181
perception/reality 148
perpetrators 34, 35–6, 40–1
personal/political 101–3
perspective, inverted 145–6
Philomela 135–7, 143, 218–19n12
Pinero, Arthur Wing 115
pleasure 67–70, 97–8, 99–100, 177
Pound, Ezra
    anti-Semitism xv, 173
    Cantos 17
    and Eliot 135
    gravity 69
    Imagist movement 141
    "In a Station of the Metro" xviii
poverty 53–4, 187
presence/absence 163–4
pronouns 68
prostitution 108–9, 110–11
Proverbs 119
psychoanalysis 62, 146–7
psychological movement 67
Punch 62
punishment 40–1
purity 60

racism xiv–xvi, 60, 64, 173
Rampersad, Arnold 178, 179
Rand, Ayn 4

rape 136–7, 138
reader
    as agent 26–7, 79–80
    and author viii–ix, 22–3, 70, 76–7, 78,
        90, 107–8, 124
    blindness 95–6, 156–7, 202
    consumerism 200–1
    defragmenting 139
    Dubliners 76–7
    expectations 152–3, 201
    experimental writers xvii–xviiii
    flexibility 202
    frames of reference 36
    hypocrisy 139
    interpretation 43–4
    To the Lighthouse 167
    mirror images 91
    modernist literature vi–vii, 200
    narcissism 160
    ordering of experiences 21
    paralysis 93
    passivity 23–4, 36
    as questioner 147–8
    responsibility 31, 69–70
    secrets 156
    as subject of experiment 24
    text 57
reading
    authority xix, 79–80
    backwards reasoning 90
    challenging 4, 7, 69, 73, 105–6, 135,
        143, 195, 201
    critical 87
    ethics x
    obedience 36, 207–8n28
    as pleasure 67–70, 69–70
    reality 153–4
    repeated 9
    as social process 26
    vicarious 79–80, 89–90
reality
    adulterated 151
    art 131–2
    created 210n46

image 150–1
modernist literature 52
oppositions 55
painting 162
perception 148
reading 153–4
role-playing 39–40
submerged 169–70
transitory 178
truth 52
relativity, theory of 62
researcher/subject relationship 66
responding 29, 31
responsibility
abdicated 29, 31, 40, 208–9n35
choice 32, 33–4
denial of 35
disobedience 29–30
reader 31, 69–70
resurrection 142–3
revolution 61–2
Rhys, Jean
Good Morning, Midnight 186, 187–8, 194
Voyage in the Dark 186, 194
Rilke, Rainer Maria 50–1
Rimbaud, Arthur 68
role-playing 38–40
Russia 7, 57, 62, 171

salvation 61, 119
Sartre, Jean-Paul 28
Schmidt-Rotluff, Karl 59
Scholer, Robert 90–1
Schreiner, Olive 109, 114
Schultze-Naumberg, Paul 59–60
secrets 156, 166
segregationists xv
self as concept 10
self-awareness 91
self-image 125
sex working 108–9, 114
sexuality
frankness 176–7
Freud 67

violence 138
women 112–13, 114, 117
wounding 137–8
Shakespeare, William
The Tempest xviii, 139–40, 143
Shaw, George Bernard
Mrs Warren's Profession 111
Sherlock Holmes (Doyle)
backwards reasoning 83, 86, 87
narrator 80–2, 88–9
partnership 78, 80–7, 106–7
stories
The Hound of the Baskervilles 79, 80, 81
The Man with the Twisted Lip 214–15n16
A Scandal in Bohemia 213–14n9, 214n10
The Sign of Four 80, 89, 106–7
sight: see visual
silence 184–5
simony 93, 97
skin color 175–6
social conditioning 3–4, 25–6, 36, 43, 119
social order 27, 28
social responsibility 29
social tension 61–2
Socrates 125–6
solidarity 37
soul as prison 41
Soviet Union 171
see also Russia
Spanish Civil War 62, 171
Spencer, Anne 181
Spiegelman, Art 212n68
Maus 64–5
spirituality 100–1
Stalin, Josef 171, 223n5
Stanford prison experiments 34, 38–40
Stein, Gertrude xvii, 74
Tender Buttons 15
Sterne, Laurence 69

Stevens, Wallace vii, x
  "Asides on the Oboe" 165
  "The Emperor of Ice Cream" 54
  "The Idea of Order at Key West" 68,
    202
  Notes toward a Supreme Fiction vii, ix
  "Sunday Morning" 20
strangeness 4, 82–3
subconscious 157–8
subtext ix, xiv, 5
suffragettes 117
  see also Pankhursts
surveillance 6, 40, 41–2, 44, 57

Taliban 59, 117
Taylor, Charles xvii–xviii
technological revolution 62
text
  fiction 152
  meaning ix
  mirror insights 126
  reader 57
  revelations 16–17
  weaving analogy 136
Thomas, Dylan 178
  "The Hunchback in the Park" 126–7
time
  divided 133–4
  modernist literature 9–13
  night watches 170–1
  present 19
  reversed 154
To the Lighthouse (Woolf)
  absence/presence 163–4
  art 160–7
  beauty/art 165–7
  darkness 182–5
  framing 164–5
  narrator 184
  reader 167
  self-image 125
  silence 184–5
  tower 43

truth/reality 52
Toomer, Jean
  Cane 174–5, 176–7
    "Blood-Burning Moon" 177–8
    "Fern" 176, 178
transformation 90, 135, 139–40,
  169
transgression 60, 61
Trapp, Wilhelm 32, 35
truth vi, 52, 94

Ullmann, Micha xvi–xvii
Ulysses (Joyce) 4
  bodily processes 54
  as challenge 8–9, 17
  Cyclops episode 130
  darkness 171, 198
  Eliot on 172
  ending 20
  equal partnerships 66
  hero xv–xvi, 18, 166–7, 173–4
  Ithaca episode 169
  Jews/Irish 62
  Nausicaa episode 155–60
  parent–child 118
  portals of discovery 68
  Scylla and Charybdis episode 21–2,
    210n46
  sexuality 68
  Stephen as learner vi
  tower left behind 43
  weaving image 10
unconscious 57, 61, 125, 131
unspeakable 143–4, 172

vampire 117
Verlaine, Paul 140
Vespera 170, 172–8
violence 138, 170
Virgil 127
visual
  experience 162–3
  framing 149

James 148
sound viii
windows/paintings 164–5
voice, loss of 46
voyeurism 53, 139, 147, 156

Wagner, Richard 125
  Götterdämmerung 142
  Parsifal 61, 140
  The Ring of the Nibelung 14
  Tristan and Isolde 142
Waiting for Godot (Beckett)
  alternative meanings 73–4
  audience response 42
  boredom 29, 54
  choice 37–8
  equipoise 119–20
  master–slave 118
  narrator 10–11
  obedience 29, 120, 122
war wounds 138–9
The Waste Land (Eliot)
  aftermath of world war 135
  "The Burial of the Dead" 141–2
  as challenge 8–9, 134, 139
  ending 20, 142–3
  falling towers 43
  "The Fire Sermon" 142
  "A Game of Chess" 136–7, 141
  music 140
  mythical method 140–1
  Philomela 136–7
  Tiresias viii, 137, 138
  "What the Thunder Said" 142
The Waves (Woolf)
  Bernard's life 11–13, 17–18,
    20–2
  darkness 186, 192
  feeling/civilization 54
  stories/experience 19
Wells, H.G.
  Ann Veronica 117
  The Time Machine 124–5

West, Rebecca
  The Return of the Soldier 52
Westminster Review 108
whiteness 175–6
Wiesel, Elie 171
Wiesenthal, Simon 35–6, 209n38,
    211n50
Wilde, Oscar 28, 29, 62, 212–13n73
  "The Critic as Artist" 87
  The Importance of Being Earnest 69
  The Picture of Dorian Gray xviii, 125,
    130–3, 154
  Salomé 109
  "The Soul of Man Under Socialism" 27,
    29–31
  trials 6–7, 61
Woman Question 107
women
  blackness 180–1
  class 141
  education 107–8, 115
  employment 108–9
  freedom 115–16
  sexuality 112–13, 114, 117
  votes for 62
  see also marriage
Woolf, Virginia
  Between the Acts 186, 193–4
  dictatorship 195–6
  education vii
  escape from words 192–4
  "An Evening Party" 16
  inner thoughts of characters 67
  "The Mark on the Wall" 9
  "Mr Bennett and Mrs Brown"
    22–3
  Mrs Dalloway 9, 15
  readers xvii
  A Room of One's Own 13, 51
  "Solid Objects" 16
  Three Guineas 110, 186, 187, 195
  The Years 186, 192
  see also To the Lighthouse; The Waves

words
  ending removed 156–7, 158, 159–60
  escape from 192–4
  meaning 14–15
World War I 62, 138

Yeats, William Butler 171, 202
  "Blood and the Moon" 51

"The Circus Animals' Desertion" 16, 51
"Crazy Jane Talks with the Bishop" 51
"Meditations in Time of Civil War" 21, 22, 43
"The Tower" 129–30

Zimbardo, Philip 34, 38–40

7 9 0 5   2 2